A Century of Parrots

A CENTURY
of Parrots

Rosemary Low

Rosemary Low

INSIGNIS PUBLICATIONS

Dedicated to the memory of Lito, my green angel
(1950s? – 4/10/2006)

ISBN 0-9531337-5-3
     978-0-9531337-5-8

Published by Insignis Publications,
P. O. Box 100,
Mansfield,
Notts, NG20 9NZ, UK.

Front cover: top left, Greater Sulphur-crested Cockatoo *(Avicultural Magazine)*; top right, Triton Cockatoo (Jurong BirdPark); bottom left, Hawk-headed Parrot *(The Royal Natural History)*; bottom right, Hawk-headed Parrot, Ron and Val Moat.

Cover by CaptainQuark, Sheffield, UK, 2006

Printed in the Czech Republic by Dona Publishing

CONTENTS

ACKNOWLEDGEMENTS

I am greatly indebted to Sonny Stollenmaier who read the manuscript with the eye of a younger generation and made countless useful comments and contributions.

Information was also provided by:
Ray Ackroyd, Australia
Guisselle Monge Arias and Olivier Chassot, Costa Rica
Enrique Bucher, Argentina
Paul Busby, UK
Gordon Cooke, UK
John Courtney, Australia
Marti Everett, UK and Costa Rica
Mike Gammond, Bahrain
Graeme Hyde, Australia
Charles MacKay, CITES Task Force, UK
Juan F. Masello, Argentina
Don Merton, New Zealand
Bernadette Plair, USA
Natalia Politi, USA and Argentina
Robin Restall, Venezuela
John Scott, UK
Sergio Shokalo, USSR
Tony Tilford, UK
Jeffrey Trollope, UK
Louise Warburton, South Africa
Photographs by the author unless otherwise stated.

My thanks go to the following who kindly answered my requests for photographs:
David Alderton, UK
British Museum of Natural History, Tring
Tim Bennetts, UK
Michael Braun, Germany
Joanna Burger, USA
Roy Chester, UK
Christopher Cokinos, USA
Gordon Cooke, UK
Werner Dobnig, Austria
Malcolm Ellis, Avicultural Society, UK
Jamie Gilardi, WPT, USA
Jurong BirdPark, Singapore
Ellen Karhausen, Netherlands
Philip Knowles, Paignton Zoo, UK
Lars Lepperhoff, Switzerland
Stewart Metz, USA
Greg Moss, USA
Rebecca Mould, Leeds Castle, Kent
Royal Zoological Society of South Australia
Michael Schooley, Australia
Roland Seitre, France
Mark Stafford, Parrots International, Inc.
Tredegar House, Gwent
Sonny Stollenmeier, UK
David Waugh, Loro Parque Fundación, Tenerife
Iolo Williams, UK
Sam Williams, UK
Rafael Zamora, Tenerife
Bonnie Zimmerman, USA

Special thanks to Elizabeth Butterworth, UK, Bernd Gerischer, Germany and John O'Neill, USA, for permission to reproduce their paintings, and to Oliver Jackson for his work on the cover.

INTRODUCTION

The 20th century saw a revolution in every sphere of life and knowledge. Whatever subject interested one, the author who might record the changes and advances during that period could produce a volume of absorbing interest. My own world has revolved around members of the parrot family (psittacine birds) since I was 12 years old. This interest altered the course of my life to the degree that I cannot visualise what it would otherwise have been like. From childhood to the present day, parrots and parrot-related issues have occupied most of my waking hours. Over a period of more than 30 years, this resulted in the publication of 22 books on parrots, covering aviculture, pet-keeping and conservation, plus monographs of certain groups (eg, Amazons, lories, cockatoos and macaws).

I have lived through half a century of what proved to be the most challenging period for parrots (and, indeed, for most bird species) since they evolved at least 20 million years ago. The urge to record what happened to parrots during the 20th century grew stronger and more compelling. I had experienced this dramatic period in their history from a number of different angles: pet-keeper, breeder, curator of parrot collections, traveller to the tropics, narrator and conservationist. My account might open the eyes of many parrot lovers, especially those who have seen no further than the parrot happily (or otherwise) in residence in their living room.

Parrots have countless numbers of devotees worldwide. Such colourful and charismatic creatures, many of whom are endowed with great intelligence, are perhaps the best loved of all birds. (Sadly, they are also among the most abused.)

Currently facing extinction are hundreds of thousands of birds and other fauna and flora in every corner of the globe. It is too late to save many of them – but others can be saved if the crisis they face becomes a matter of concern to more and more people. Natural extinction is usually a slow process, but extinction has accelerated to a pace that few would have predicted at the start of the 20th century. Relating the history of parrots and man's association with them during this short period (short compared with the eons during which parrots have existed), has painted a vivid and disturbing picture of the impact man has made on parrots and their environment.

The 21st century will be the one during which the fate of many (perhaps most) species is sealed, for better or for worse, for survival or for extinction. Perhaps by looking back at the 20th century, and learning from the mistakes made then, we can help to secure a better future, in their natural habitat and in our homes, for the colourful, incomparable and endlessly fascinating creatures that we know as parrots.

In this book I have used the past tense throughout (even when describing, for example, parrot collections still in existence) in order to emphasise its historical narrative. For the same reason, I have sometimes used old photographs where modern ones would have been technically superior but less appropriate.

PART I.

AVICULTURE AND TRADE

1. AVICULTURE: THE EARLY YEARS

In the early years of the 20th century, when the industrial age was at its height, there was a house in Cambridge constructed of 1in (2.5cm) tongue and groove wood. It was lined with teak and insulated with thick felt; the floor was of oak boards. All the windows were on the south-east side, glazed with rolled glass and fitted with Venetian blinds. Outside the windows were fitted with striped blinds. The house stood on brick and cement pillars and was heated by hot water pipes. It was painted pale green outside and eggshell blue inside. It was a parrot house and cost as much to build as the average working man's home. Massive cages housed the birds. Mrs Anningson loved her parrots and spared no expense to give them a good life.

A few streets away in a dingy living room, in a back-to-back terraced house, Mrs Harvey sat by the cage of her Cockatiel, listening to its shrill warbling. In a home that lacked all the modern comforts, her "Alfie" brought joy to the colourless drudgery of her life. He was her pride.

In those days there was an enormous gulf between the classes, between the owner of a single pet bird and the wealthy aviculturists who even sent collectors to far-flung lands to bring back species never previously seen in captivity. By the end of the century all that had changed. There was no class divide in parrot keeping; it attracted people from every walk of life, from postmen to professors and from farmers to pharmacists. They all spoke the same language – one that can sound foreign to an outsider.

In Europe the bird-keeping tradition is strong and dates back many centuries. Research suggests that around the beginning of the 20th century there was a cage bird in every other home in Britain, mainly Canaries and British finches. Members of the parrot family were in the minority, with the exception of the Budgerigar, sometimes called the Undulated Grass Parakeet. Two much-loved species, the Budgerigar and the Cockatiel, were the first parrots to rear young to countless generations. Even in 1879 in Britain Cockatiels were said to "breed freely, and require no more attention than would be given to pigeons".

◼ *Mrs Anningson's Parrot House.*

Reproduced from *Bird Notes*

Budgerigars were as common as Canaries and it was estimated that approximately 25,000 were bred every year in Europe.

In the early years of the 20th century parrots were valued mainly for their ability to mimic. The advice in *Enquire within upon Everything* (published in 1891) was that they should not be kept in places "where they were liable to hear disagreeable noises, such as street cries, and the whistling and shouts of boys at play, for they will imitate them, and become too noisy to be tolerated."

In 1902 (when Arthur Balfour was Prime Minister and there were only 7,000 cars in the entire country) bird keepers were united by the publication of a new weekly paper, *Cage Birds*. It cost one penny, or 1 ½d posted*. For 3s 3d (16p) one could take out a subscription for six months. (In 1996, £51.86 had the equivalent purchasing power of £1 in 1900.) That very first issue had a line drawing of a Blue-fronted Amazon on the front page. There were not many advertisements in those early days. Line advertisements cost 4s 4d for 12 words and one penny for every three extra words. A typical advertisement read: "Amazon Parrot; thorough good talker, very tame, 2 guineas" and came from Shaftesbury Avenue in London's West End. (It is interesting to compare the prices over the years. In 1981 a similar Amazon, with cage, was advertised for £240; by the century's end the price was at least double.)

In comparison, an imported Grey Parrot cost 17s (85p) in 1902. Another Grey, a "good talker", aged four years, was on offer at £7 in the September 6 issue. This must have been a very talented bird indeed. It cost the equivalent of five week's wages, before deductions, for a working man. A tram conductor working a 90-hour week in 1900 earned 22s (£1.10) and a tram driver at the same depot earned 27s (£1.35). The latter sum would have been just enough to buy one Redrump Parakeet ("good songsters, very beautiful"), while Rosellas were only £1 per pair. A Rock Parrot *(Neophema petrophila)* (unknown in aviculture outside Australia since the 1960s) cost 15s (75p) and Senegal Parrots were 12s 6d each (62p).

At the start of the 20th century, according to the (*Modern Cyclopedia of Universal Information*, volume VI, 1903), the best-known species was the "Grey (*Psittacus erythacus*) of Western Africa, which can be most easily trained to talk. The Green Parrots (*Chrysotis*) [*Amazona*] are also common as domestic pets, being brought from the tropical regions of South America. The Carolina Parakeet (*Conurus carolinensis*) is found in the U. States, and is gregarious in its habits." Ironically, the Carolina became extinct 11 years after this was published.

Another encyclopaedia, undated but published during the reign of Queen Victoria (her reign ended in 1901), was accurate and informative on the subject of the Grey:

"... frequently kept in confinement, in which it displays the greatest docility and intelligence, surpassing in powers of speech any other parrot. It is an inhabitant of tropical Africa, where it dwells in the woods, feeds upon seeds and the kernels of fruits, and breeds in holes in decayed trees, laying about four white eggs. In confinement... the strength of its bill enables it readily to break the shells of nuts and almonds, so as to get at their sweet kernels."

Avicultural journals are born

Much information was published about members of the parrot family at the beginning of the 20th century because two magazines for aviculturists existed. Founded in 1896 (when the Marquis of Salisbury was Prime Minister) the Avicultural Society invented the word aviculture to mean the care and breeding of non-domesticated birds in captivity. It was derived from *avis*, the Latin for bird, and culture (breeding). The Society published *The Avicultural Magazine* each month. Its eight pages doubled after the first year when the society had built up its membership to 173. The annual subscription was 5s (25p) at a time when an agricultural worker took home about 10s (50p) for working a 72-hour week.

In 1901 The Foreign Bird Club started to publish its monthly journal, *Bird Notes*. The two magazines looked almost identical and included

---

* 1 ½d = one and a half pennies in the days when there were 240 pence to the pound. Shillings and pence were abbreviated s and d, for example 2s 6d.

■ **Left:** *The first issue, in 1902, of the weekly magazine* Cage Birds. *It cost 1d.* **Right:** *At the end of the century the same magazine was entitled* Cage & Aviary Birds *and cost £1.05.*

fine colour plates. Until 1914 these plates were hand-coloured lithographs and, at least into the 1930s, of very high quality from the brushes of leading bird artists. The enthusiastic editor of *Bird Notes*, Wesley Page, FZS, must have spent about half the month travelling around the British Isles, visiting members' aviaries and recording what he saw in the magazine. This is very fortunate from the historical aspect. Softbills and finches were favoured because large aviaries (often very large) containing mixed collections were popular.

Parrot species available

Australian parakeets and small parrots such as lovebirds and parrotlets were often kept in these aviaries. The one-pair-per-aviary concept was unusual, except for the larger or more aggressive species. Lord Poltimore in Exeter kept lories in pairs on their own. Lorikeets, especially Swainson's and Red-collared from Australia, were readily available, as well as Indonesian species such as the Black-cap and the Purple-cap.

■ Bird Notes, *magazine of the long-defunct Foreign Bird Club.*

Another noble aviculturist was the Hon. and Rev. Canon F. G. Dutton, who became Lord Sherborne. A great figure of aviculture in the Victorian age, he died in 1920 at the age of 90. He was said to have kept more species of the parrot family than any other aviculturist of his time – in cages, aviaries and at liberty, especially during his years at the beautiful vicarage of Bibury. In 1917 he gave up his parish and moved to a small house, taking with him his pet – a St Lucia Parrot (*Amazona versicolor*)! Used to flying at liberty, its health deteriorated. Willed to the Marquis of Tavistock, it made a remarkable recovery when it again enjoyed its freedom.

In that era taxonomic relationships were not well understood. The Crimson-winged Parakeet (*Aprosmictus erythropterus*) (called Red-winged Parrot in its native Australia) was believed to be closely allied to the lories. C. W. Gedney, in his book *Foreign Cage Birds*, volume I, stated that as a cage pet it would always hold a foremost place and that: "the vivid beauty of his coat and the gentleness of his nature are alike attractive, and there is something exceptionally fine in the colours of his plumage which raises him above the level of any other bird of kindred variety."

Adults were rarely trapped. Most of those that reached Europe were young birds that had been taken from the nest. Gedney warned, however, that this species was unlikely to breed because it was too timid in an aviary. But in any case it would not become commonly known by English fanciers! Time was to prove him wrong.

The Blue-front was the best-known member of the genus *Amazona* in that era, when Amazons were called Green Parrots. Occasionally available were Cuban, Festive, Salvin's, Double Yellow-headed and Green-cheeked Amazons. Orange-winged Amazons were more commonly imported than Grey Parrots but were known not to be such good mimics. Most of the larger macaws were imported and were usually kept on a perch, restrained by a leg chain. This inhumane method could be seen for another half century – and some of the largest zoos were the major culprits.

Among the conures available was the Cuban (*Aratinga euops*), the smallest of the red and green *Aratingas* (see colour page 34) – now an endangered species and very rare in aviculture. One writer noted that they looked at their best when flying in a large natural aviary when the brilliant scarlet of the under wing coverts showed to great advantage.

Apart from the Grey, African parrots were represented mainly by the Senegal Parrot and by lovebirds, especially the Black-cheeked. One lady member wrote with some insight on the behaviour of her pair of Madagascar Lovebirds:

... the cock had little time to be bad-tempered or anything else with his constant attendance on his dame. As a reward for his devotion, he often received a gentle scratching of his poll, first one side and then on the other. For the rest he was humbly at her beck and call... His daily duty seemed to be to answer his lady's two sharp notes, to fetch seed for her and be hurried up over it, too, by her querulous calls. Then they would sit quaintly feeding each other backwards and forwards.

Mrs Cook's description (*Bird Notes*, March 1918) might seem anthropomorphic but it was well observed: in lovebirds the female is dominant. Her miniature painting of the pair, used to illustrate the article, had been exhibited in the Royal Academy.

All the white cockatoos were available, although Ducorp's and Goffin's (*Cacatua ducorpsi* and *C. goffini*) were rare. The

■ *Crimson-winged Parakeet.*
Reproduced from *Foreign Cage Birds*

Australian species were common, especially the Sulphur-crest, trapped as a pest. The Bare-eyed Cockatoo or Corella was equally numerous but it was less popular with bird keepers. Many Galahs and Sulphur-crests were kept in England as treasured pets. The Galah, or Rosy Cockatoo (*Eolophus roseicapillus*) as it was often known (sometimes now called Roseate or Rose-breasted), was the most plentiful. "Immense numbers being reared from the nest for importation to this country... they are the most amiable of the cockatoo family" (Gedney, 1879). Gedney recommended that they should be kept in an aviary during the summer, as this "would greatly improve them in health and plumage, whilst the winter caging keeps them both tame and affectionate".

He dispensed excellent advice! Even then breeding attempts were not uncommon. When the female of a pair died, and the two chicks were neglected by the male who was "stricken with grief", Gedney hand-reared them. He chewed up maize and shelled oats but then, he wrote, it "required a considerable amount of consideration before I could summon up sufficient enthusiasm to go through the process of feeding ... but I will spare my sensitive readers these unsavoury details".

Presumably he fed them from his mouth! The days of hand-rearing foods and parrot incubators were nearly a century away! The young cockatoos were brooded by a bantam. She tried to persuade them to feed by picking up morsels of food and calling them. When they tried to thrust their beaks into her mouth, she was "utterly astonished"!

Early breeding attempts

Referring to a breeding attempt by his Swainson's Lorikeets in 1917, Maurice Amsler, MB, FZS, wrote: "I hope for the best and am prepared for the worst." This summed up the situation for most parrot keepers. The breeding success rate was low, partly because of the difficulty of sexing parrots. Even in some sexually dimorphic species the sexes were in doubt. Mrs Anningson had a Banksian (Red-tailed Black) Cockatoo, a greatly admired winner at many bird shows. She felt it was a male but there was much debate about its sex even although this is a sexually dimorphic species. The bird finally provided a definitive answer by laying an egg!

▌*Swainson's Lorikeet drawn by Mrs Cook.*
Reproduced from *Bird Notes*

Breeding results were poor because many parrots were kept in mixed aviaries. A typical example was an aviary 19ft (5.7m) long in which finches and cardinals were kept alongside *Aratinga* conures, Budgerigars, Cockatiels, Lovebirds and Redrumped Parakeets. Nevertheless, the latter three species reared young there. William Shore Baily's Alexandrine Parakeets (*Psittacula eupatria*) reared three young in a large mixed aviary in 1914. When the first young one left the nest (a "banjo" nest-box), it clung to the wire. The father was on one side shouting "Hullo, Polly" and the mother was on the other side whispering "Pretty dear"! Mr Shore Baily found this most amusing because the female had never previously been heard to utter a word! Some breeders were prepared to go to some trouble to make a suitable nest-box for a common species. Financial reward played no part in their desire to encourage their birds to breed.

Another reason for lack of breeding successes was inadequate diet. Many females died of egg-binding due to calcium deficiency. One owner of a pair of Grey Parrots in Germany solved this

▌ *The "banjo" nest-box.*

Reproduced from *Bird Notes*, July 1914

problem. The female's first three eggs nearly killed her because they were so thin shelled she could not pass them. The owner crushed the egg inside the body (a risky procedure that could lead to death). When the pair mated again he added ground eggshells to the softfood; the result was two perfect eggs. Soon after the first chick hatched it was killed by the male. The survivor was reared on cooked maize, hazelnuts, stale white bread and hard-boiled egg.

Wealthy owners

Most bird collections were owned by the wealthy and titled who employed people to look after the birds. Some of their large aviaries had elaborate and expensive indoor houses. E. J. Brook's aviaries at Hoddam Castle in Dumfriesshire, Scotland, were pleasingly constructed in a half-timbered Tudor style, near to an animal house that contained an "amiable" Himalayan bear. Some of these collections were more like zoological gardens – except that they contained more rarities! At Hoddam Castle there was an impressive range of aviaries for birds of paradise and lories (see photograph above chapter heading), a small birds' house and a kitchen, all very clean and

tastefully decorated in pale green and white (*Bird Notes*, June 1911).

Mr Brook achieved several first recorded breeding successes during the first decade, including those for the Black Lory (*Chalcopsitta atra*) and Stella's Lorikeet (*Charmosyna papou*). He also had a sub-species of the Green-naped, *brooki* (no longer recognised) named after him – a rare honour. Such was the wealth of some of the leading private aviculturists that they helped to fund expeditions by the most skilful bird collectors of the day. New Guinea was often their destination and birds of paradise the sought-after species. The area was also rich in lories so private aviculturists received lories that were otherwise unknown to aviculture until commercial exports became common in the early 1980s.

"A more artistic, humorous, tasteful and, at the same time, a more upright, kind and generous man never existed," wrote Jean Delacour of Hubert Astley. At Benham Park, near Newbury, Astley lived in a 14th century moated house with an interior courtyard. In these picturesque surroundings his large mixed collection included some rare parrots. His aviaries were spacious and the bird houses were heated by hot water radiators. Each flight had a gravel path along the front and on each side, the centre was of turf and planted with bamboos,

▌ *Aviaries for lories and birds of paradise at Hoddam Castle in Scotland.*

Reproduced from *Bird Notes*

1 Always rare in aviculture, the gorgeous Tabuan Shining Parrot *(Prosopeia tabuensis)* was bred in New Zealand in the early 1940s (CHAPTER 1). **2** Whitley's Conure (CHAPTER 1). It was a hybrid! **3** Waddesdon Aviaries in Buckinghamshire (CHAPTER 3).

④ The entrance to **Loro Parque**, Tenerife, in 1987 and, ⑤ the new entrance through the Thai Village in 1994 (CHAPTER 3).

6 Parrot aviaries at Vogelpark, Walsrode, a major European parrot collection. Its rarities included **7** the Imperial Amazon Parrot *(Amazona imperialis)*, (CHAPTER 3). In the 1980s **8** this Ground Parrot *(Pezoporus wallicus)* was an extreme rarity in captivity (CHAPTER 3).

9 In the 1980s, Jurong Bird Park's waterfall aviary was home to a lory spectacle second to none (CHAPTER 4). **10** When hand-rearing for other breeders was a business, an intriguing range of species might be reared together, from Mountain Parakeets to a Leadbeater's Cockatoo, Meyer's Parrots, Eclectus and Blue-throated Conures (CHAPTER 4).

Photo: Thomas Brosset

■ *Hubert Astley's aviaries at Benham Valence, near Newbury.*
Reproduced from *Bird Notes*

crown, grey-blue nape and orange-yellow band on the upper mantle. Mr Page had measured its tail: the two central feathers, which ended in spatulas, were 6.5in (16.5cm) to the tip and the outer feathers were 3.6in (9cm) long.

In that era some aviaries were so large that the owner was unaware that a pair had nested until three birds were sitting on the perch. This happened to Lord Poltimore with his Chattering Lories. Amazingly, the aviary, measuring 43ft (13m) long, 36ft (12m) wide and 12ft (3.6m) high, also contained Yellow-backed and Purple-capped Lories and Swainson's and Red-collared Lorikeets (*Bird Notes*, January 1914). (Don't try this at home!) Lord Poltimore's aviaries, in Exeter, were situated in an extensive park where a huge herd of deer grazed. Peaceful scenes such as this throughout Europe were soon to be no more than fond memories.

and a fountain with running water enhanced the pleasing environment. His parrots included a pair of Lear's Macaws (*Anodorhynchus leari*), described as amiable and intelligent. Nothing at all was known about these now Critically Endangered macaws, except that they were shipped from the ports of Bahía, Santos and Rio de Janeiro (*Bird Notes*, April 1910).

Another rarity was a Golden-mantled Racket-tail (*Prioniturus platurus*), a softly-coloured 11in (28cm) parrot with a tiny red patch on the

■ *One of Lord Poltimore's aviaries.*

Reproduced from *Bird Notes* September 1914

The First World War

Bird Notes gave a wonderful insight into aviculture during the first two decades, with its regular contributors and news items. During the First World War, 1914–1918, occasional sad notices were published of members who had died in action. One contributor was killed in a native mutiny in Abyssinia. The news came in a cable "brief and sword-like". Perhaps saddest of all was the obituary of an enthusiastic and regular contributor who died from pneumonia two days before his 18th birthday... The war inevitably led to a reduced membership and, for *Bird Notes*, the loss of valued contributors. In 1925 it was absorbed into *The Avicultural Magazine*.

The war had devastating and tragic consequences for birds and owners. When Belgium was occupied by Germany, British friends of Dr J. M. Derschied, who had an outstanding bird collection, waited anxiously for news. When it came it was heart-breaking. The aviaries of the parakeets and lories were opened in the vain hope of preventing the birds from starving to death. Dr Derschied had been executed. Among the wonderful species in his collection were Shining Parrots from Fiji, Tahiti Blue and Ultramarine Lories, and Keas.

∎ *Captain Jean Delacour, a great aviculturist and ornithologist.*
Photograph by kind permission of the Avicultural Society

One of the greatest bird collections in Europe, that belonging to the famous French aviculturist and ornithologist Jean Delacour, was destroyed, along with his home, Villers Brettonaux. Thousands of shells hit it daily. He wrote: "Naturally, all my birds were killed, all the trees and plants destroyed and all the buildings wrecked... Where the gardens, conservatories and aviaries had been, only tangles of broken steel, glass and wood remained" (Delacour, 1966).

The war had a serious impact on all bird-keepers. It was difficult to obtain seed. Parrots were fed on table scraps or foods of inferior quality. Maud Knobel noticed that her parrots took longer to moult and some of the feathers of green parrots were blotched with yellow, signifying a dietary deficiency. Many parrots were offered what was left from the table, such as soaked bread and mashed potatoes.

After the war

"Why is it," asked Capt. L. Lovell-Keays in 1919, "that with no fresh importations breeding results have suddenly dropped to nil, and most private aviaries are to-day standing practically empty? Let us face it and think how we can minimise our losses."

Lovell-Keays inferred that many losses were due to neglect. He did not mince his words but stated emphatically that "aviculture is not a thing that 'any fool' can pick up by reading a text book that may perhaps only advocate the writer's particular views. If he tries he will, instead of picking up all the necessary knowledge, spend most of his time picking up corpses."

Many birds died during the war because their owners, normally ladies and gentlemen of leisure, were involved in war work. Lady Dunleath wrote that she had been obliged to "hand my aviary and all my birds to others to look after; consequently they gradually died off..."

Nevertheless, the wealthy enthusiasts built up their collections. Delacour acquired a new chateau, parts of which dated back to the 11th century, that of Clère, 15 miles north of Rouen. In 1920 (when Pablo Picasso was astounding the art world in Paris) he moved in, along with hundreds of animals and birds. Soon macaws were flying at liberty. He amassed the finest private zoo in the world, with 3,000 birds and animals of more than 500 species.

Jean Delacour wrote of the post-war era: "England was such a paradise for a lover of gardens, animals and birds that I returned regularly... The art of aviculture was never practised in Europe on a larger scale, or with greater success, than between the two wars." The wealthy bird owners were more interested in creating pleasing aviaries containing beautiful birds than with the challenge of breeding.

However, in the spring of 1920 Wesley Page acquired a pair of Blue-fronted Amazons which he placed in "a small aviary with a flight 12ft x 10ft and a shelter 8ft x 8ft". (By today's standards this 3.6 x 3m aviary, with a shelter 2.4m square, would be large.) He loved these birds. They made "a glorious picture in flight" and their demeanour was delightful and friendly. In July he saw the first egg laid by a Blue-fronted Amazon in England. Alas, his satisfaction was very short-lived. Two days later the female was dead in the nest; the second egg had killed her (*Bird Notes*, August 1920).

A well-known aviculturist who very familiar with corpses was the Marquis of Tavistock, who became the 12th Duke of Bedford in 1940. The author of a highly respected book, *Parrots and Parrot-like Birds in Aviculture*, published in 1929, he attempted to keep his parakeets at liberty, usually with disastrous results. Pages and pages of *Bird Notes* were filled with tales of birds released soon after purchase, many of which were never seen again. These losses, including a pair of Lear's Macaws, made very sad reading. In later years he was successful in establishing a rare strain of liberty Budgerigars. His early attempts were disastrous. He obtained several aviary-bred pairs and released them in the early summer. Sadly, most of the females died egg-bound and one or two survivors were killed by a larger parakeet. Despite the tragedies, the Duke of Bedford remained a committed aviculturist until his death in 1953.

One young enthusiast, a keeper at Dudley Zoo, later the founder of the Tropical Bird Gardens at Rode, Somerset, recalled how difficult it was to acquire birds when he set up his aviary in 1929. Donald Risdon had long wanted a pair of Cockatiels. Suddenly they became popular and difficult to acquire. If they were advertised one had to telegraph money immediately. The

■ *The Duke of Bedford.*

birds would be sent by train, in an era when horse-drawn traffic was fast disappearing. In this way he acquired his first pair – but what a disappointment! The female was sick and died soon after. Today it is so easy to acquire the birds we want that we take this for granted.

Despite the problems, many Cockatiels, Australian parakeets, some lorikeets and plenty of lovebirds were reared. An article written in the 1931 *Cage Birds Annual* was entitled "Profits from Parrakeets". No members of the parrot family were being imported thus parakeets could be regarded as "profitable speculation". Abundant supplies of seeding grasses were "a great help" when they were rearing young. The price of Redrump Parakeets was maintained at about £3 per pair but "the Common Indian Ringneck really does not pay to breed". Budgerigars and Black-cheeked Lovebirds also provided a good financial return. In the early 1920s young Budgerigars fetched 10s or 12s a pair but by the end of the decade their value had halved. David Seth-Smith (Curator of Birds at London Zoo) advised "Even at these prices, a schoolboy may do worse than invest his spare pocket-money in a few pairs of Budgerigars...".

Refusal to accept the nest-box offered was not uncommon and coconut husks were provided for Budgies and other small parrots. Today we tend to forget that because these species have been bred in captivity for many generations, they are easier to breed than their wild-caught ancestors.

Australian parakeets were very popular, especially the grass parakeets (*Neophemas*). In 1918 the Bourke had died out; the most common species were the Blue-winged and the

Rock, the latter unknown in aviculture outside Australia since the middle of the 20th century. The Marquis of Tavistock sent the Splendid and the Turquoisine to join the Dodo and the Great Auk! They were apparently extinct and he had owned "the very last living Turquoisine that will ever be seen in England". He commented: "This species was once a common aviary bird and bred freely, but aviculturalists, with a stupidity which cannot adequately be described in polite language, allowed it to vanish like the Paradise parakeet."

Sadly, he was right about the latter. The Splendid and the Turquoisine, probably due to a combination of agriculture and climatic conditions, declined drastically – but within a few years they were again being exported. They became two of the most frequently bred parakeets in aviculture worldwide.

Australian parakeets maintained their supremacy until at least the early 1980s. Their readiness to breed, pleasant voices and lovely colours were the combined factors that kept them at the forefront. An early breeding account is notable for the resourcefulness of a breeder before the days of incubators. A young pair of Rosellas ceased to feed their three young just before they were due to fledge. The chicks were found cold and hungry. The problem of keeping them warm was solved by putting them in the basket of "Nanki-poo" the Pekinese dog! After a feed they snuggled into his long coat and went to sleep! They were fed on chewed up apple and biscuit and a liquid vitamin supplement. After the first day they no longer needed the warmth of the dog (*The Foreigner*, October 1936).

The Great Depression

The decade of the 1930s was one of the bleakest in British and American history. The collapse of the New York Stock Exchange in 1929, due to the sudden fall in the prices of commodities, soon affected much of the developed world. It caused many wealthy people to lose fortunes and resulted in all-time record unemployment among the working classes. Wages were kept low and strikes were numerous, resulting in more poverty. Most families struggled to make ends meet. There was no room for luxuries such as parrots. In Britain the National Grid was completed in 1933, bringing electricity to those

who could afford it. Working class people did not own aviaries; their houses had a backyard with an outside lavatory. In 1930 two million people in Britain were living in houses classified as unfit for human habitation or in slum conditions. Only the fortunate few possessed gardens, and only the wealthy with large properties built aviaries. In 1931 they could have bought a ready-made one, measuring 10ft (3m) long, 4ft 6in (1.5m) wide and 7ft (2.1m) high for £9.10 shillings. This was twice as much as was needed for the £5 deposit that could secure a three-bedroomed house with a price of £400 to £500. Nevertheless, the wealthy collectors had huge aviaries, lavishly planted and often of ornate construction.

In this era there were few places of entertainment. In London, the Crystal Palace in Sydenham, Joseph Paxton's superb feat of engineering, was built in 1851 to house the Great Exhibition. It was moved from its original site in Hyde Park in 1852 and was then used for exhibitions, plays and concerts. In later years many bird fanciers were familiar with this venue as the home of the National Exhibition of Cage Birds. Its grounds contained aviaries as well as an amusement park with life-sized models of dinosaurs. In November 1936 the Crystal Palace was destroyed by the biggest blaze in the capital for five decades. Officials risked their lives to release the birds to save them from the flames. Miraculously, parrots in their winter quarters in the tunnels were unharmed. The dinosaurs also survived the blaze and became "listed buildings"!

In 1902 there were parrots inside the Crystal Palace. In the *Avicultural Magazine* for March of that year, the Rev. Canon Dutton commented

■ *London's Crystal Palace.*

that in the room devoted to birds: "The parrots are almost all Sulphur-crested Cockatoos 'presented' by their owners!" A century later, when Greater Sulphur-crested Cockatoos were rare in Britain, the Moluccan Cockatoo had replaced the Greater but the problem was the same. The message had not been understood that white cockatoos are too intelligent to be caged.

■ *Greater Sulphur-crested Cockatoo.*
Photograph: *Avicultural Magazine,* **March 1902**

The Second World War

Soon after the country started to recover from the economic downturn, the Second World War was declared. Once again Britain was plunged into austerity. In 1940, after a year at war, seed became difficult to obtain. Giving food suitable for humans to birds and animals was banned; nevertheless, "breakfast biscuits" (whatever they were) were suggested as a substitute for seed. Throughout the war many parrots and parakeets had to survive on scraps from the table. It was not permitted to grow seed on vegetable plots. Breeders were advised to dig up their lawns and plant millet. One man planted the seeds from one and a half millet sprays that he had left in his greenhouse. From these seeds he produced 700 ripe millet sprays and 300 green ones!

At a meeting of the Budgerigar Society held in 1942, it was naïvely suggested that in order to make seed available to members the Government should be approached. The Ministry of Food replied that it was more important to import food for people! The situation was so serious that a small corn merchant with illegally imported seed was fined £2,750 (a sum that could have bought six semi-detached houses) or six months' imprisonment. He went to jail (Stringer, 2004). At this time canary seed cost £700 a ton (70p per kilo). Budgerigar breeders fed their birds on oats, soaked wheat and stale scraps of bread soaked in milk or water and squeezed dry. In 1946 the seed situation in Britain was still desperate. The National Council of Aviculture sent a circular to MPs, appealing on behalf of bird breeders for the resumption of seed importation. Before the war 300,000 tons of bird seed had been imported every year.

Hybrid breeding

Up until the 1980s breeding hybrids was accepted in all sections of the bird fancy, and it was a traditional part of finch and Canary culture. Parrot hybrids were bred deliberately and accidentally in mixed aviaries. Today, as Joseph Forshaw, author of *Parrots of the World*, says: "Hybridisation is to be discouraged. It poses a threat to the gene pool of captive stock." This fact is recognised by all responsible aviculturists.

During the first half of the 20th century hybrids between the white cockatoo (*Cacatua*) species were common. Herbert Whitley of Paignton (who established the collection that was the forerunner of Paignton Zoo) maintained one of the best and most interesting parrot collections in the country until the war forced him to give up his birds. He delighted in breeding the most unlikely hybrids as well as the more common ones such as Galah x Lesser Sulphur-crested Cockatoo. It was said to bear "the most striking and inexplicable resemblance to a huge short-tailed Cockatiel!"

This is not inexplicable. At a certain age the chicks of the two species bear a resemblance to each other, indicating a common ancestor. Cockatiels are closely related to cockatoos and not, as many people believe, to parakeets. There is no genuine record of a Cockatiel hybridising

Herbert Whitley.
**Photograph by kind permission
of Paignton Zoo**

with any other species. However, that did not prevent spurious claims being made of breeding successes that included Cockatiel x Redrump Parakeet and Cockatiel x Blue-winged Grass Parakeet. There was little understanding of taxonomic relationships and the fact that distantly related species cannot produce hybrids.

Neotropical parrots, on the other hand, are closely related and size is almost the only barrier to hybrid production. Herbert Whitley had a large conure named after him – *Aratinga whitleyi*. He acquired this unidentified bird from a dealer and exhibited it at the most important bird show, Crystal Palace in London, in 1926. It was then taken to the Natural History Museum in South Kensington to be "identified". A conference of ornithologists met and pronounced it to be an undescribed species! It was the first and last "Whitley's Conure" ever seen! A plate in the *Avicultural Magazine* for October 1926 (see colour page 1), by the excellent artist Roland Green, shows a bird that I would guess was a hybrid between a Patagonian and an *Aratinga* conure, or possibly a Nanday. Whitley knew a lot about hybrids. It is highly unlikely he did not know one when he saw it but he apparently enjoyed fooling the "expert" ornithologists! And having his name recorded in the ornithological literature!

The Duke of Bedford bred some hybrids that attracted much attention. The male parent was a Crimson-winged Parakeet and the female was a Sula Island King Parakeet (*Alisterus amboinensis sulaensis*) from the Indonesian island of the same name. This sub-species has always been rare in aviculture. (It differs from the nominate race, the Amboina King, in having a variable green band across the blue mantle.) One of these hybrids, described as "strikingly handsome", was presented to London Zoo in 1929. It was returned to him in 1949! Another won the hybrid class at the Crystal Palace Show in 1930. Today a mainstream zoo would not exhibit a hybrid and there are no classes for hybrid parrots at shows.

The King x Crimson-wing hybrid occasionally occurred in the wild. It fooled even the famous 19th century ornithologist John Gould. When he came across a specimen he named it *Aprosmictus insignissimus*! The specific name referred to its remarkable beauty. I have seen this hybrid produced in an aviary in Australia and admit that it is beautiful. It was not difficult to see why Gould was deceived because unlike many hybrids it looks as though it should be a genuine species!

The interest in hybrid parrots was mainly fuelled by the desire to breed something new and different. When colour mutations arrived on the avicultural scene, hybrid breeding declined to become the occasional accidental event. Just after the Second World War the first mutation parakeets were established. Alfred Ezra maintained a famous bird collection at Foxwarren Park in Surrey. By 1944 he had more than 30 lutino Ringnecks as well as half a dozen blue Alexandrine Parakeets. It would

King × Crimson-wing hybrid.

be another 30 years before mutations took a big hold – to the degree that it became hard to find the original colour in commonly bred Australian parakeets and lovebirds.

In the USA

Between 1901 and 1942 an average of 350,000 birds were imported into the USA annually, of which 71% were Canaries (Nilsson, 1981). According to Lee Crandall, Assistant Curator of Birds at the Bronx Zoo, New York, aviculture was not a popular pursuit in America. Writing in 1911 (*Bird Notes*, December), Crandall stated that this was not due to lack of interest in living birds "for thousands of Canaries and large numbers of more interesting species, are imported annually by the two or three dealers who monopolize the greater part of the trade". The reason, he thought, was that laws prohibited keeping native birds, thus reducing the impulse to keep birds. However, one could argue equally that these laws would encourage an interest in keeping exotic species.

Mr Crandall reported (*Bird Notes*, December 1911) on a large private collection in New York, belonging to Mrs Frederick Ferris Thompson. It could be regarded as a model of its kind. Housed in a one-acre area of her estate, Sonneberg extended over 52 acres. The owner generously opened to the public on Saturday afternoons and visitors could see the parrot house, adjoining hospital and large aviary, the jay house and pheasant aviary. In July 1911, 891 birds of 246 species graced the aviaries. The huge flying cage contained 600 birds. In other enclosures the Greater Vasa Parrot and Jardine's Parrot were notable.

In the 1920s commercial breeding of Budgerigars (already established in Japan) commenced. Mr J. S. Edwards of Los Angeles was the largest breeder. In 1928 he bred and sold 15,000 young, including the sought-after skyblue, cobalt and mauve.

One could say that the birth of aviculture in the USA came about with the formation, in 1927, of the Avicultural Society of America. Almost at once it was hit by the Depression and was compelled to suspend operations until 1934. By the 1930s aviculture had become more popular, despite the fact that it was "often looked upon with askance by otherwise very intelligent people. Among these are the self-styled bird protectionist and his first cousin, the maudlin sentimentalist", wrote Dr Leon Patrick (*The Foreigner*, September 1937). First published in 1934, *The Foreigner* was a magazine about exotic birds published in England. It survived only a few years.

In Chicago, a life-long bird enthusiast was Dr Karl Plath, who was credited with the best-arranged and most beautiful outdoor aviary in the Middle West, with indoor accommodation for the winter months. In 1930 (at a time when Herbert Hoover was president of the USA) he wrote that his very tame Spix's Macaw was becoming more lovable every day, it talked in a feminine voice (but not always distinctly) and frequently burst into song "in a laughably quavering manner" (*Avicultural Magazine*, May 1930). Seventy years later his single Spix's was one more than existed in the wild...

California was where it was happening – and this included Hollywood. In 1934 two press agents were assigned to publicize Mae West's next picture. They bought 300 parrots and every day for two months repeated to them the film's title, *It Ain't No Sin*. They intended to send the parrots to film reviewers across the country, who would unwrap the cage and, they thought, would immediately hear the parrot plug the film. The very day the agents crated the parrots to ship, a memo came from the front office changing the title of the movie to *Belle of the Nineties*. The humour contrasts with the attitude of the press agents for whom parrots were just tools of publicity.

On Sunset Strip, the Mexican-themed nightclub Mocambo opened in 1941. It featured big bands and an aviary of macaws and other parrots. The hottest night scene in town, it was frequented by Frank Sinatra, Judy Garland and Errol Flynn.

In Australia

Bird breeding in Australia commenced soon after European settlement in 1788 when early settlers brought Canaries with them from Europe. The Avicultural Society of Australia was founded in 1940 (when Robert G. Menzies was Prime Minister) in Melbourne. Graeme Hyde who, in 2004, had been a member for 50 unbroken years, said that it was not surprising, therefore, that methods used by early Australian aviculturists were based on the management and breeding of these birds. They were inappropriate to the requirements of the Australian species they trapped and placed in an aviary environment.

Although earlier aviculturists had relatively easy access to native birds, especially those that were close to major towns or cities, only certain species seemed to attract their interest. Apart from the various birds that were caught for pets, and often kept under appalling conditions, the more colourful and easy to trap species such as the Eastern Rosella, Port Lincoln Parakeet (Parrot) and Cockatiel, were among the first birds to be housed in cages and aviaries.

▌ *Graeme Hyde, stalwart of Australian aviculture.*

Photograph: Graeme Hyde

New Zealand

The Avicultural Society of New Zealand existed during the Second World War and published its "War-time Report and Bulletin". W. K. Boulton of the Wanganui Hospital recorded how an infra-red lamp saved the life of a Budgerigar who had been teased with a cigarette. The poor bird became very ill after ingesting a shred of tobacco. The pain resulted in it tearing out the feathers over its crop and seemed to be relieved by the use of the lamp. Today these dull emitter lamps are used by bird keepers all over the world. But who discovered their beneficial use for sick birds? Mr Boulton recorded that the Royal Veterinary Hospital in London had been using them for some time.

Parrots endemic to Fiji, which wisely maintained a non-export policy, have always been rare in aviculture. The wonderful, gorgeous Shining Parrots (*Prosopeia*) are among the few genera of parrots that have remained largely unknown to aviculturists. The occasional pair that left those shores always attracted attention – but rarely reproduced. However, the wartime bulletin from New Zealand related how Mrs G. Collins met with success. She kept the Tabuan (*P. t. tabuensis*) sub-species, a somewhat variable form in coloration. (See colour page 1.) After a number of clutches which all ended in egg-binding the female laid two eggs in September 1940. She incubated them on the floor. When a chick hatched and was reared Mrs Collins was astonished. She wrote: "Possibly owing to the fact that his mother has always been a great pet in the aviary, the young bird quickly gained confidence and will come to me at any time."

In Japan

There is an ancient tradition of keeping birds in Japan, usually songbirds in ornate cages. In 1922 Prince N. Taka-Tsukasa recorded that parrot-keeping consisted mainly of parrots and parakeets kept chiefly in bell-shaped cages, singly or in pairs. A few people attempted to breed them. He had bred Cockatiels, Redrump Parakeets, Peach-faced and Madagascar Lovebirds, and White-fronted Amazons in outdoor aviaries. Others had raised Rosellas and Swainson's (Rainbow) Lorikeets. Many species of cockatoos, macaws, lories and lorikeets were also available (*Avicultural Magazine*, March 1922).

Parrots in art and design

During the early part of the century exotic themes, including parrots, were becoming fashionable in art and design. Parrot-motifs were seen on wall decorations and other everyday items. Macaws, especially the Scarlet, seemed to be as popular then as they are today. About 1910 an elegant polychromed (appropriately!) bronze of a Scarlet Macaw was made in Vienna. It stood 29in (74cm) high and was signed by Namgret.

Also in 1910 a unique lampshade was reverse hand-painted with three Scarlet Macaws in a tropical setting. Nearly a century later in

■ *Lamp made in the 1920s featuring a macaw.*

Memphis, Susan Grannis took this Handel lamp to an antique dealer. It was valued at $15,000 to $20,000! During the 1920s beautiful lamps were made to look like a parrot sitting on a perch holding a small cage in its beak. The light was inside the cage. Parrots featured in costume jewellery and in Germany bisque doll accessories even included a parrot (to be held by the doll). In Hollywood, Metro film studios used a parrot as its mascot until it merged with Goldwyn. Most bizarre of all, made in 1937, was a parrot music box containing a stuffed Grey Parrot (now in the Peggy Guggenheim Collection.)

German makers of the finest porcelain, such as Meissen and Rosenthal, produced exquisite figures of parrots, especially cockatoos and macaws. Many were large and impressive and all were highly collectible works of art. At Loro Parque, Tenerife, a museum is dedicated to porcelain figures of parrots and surely has the world's best collection. One of the most interesting is an albino Grey Parrot made by Dorothea Moldenhauer in 1929.

"Too late"

In Britain some pet parrots survived the Second World War on scraps from the table. H. P. Williams had a Blue-fronted Amazon who was taken into a cellar with a cat and a dog during air raids. He wrote: "It was quite amusing to see them all grouped round the same dish partaking of the same kind of food." After the war the Amazon was given seed but preferred cooked vegetables, including chips, dog biscuits, bread and butter and jam, and egg, whether boiled, fried or scrambled. He ate custard and rice pudding while holding it in a spoon! At the time of writing he was 30 years old (Williams, 1951).

Nancy Price related a sad story from this era. A bomb fell in Knightsbridge, London, destroying many buildings. Three days later a voice was heard calling over and over again from under the rubble: "Come quick, come quick!" The rescuers worked determinedly towards the source of the calls. Eventually they found a caged parrot who, reputedly, called out "Too late! Too late!" Against the cage was huddled a cat. All the other occupants of the house were dead. The parrot and the cat were taken by a friend of Nancy Price but the parrot died, refusing all food and, it was said, continually repeating its call of "Too late". The cat lived on.

■ *Meissen cockatoo, c 1930.*

■ *Salvadori's Fig Parrot hatching.*

2. AVICULTURE: THE SECOND HALF OF THE CENTURY

If the century were to be divided in two from the avicultural perspective, the Second World War would seem to be the logical division. Soon after it ended in 1945 the modern age was born, with the invention of the transistor (leading to computers) in 1947 and the first flight of the turbo-prop airliner in 1948.

Perhaps the most famous location with an aviary was Windsor Castle. In 1946 the Queen, then Princess Elizabeth, her sister Princess Margaret and King George VI were photographed standing in front of the Budgerigar aviary. Made at about the same time, an informal home video (televised in 2006) showed the future queen, with short hair, parted in the middle, typical of the era. Smiling and carefree, she was inside the aviary with Budgerigars climbing over her. In 1937 the King had been described as a "very keen devotee of our hobby" in one of the avicultural magazines. He kept grass parakeets (*Neophemas*), among others.

Most European bird collections were lost during the war – and, sadly, some were bombed. With male members of the family away at war, even putting food on the table was a struggle for most families and the purchase of scarce bird seed was impossible. Survivors included Indian Ringneck Parakeets, Rosellas, Redrumps and Cockatiels. All eight species of lovebirds were still available but their prices had increased from £5 to £12 a pair. The cost of seed had escalated. Sunflower had soared from 14 shillings (70p) per hundredweight to £25, hemp from 24 shillings (£1.20) to £28, and canary seed from 28 shillings (£1.40) to £30 (Vane, 1947). These prices were unattainable to all but the wealthy.

It took some years after the end of the war for the nation to attain a degree of affluence. Parrots had become high-priced due to the short supply. People were not used to paying the £20 asked for a Roseate Cockatoo (Galah) in 1946, or £25 to £30 for a Blue-fronted Amazon. In that year the purchasing power of £1 was equivalent to the purchasing power of £21.20 in 1996, thus by 1996 standards the Galah was offered at £420 and the Blue-front at £530 or more. This is interesting because the value of the Amazon has changed little while that of the Galah had increased much more. (It experienced a new popularity in the 1990s.)

The 1950s

Not until May 1950 did the Ministry of Food announce that it would issue an open licence to permit the free importation of canary seed, millet and millet sprays. Most human foods were still in short supply, and one tenth of all that consumed in the UK was grown in allotments and gardens. There had been no space to grow bird seed. Human food remained rationed until 1954. This coincided with the start of a new Budgie boom in Britain, with numerous hobby breeders making a little cash by supplying the pet shops with young birds. Almost every town had a cage bird society, attended mostly by breeders of Budgerigars and Canaries. Indeed, during the mid- and late 1950s cage bird society meetings hit peak attendances that have never been equalled. (By the end of the century, many such societies were struggling while others had been disbanded during the previous two decades.)

Lack of timber affected aviculture – and it was never to recover. The traditional 30ft (9m) flights for parakeets were reduced in length to 12ft (3.6m) or 15ft (4.5m) long and 3ft to 4ft (1.2m) wide. Timber on the roof was replaced by asbestos sheet (some types of which were later found to be deadly to man) and corrugated or flat sheet iron. Some aviaries were thatched! Shelters were only 3ft (91cm) in depth and the front was left open or only half enclosed. The height of nest-boxes was also reduced. Netting usually consisted of 1in (2.5cm) chicken wire.

Wood and chicken wire were more freely available by the end of the decade. Many people bred Budgerigars because they were enormously popular pets and the sale of young birds paid the seed bill. In the mid-fifties a pet shop would offer a breeder about 12 shillings and 6 pence (62p) for a young male and only about 7 shillings (35p) for a female. Males were in greater demand because of their superior talking ability. Seed was again in good supply and the Budgerigar fancy was booming. Cage bird societies staged two shows a year and a few Cockatiels, lovebirds and Ringnecks might be exhibited.

There were few birds in pet shops, except Budgerigars and Canaries. If you lived in London *the* place to buy birds was the Sunday morning livestock market known as Club Row. It was held in the dreary, depressing East End Sclater Street. Pushing their way through the crowds, prospective purchasers examined all the stalls for a bird that caught the eye or for an unusual species. If they found one, it was pushed into a cardboard box and handed over.

The 1960s

At the start of the 1960s (when Harold Macmillan was Prime Minister and the Russians were about to build the Berlin wall) the availability of species was still limited. Cockatiels cost £5 10 shillings for a pair. At this time the basic wage of an agricultural worker, for example, was £8 12 shillings. (By the end of the century normal Cockatiels cost £10 each.) In the mid-1960s everything started to change – for better for humans, for worse for parrots. Many people had money to spend and the demand for exotic wild-caught birds, in home and aviary, multiplied. Coupled with the growth of air transport, bird imports increased enormously (see Chapter 5). The ban on the importation of parrots into the UK was lifted in November 1966. Within two years the prices of parrots had fallen dramatically, due to the large numbers available.

These prices should be put in the context of an average minimum basic wage. That for an ordinary agricultural worker was £11.11s per week in 1968. For the first time parrots were affordable. Indeed, they were actually cheaper, judged against such a wage, than they were at the end of the century. Thus it was not surprising that the 1970s and 1980s saw a huge influx of new parrot keepers in Europe and in the USA.

During the late 1960s and early 1970s parrots were not imported into the UK in huge numbers and many of them arrived in good condition. In 1967 I visited some friends in the north of England. They took me to the premises of a small-scale bird dealer who had just returned from the airport with a batch of wild-caught parrots. When he opened one box an adult Yellow-fronted Amazon walked out – tame and friendly and talking in Spanish. I was enchanted! She stepped on to my hand and I picked her up and took her away. She has been with me ever

Species	Early 1966 prices	mid-1968 in the UK
Moluccan Cockatoo	£120 per pair	£30 to £60 per pair
Blue-fronted Amazon	£35 each	£10 each
Blue-headed Pionus	£30 each	£7 to £10 each
Blue and Yellow Macaw	£40 each	£25 each
Plum-headed Parakeets	£14 per pair	£4 per pair

▌*The author with her Amazon –*
after 20 years together.

since, my most precious avian companion, acquired for the sum of £10 (about 27p a year to date!).

In those days it never occurred to anyone to quarantine new purchases. Disease was not seen as a problem and viral diseases appeared to be uncommon or were not identified. The two main sources of parrots were western European breeders who supplied Australian parakeets and the importers who brought in wild-caught parrots. Under normal circumstances such birds travelled in the heated hold of the aircraft – unless the importer had friends in high places! During the 1960s Australian parakeets enjoyed enormous popularity and there was little interest in other parrots. One of the best parakeet collections in the UK belonged to the Anglo-American heiress, Olive, Lady Baillie, who had bought and renovated Leeds Castle in Kent. In acres of parkland and surrounded by a moat, it has been described as the most beautiful castle in the world.

Lady Baillie's passion was bird-keeping, primarily parakeets and waterfowl. During the 1960s she sometimes travelled to Germany, Belgium and Holland, which region was then the hotbed of Australian parakeet breeders. She went to Germany to visit a dealer and bought a large number of birds. However, she was somewhat naïve about importation procedures – and she was also used to getting her own way. When told the birds must travel as freight, she refused to accept this. As luck would have it, her cousin, Whitney Straight, was chairman of British Overseas Airways (as B. A. was then). Due to his influence, the front row of seats on the aircraft was removed and the birds travelled in the cabin, with Lady Baillie and her agent! (Bignell, undated.)

This was before the days of compulsory quarantine, when some importers would advise their regular customers of impending importations. The day the birds arrived was an exciting time as the importer could never be sure which species would turn up. All this was to change; in years to come if the birds that arrived did not match those listed on the import licence, the whole consignment could be seized. But back in the 1970s there was little regulation. At that time, it was not parrots that were the sought-after birds but small exotic softbills, such as hummingbirds and sunbirds. There was a band of foreign bird exhibitors who were always looking for the rare or the unusual. They congregated in the dingy shop not far from London Airport of the self-styled king of the

▌*Lady Baillie at Leeds Castle during the 1960s.*
Reproduced by kind permission of Leeds Castle

importers, an amiable man with a cigar hanging out of his mouth. Many of the birds they found there were on the show bench less than three weeks later, often with a best-in-show rosette on the cage! Into this shop there arrived from Colombia on two occasions, single specimens of one of the rarest parrots on earth. The year was 1965 and the species was the Yellow-eared Parrot (*Ognorhynchus icterotis*) (see Chapter 12 and colour page 19). The two birds were bought by different collectors.

The only parrots in which the exhibitors were interested were the gem-like Hanging Parrots (*Loriculus*) – but these usually arrived in poor condition and took months to attain the perfect plumage needed for the show bench. In general there was little interest in unusual parrots; the delicate softbills had a higher value.

Rarely imported parrot species could go unidentified. At the 1969 National Exhibition of Cage and Aviary Birds, I saw a Massena's Parrot (*Pionus tumultuosus seniloides*) on a trade stand. No one was interested in it or even knew that it was a rarity that was virtually unknown in aviculture. I bought it for £13. During the 1980s collectors would have been fighting over it. I suspect that a decade later it would again have been unrecognised. The esoteric was not fashionable.

■ *The author's Massena's Parrot.*

The 1970s

Seen only in zoos were rarities that would soon become commonplace. In 1971 I saw for the first time a Yellow-streaked Lory (*Chalcopsitta scintillata*) at West Berlin Zoo. The species had yet to be imported commercially. I was stunned by its beauty: the scarlet head and under wing coverts, skyblue rump and yellow-streaked green head and underparts. Today I still keep this species (my male is from the 1970s) but no longer breed it. You cannot even give the young away. Emphasis has changed from the enjoyment of keeping beautiful parrots with character to breeding for the pet trade – and that usually means Grey Parrots.

Meanwhile in the UK of the 1970s some enterprising bird keepers imported parrots after seeing the low prices on Singapore dealers' trade lists. One friend imported Lesser Sulphur-crested Cockatoos and lories from Singapore. The cockatoos (now Critically Endangered due to over-trapping) cost about £5 each. Amazing species that until then had been only pictures in books were appearing on the lists of dealers in Guyana and Singapore. An adventurous friend, Stephanie Belford, went to Georgetown, and came back with Hawk-heads, Queen of Bavaria's (Golden) and Sun Conures. The latter were not the first in the UK. Two of these striking orange, yellow and green parakeets imported by a dealer in July 1971 caused a sensation, the first in living memory. How familiarity breeds not contempt but certainly a lack of appreciation!

Stephanie Belford brought in parrots from Singapore in advance of the professional importers. Driving over to her house in Welwyn, sometimes with the expectation of seeing a species I had never seen before, was exhilarating. "Darling," she would say in her theatrical manner, puffing on the inevitable cigarette, "Look what I've got here!" In 1977, before anyone had seen Goldie's Lorikeets in the UK, she had a cage containing thirty. It took about six months to sell them all and she lost not a single bird. In this same house in the same year I saw my first Salvadori's Fig Parrots, enchanting stocky little parrots, with a jerky way of moving. Soon Goldie's and Fig Parrots were gracing my own aviaries. When she opened up a box and saw her first Palm Cockatoo she panicked and sold it by picking up the phone!

Later she imported more of these gentle giants and loved to demonstrate their lack of malice by placing your finger in the cockatoo's beak! She even brought in Pesquet's Parrots! (See colour page 5) They were amazing days, never to be repeated. Most small importers looked after their birds well; there was little disease and suffering associated with the huge commercial importations.

The 1980s

The 1980s was a decade of remarkable change. New technology and television brought the world into private homes as never before. It encouraged people to broaden their outlook and to travel. Parrot keeping and travel were not compatible. In Britain some parrot breeders began to reduce their stocks so that it was easier to jet off to the Costa Brava: parrots tied you down. It was an era of free enterprise and the consumer culture boomed. Many people had spare cash for the first time and were prepared to spend large sums on a parrot and cage. However, it was also an era of unrest in Britain. An IRA bomb nearly destroyed the entire government Cabinet at a party political conference in Brighton and the war between the miners' union and Margaret Thatcher's government bred an atmosphere of violence and confrontation. Some miners had lost a year's pay by the time their strike collapsed in March 1985.

By the early 1980s there was much more interest in non-Australian parrots. Never before had so many parrot species been available. Up until then the rarer Australian parakeets such as Kings and Princess of Wales were the most collectable, the most expensive parrots. They were all aviary-bred but were less prolific then. It was the importation of many parrot species from New Guinea, Indonesia and South America, an eclectic variety of rare and electrifying birds that no-one had seen before, that set the non-Australian parrot scene alight. Stella's Lorikeets, those elegant long-tailed scarlet beauties, were offered at £1,000 per pair! By the end of the century they were worth about £70 each.

In Europe

In Western Europe parrot breeding was thriving in Germany, the Netherlands, Belgium and Denmark. In Eastern Europe gradually the Cold War faltered and died away. In 1989 the Berlin Wall, a potent symbol of the division of Europe, fell. Now aviculturists from the east and the west could exchange birds and ideas. The eastern European countries were not affluent, thus there were few parrot breeders, except in Czechoslovakia and Eastern Germany but as their economies improved, the interest in parrots grew.

In the USSR some Greys, Amazons and cockatoos were kept but breeding was rare. The most common parrot was the Cuban Amazon – more than 200 in the late 1980s. These wild-caught Amazons ceased to be available after the withdrawal of military forces from Cuba in 1995 but by this time they were breeding in good numbers. From the USSR, Cuban Amazons reached other eastern bloc countries. In 1986 world attention was focused on Chernobyl, near Kiev, where there was a catastrophic accident at a nuclear power plant. Thousands of people died from radiation. For some unfortunate people, the pleasure of keeping Budgerigars and parakeets was brought to a sudden end. By the close of the century the most common and popular species in the USSR were Australian and Ringneck Parakeets that had been acquired from the Czech Republic.

■ *The elegant, long-tailed Stella's Lorikeet.*

In south-eastern Europe in the early 1980s it was rare to encounter parrots other than Budgerigars and Cockatiels. Todor Nikolov lived in Macedonia and bred Budgerigars. Even as a child he longed to own the bigger parrots that he had seen depicted in a German book. They were literally an elusive dream. He had a recurring dream that he was walking down his street when he saw an escaped cockatoo. When he tried to catch it, it flew away. This fantasy haunted him for years. By the end of the century it was answered in the form of a Yellow-collared Macaw. In the more affluent countries, we take so much for granted...

▮ *Horned Parakeet.*

During the 1980s parrot collections in western Europe reached their zenith. Germany, the Netherlands and Belgium led the way. It seems unfair to single out a couple for mention, when so many were good. However, the collection of Dr Romuald Burkard in Zurich was outstanding for its avicultural rarities and the size and extent of the meticulously planned aviaries. Dr Burkard (who died in 2004) managed to acquire species from Fiji that were virtually unknown in aviculture, such as the exquisite little Collared Lories and two species of Shining Parrots (*Prosopeia*), including the Masked (*P. personata*). He was extremely knowledgeable about his birds and it was always a pleasure to listen to or to correspond with him. The same could be said of Dr Quinque in Paris whose speciality was (and still is) birds from New Caledonia. He bred the delightful Horned Parakeets when they were otherwise unknown in aviculture. These two men were aviculturists of the "old school".

Up-and-coming younger men whose enthusiasm for parrot breeding was as strong decades later, included Robert Peters near Munich. He maintained one of the most impressive private collections in Germany, breeding neglected species such as Eastern Long-billed Cockatoos and hard-to-acquire ones such as Keas and Rajah Lories. He was the first person in Germany to breed the Palm Cockatoo. His rows of aviaries were built on sloping ground and the shelters were underground!

Advances in the 1980s

Interest in breeding sexually mono-morphic species (those in which male and female are alike in appearance) increased dramatically during the 1980s. Previously years could be wasted before discovering that both birds were of the same sex. It was in California, that hotbed of parrot breeders, that an enterprising vet, Raymond Kray, solved the problem with the use of the laparoscope. This instrument, borrowed from human medicine, consists of a light source, a flexible light cable of glass-fibre elements and a viewing piece called an endoscope. A small incision was made in the bird's left side, behind the last rib, and the laparoscope was inserted, revealing either ovaries or testes. Ovaries have often been described as looking like a bunch of grapes, while the male's testes are elongated. In the early 1980s the laparoscope was used for the first time in the UK to determine the sex of parrots. A small number of vets specialised in this work. Breeders would travel long distances to reach one so the journey and the anaesthetic could prove quite stressful to the birds.

Surgical sexing was normally a quick and simple procedure: the anaesthetic was the most dangerous part. In about five minutes the bird would be up and on the perch. There were a few deaths – 11 in the first 2000 birds sexed by one vet. Such deaths were usually due to the bird being overweight or in poor health. The advantage of surgical sexing was that the laparoscope gave a view of internal organs, indicating if the bird had a health problem such as airsaculitis, and if it was mature enough to breed. The disadvantage was that too many incorrect results were obtained, often with birds too immature to sex in this way.

During the decade of the 1980s parrot breeding was revolutionised by artificial incubation of eggs and hand-rearing of the chicks. It became common practice rather than an emergency procedure. The age of innocence was over. Parrots had become big, commercial business in the USA and even in the UK a few breeders gave up their jobs to breed parrots for a living. They had to choose the species very carefully and to know the market trends.

Hand-rearing of larger parrots, cockatoos and macaws for the pet trade became common among small breeders. There was more money to be made which, given the expenses of parrot keeping, was welcomed. Productivity increased because when the eggs or small chicks were removed the female would lay again. Ten or more young from a pair of Blue and Yellow Macaws was achievable with luck. Then a breeder might live off the income. (But no one gave any thought to the psychological effect on the female whose eggs or young chicks were repeatedly snatched away.)

Soon a new kind of business venture emerged: hatching eggs and rearing the young for other breeders. With the higher-priced parrots there was still money to be made by breeders even after paying for this service. One well-known enterprise in Cambridgeshire invested in what was described as a "purpose-built high-tec psittacine breeding centre". During the height of the season, from April to August, the three feeders were working shifts to feed up to 300 parrots during a 21-hour working day. One visitor recorded seeing more than 250 chicks, including 70 macaws, 40 Greys, countless Amazons, lorikeets, three species of Fig Parrots and many cockatoos, including Palm, Red-tailed Black, Leadbeater's and Moluccans. It is difficult to give sufficient attention (especially at the weaning stage) to or to take sufficient hygiene measures when rearing such large numbers. Production on this scale might have been one of the factors that caused the market to slow down but it was the inevitable introduction of disease that brought this particular venture to an end.

Many new breeders had no knowledge of rearing chicks – or no time – and simply took the eggs or the chicks to a commercial rearer. This sounds good in theory but in practice it was a recipe for disaster. Eggs and chicks coming in from all over the country meant that sooner or later serious disease outbreaks would occur. None of these places survived in the long-term.

In every country where aviculture is practised there will be some commercial breeders but not on the scale with which they proliferated in the USA in the 1980s and 1990s. Many people envisaged parrots as a means to rapid wealth! They saw the high prices and calculated these by the number of parrots they thought they could breed in a year. They were so naïve! The lure of what was perceived as easy profit drew into parrot breeding many people who lacked experience with livestock. This was disastrous for the birds and many died in inexperienced hands. A keen young man, an avid reader of parrot literature, on the point of obtaining his first pair, told me that he could not understand why anyone would want to keep Budgerigars and Canaries. He was discarding the important role of easily-bred species. They provide something that is indispensable to the aviculturist – experience. In that respect, the most valuable birds I ever kept were the Budgerigars that reared young for me before I reached my teens.

Big in America

Parrot stocks in the USA declined dramatically because after the psittacosis scare of 1930 there was no legal importation until 1968. By then antibiotics had been developed to treat psittacosis in humans. Parrots had to be treated with chlortetracycline before export and then spend 30 days in quarantine on arrival in the USA. (By the early 1990s there were at least 90 quarantine stations throughout the country.)

In the early 1970s the worldwide trade in wild-caught parrots escalated – literally out of control. The big importers in Florida and California brought parrots (in thousands) from all over the world into their quarantine stations – and mixed them indiscriminately. Disease was rife. In 1972 exotic Newcastle disease (VVND) spread from parrots to poultry. The poultry industry was threatened. In some areas hundreds of parrots were euthanised by the authorities. One can only guess at the agonies suffered by these parrot keepers who had all their birds destroyed. Photographs showed mountains of euthanised cockatoos and parrots.

Speaking at the 1979 American Federation of Aviculture (AFA) Convention, Bob Berry, Curator of Birds at Houston Zoo, said: "It was this chaotic nightmare which was largely

▌ *Bob Berry speaking at the 1979 AFA Convention.*

responsible for forging the AFA. It also caused aviculture to unite and to rally to a common cause, that cause being the survival of aviculture as we know it... The abrupt halt of bird importations shook us into reality. Most of us were not doing our jobs. Zoos certainly did not place any real emphasis on breeding birds, and many aviculturists' attempts were only half-hearted. If this or that bird died we simply went out and bought some more. Today this story is quite different. Most major zoos now place a great deal of emphasis on breeding birds, and many have constructed extensive off-exhibit areas for this purpose."

Nevertheless, not long after the 1972 catastrophe, the importation of parrots resumed – in a big way. Parrot mania had arrived – to the detriment of thousands of hapless wild-caught birds. Jane and Michael Stern were writers. Their Yellow-naped Amazon inspired them to contribute a long feature on parrots to the prestigious magazine *The New Yorker*. They wrote: "... when many stylish people sought extreme ways to express their individuality, one well-publicized method was to keep a wild animal as a pet. Compared with a dog or a cat, a big parrot is flamboyant and conspicuous – a good advertisement for someone trying to be seen as unconventional" (Stern and Stern, 1980).

It was a tragedy for cockatoos that a television programme called Baretta, which was shown from 1975 to 1978, starred a police detective who kept a cockatoo named Fred. The demand for cockatoos skyrocketed. Most of the people who bought them had no idea that they had obtained one of the most sensitive and demanding creatures on the planet. They were unable to cope with them. The Sterns wrote: "Unlike a hula hoop or a pet rock, a parrot that outlives its appeal as a fad cannot be stored in the attic. Hundreds of these sensitive-souled creatures, taken from their mates and families in the South Pacific, wound up neglected or mistreated, and soon dead."

The 1980s

One of the first organisations to take up parrot breeding was Busch Gardens in Tampa, Florida. Established as an entertainment centre by the Anheiser-Busch family of beer producers in the 1950s, it had an impressive parrot collection that I visited several times in the 1980s. There was a famous walkway, lined on both sides with unusually shaped cages each containing a single parrot. (Welfare standards had improved by the end of the century when this type of exhibit would have been unacceptable.) Nevertheless, some interesting species were seen there, also in the traditional aviaries in which breeding successes were sustained. A pair of Queen of Bavaria's Conures, for example, reared more than 50 young.

In 1984 Busch Gardens opened an off-exhibit parrot breeding facility. All the pairs were maintained in small wire cages, elevated and covered for protection from the sun; they stood on a concrete base. This was the first time I had seen numerous breeding pairs kept in such soul-less conditions. Sadly this was to become the norm in the USA and elsewhere. The policy was to remove all chicks at the age of three weeks for hand-rearing.

This trend quickly became established. In my mind it was "the dark age" of aviculture. In 1981 I had visited California and was invited to the homes of a number of parrot breeders – or would-be breeders. I was shocked. It was now the vogue to keep pairs of parrots in tiny wire cages inside buildings. The size of these cages and the total lack of quality of life left me sad and bewildered. One of the first pairs I saw were of Goffin's Cockatoos, set up in a 6ft (1.8m) cage with a nest-box on the outside. These were, of course, wild-caught birds, only a few months (or

■ *Off-exhibit breeding cages at Busch Gardens, Tampa, in 1984.*

even weeks) away from their Indonesian forest home. They were not Budgerigars or Cockatiels that had been captive-bred for generations with no memory and little instinct of life in the wild. They were truly wild creatures, highly intelligent and needing far more stimulation and occupation than a wire cage could provide.

This method so quickly became the norm in the USA that new recruits to parrot breeding (and there were hundreds) did not question it. They accepted that this was how it was done, like keeping battery chickens. I imagine that many soon gave up, disillusioned. No cockatoo chicks were hatched, or the male killed the female out of frustration. Yet some species, such as Grey Parrots did breed well. The birds spent their entire lives in small cages, with nothing to do but breed and, in many cases, with nothing to eat but pellets. Most breeders who kept parrots in this way had absolutely no understanding of their lack of quality of life, of the things that parrots look forward to – a rain shower, their favourite fruits, branches to gnaw and early morning sun. All these things were missing.

Some breeders, especially those who paid great attention to hygiene and disease elimination, became very successful. Annually they turned out dozens or even hundreds of hand-fed young parrots for the pet trade. They sold them unweaned; weaning would have taken too long, reducing profits dramatically. Unweaned young went to pet shops where they picked up infections from parrots from other sources and died, or succumbed due to lack of expertise on the part of those feeding them. Or they died in the hands of inexperienced purchasers. It was a very sad situation but many breeders were operating for profit only, and few cared about some losses.

Avicultural conventions

The conventions hosted by the AFA during the 1980s were the most successful ever held in the USA, reflecting the hey-day of parrot breeding. I recall that staged in San Diego, California, in 1981 as probably being the largest in terms of attendance, with over 750 participants. Breeders came to learn from the 30 speakers, aviculturists and zoo curators, plus 11 vets, who presented papers. The American meetings of the 1980s were alive and buzzing with interest. By the end of the century they were more mundane affairs with fewer speakers and a much smaller attendance.

There was nothing like these meetings in Europe. In 1984, when I met Wolfgang Kiessling for the first time, I suggested that Loro Parque should host an international parrot convention. He instantly jumped on the idea! It took some planning and the first meeting was held in 1986. These meetings, held every four years in Tenerife since then, have become a focal event for the world of parrots, combining lectures with social occasions. Such is their popularity that numbers must be limited, usually to 700 participants. Over the years the emphasis of these meetings has shifted gradually from breeding to conservation.

The 1990s

In the USA parrot importation continued unabated until 1992 when the import of all wild-caught birds was strictly regulated. This changed the face of aviculture forever. Unfortunately at a time when there were many advances that could enhance the lives of captive parrots, some breeders were cashing in on the end of the import trade. One breeder of Amazons told me that he sent all his chicks to a broker in New York when they were five weeks old. They were then exported to Japan for the pet trade. It appalled me to think of such young and vulnerable chicks being shipped around the world.

Guidelines for breeders

One aviculturist who did care was Laurella Desborough. In an article in the American publication *Bird Breeder*, in July 1994, she wrote:

"There is a problem occurring with the sale of unweaned chicks to inexperienced buyers. For many of these buyers, the result is stunted chicks, chicks with heavy bacterial infections, and eventually very sick (or dead) chicks. I have seen 1-year-old parrots that are misshapen and that have poor posture, poor feathering, lack vitality and have low weights. Macaws may be low in weight by hundreds of grams and other parrots by one quarter body weight... It is clearly an irresponsible act to sell an unweaned exotic bird to an inexperienced person who has neither the brooding nor hand-feeding equipment, nor the knowledge of the chick's behaviour and development to guide its daily care."

Parrot breeding had become an industry – one that was beset by problems caused by irresponsible or ignorant breeders. The industry had been born so suddenly that there were no controls, no guidelines. In 1984 Laurella Desborough and a few other caring individuals in the USA set up MAP – the Model Aviculture Program. (By then, parrot breeding accounted for perhaps 85% of aviculture.) It was designed by aviculturists and avian veterinarians to improve basic husbandry and management, and to enable responsible breeders to be recognised as having achieved certain standards in caging, nutrition, record-keeping, quarantine and disease control. It operated on a voluntary aviary inspection and certification basis.

▌*Laurella Desborough.*

Increasingly the words "A MAP Certified Aviary" were appearing in advertisements, giving the prospective purchaser some guarantee of the standard of husbandry. Although only a minority of breeders choose to participate, it was a step in the right direction. In the event that governmental controls were imposed on breeders, the framework for these would already be in place. In Canada, in 1994, the Parrot Association of Canada set up a similar programme.

When breeding cages were large and erected outside, amid shady trees, there were various risks, but the birds' lives were immeasurably improved in comparison with those kept in buildings. In enclosed spaces such as barns and lock-up buildings away from the breeders' home, the disease risks were enormous. Few people quarantined their new purchases, and with wild-caught birds pouring into California and Florida from different continents, avian pox, Pacheco's disease, papillomatosis and proventricular dilatation disease proliferated. Yet the number of indoor breeding facilities grew and grew.

Disillusioned breeders

The move towards keeping breeding parrots in confined spaces, such as barns, ultimately resulted in disillusionment for many breeders. Serious infectious diseases were rife. Polyoma, PBFD (psittacine beak and feather disease) and the wasting disease PDD (proventricular dilatation disease) were the worst of these and accounted for the deaths of thousands of parrots. Before the early 1980s it was almost unknown to keep breeding pairs of the larger parrots in indoor accommodation. With the increase in parrot thefts and the reduction in the size of gardens (resulting in closer neighbours and complaints about the noise) many people ceased to keep parrots outside. The infectious diseases spread easily with fatal consequences in a confined space. Most people who suffered serious losses as a result gave up parrot-keeping. Those who kept parrots in outdoor aviaries did not suffer disease epidemics but their birds were horribly susceptible to theft (see Chapter 6).

During the last decade of the century there was an interesting shift away from keeping breeding pairs permanently in small cages. More and more breeders in North America and elsewhere were building large aviaries in which they could enjoy seeing their pairs flying out of the breeding season. Or, in the case of Grey Parrots that might breed in any month, pairs were rotated so that they all spent some months in a large flight. The birds became much fitter thus, in theory, should have produced more young and over a longer period.

It was not only attitudes that changed. Until the 1970s parrot breeding was a hobby. Science hardly came into it. There was little technique and a lot of the hit or miss approach. Vets knew nothing about parrots. But when parrots became valuable commercially, some breeders worked hard to find methods to maximise their profits. This was especially the case with parrot incubation techniques which had advanced to scientific status by the end of the century. Many breeders learned how to manipulate the humidity in the incubator, or for an individual egg, to maximise hatching success. They weighed eggs daily and kept graphs of their weight loss. (This should reach a certain percentage, usually in the region of 16%, for optimum hatching results.)

This information contrasted starkly with that of 20 years previously when even the incubation period of some species was unknown. Lack of knowledge of how this could be extended (or shortened) by environmental conditions often resulted in impatient breeders opening an egg to discover the embryo was still alive, an action which resulted in its death. By the end of the century a sophisticated piece of equipment had been invented and marketed which tested an egg and indicated if the embryo was alive.

The micro-chip was another facet of the late 20th century that would, only 50 years earlier, have seemed about as likely as a visitor from Mars. All but the smallest parrots could be safely implanted with a microchip. Once implanted, it was not possible to detect the precise location in a bird's body, but the unique number could be read with a scanner. This technology was later used by parrot owners who realised that it was the only positive method of identifying their parrot, should it be stolen, and later located.

During the 1990s DNA sexing for parrots became widely available. Most breeders preferred this method because it was non-invasive, and because pulling a few breast feathers was much less stressful for the bird than an anaesthetic. The feathers were placed in a little envelope and sent off to the appropriate company.

■ *Implanting a microchip in an Amazon Parrot under anaesthetic.*

Outside Europe

In Australia Paul Sperber recalled of the 1950s: "There were not many aviculturists around. We would look through *The Age* newspaper on a Saturday to see what birds [wild-caught] were available at the Melbourne bird dealers... We started going to dealers in Melbourne where we would buy, for example, six pairs of birds ... if we still had a pair alive after two weeks we were very lucky. They would die mainly because of stress and because no one knew anything about disease" (Sperber, 1996).

Sperber recounted how English cars were transported to Australia in large wooden crates. These crates were then used to legally export Australian birds overseas. "I vividly recall when we were at a place in Melbourne there were over 70 Major Mitchell's Cockatoos packed ready to go in these car crates."

Parrot aviculture in Australia improved rapidly. By the end of the century breeding results were good due to a better overall understanding of the birds' needs, combined with good climatic conditions in many areas. Breeding formerly "difficult" species, such as the Golden-shouldered Parakeet (Parrot) (*Psephotus c. chrysopterygius*) had been mastered. Graeme Hyde of Victoria, an aviculturist for 50 years, commented that by the end of the century some Australian parakeets were no longer bred due to lack of demand. Some former keen parrot breeders still kept birds but did not allow them to breed.

In Australia the development of a wide range of mutations, such as those of the Rainbow Lorikeet, Red-rumped Parakeet, Bourke's Parakeet and Cockatiel, had a significant impact on the surplus bird market. It became extremely difficult to obtain birds of the species mentioned that were genetically pure for the original colour. The same applied in Europe. In Australia a few breeders felt strongly enough to form the Pure Species Group. In the USA there was much more interest in neotropical parrots than in parakeets. Hand-reared Hyacinthine Macaws were advertised as "the ultimate pet". With a price-tag of $7,000 to $12,000 each in 1990, they were well beyond the means of the average wage earner.

In Japan since the 1980s the huge demand for tame parrots was mainly met through importation. Very few breeders existed. In

▌ *Elaine Judd in Australia feeding chicks of mutations of Redrump Parakeets in 1994.*

Indonesia, where songbirds (such as thrushes) were, by long tradition, kept for singing contests, there was an unusual twist on this theme. Young lovebirds were reared in the company of songbirds, whose songs they copied. The lovebirds were then entered in singing contests!

Trends in parrot breeding

Trends in breeding are, on the whole, perceived rather than proved. However, members' breeding results published by The Parrot Society UK reinforced the suspicion that in the UK, by the end of the 20th century, there were fewer parrot breeders than ten or 20 years previously and that the number of birds produced by each breeder was lower. In the 15 years for which Breeding Registers were published periodically between 1976 and 2000 the average number of birds bred per year per contributor was 24. 3. (The majority of these would be easily bred species such as Cockatiels and lovebirds.) It fell below 20 for the first time in 2000, when the average number was 16, and it exceeded 30 only in 1984 and 1987. The early to mid-1980s were indeed the heyday of parrot breeding in Europe and the USA.

The mid-1980s showed the highest averages bred per member and the early 1990s the highest total production. Perhaps surprisingly the number of species (and sub-species) bred peaked in 1998 – but the picture was not quite

Parrot Society Breeding Registers

Year	species *	contributing members	number bred	average per member
1977	91 (97)	604	13,256	21.9
1979	78 (120)	676	14,584	21.6
1980	98 (105)	625	15,670	25.0
1981	98 (92)	583	14,340	24.6
1984	119 (133)	859	31,326	36.4
1987	--- (133)	676	20,134	30
1991	146 (163)	1,401	34,287	24
1992	149 (173)	1,260	32,384	26
1994	--- (182)	1,357	29,809	22
1998	160 (201)	1,275	27,092	21
2000	146 (229)	725	11,497	16

* The figures in brackets are the numbers shown in the registers but they include sub-species.

as rosy as it might appear because of the 160 species bred, 21 had but a single breeder. I predict that the number of species reared will decline significantly, possibly quite rapidly.

By the very last years of the century there were more parrot keepers who were not breeders, and far fewer breeders than at any time since the 1970s. I suspect that the main reason was over-production leading to difficulties in selling young birds. In that situation I kept my birds and stopped breeding from them, but most breeders reacted quite differently: they sold their pairs (many of which were exported). They become disillusioned, as though breeding was the only reason to keep birds.

This indicates another change that gradually became evident from the 1980s. Previously aviculturists had kept birds for the pleasure of their company. If they produced young it was a bonus. All this changed. For many breeders profit was the over-riding motive. In 1985 the magazine *Harper's & Queen*, published in London, carried an article entitled "Parrot Passion" by Amanda Atha who "penetrated the world of the polymaths and found ways of making them squawk"! She interviewed a "well-known breeder called Sid Pretty". This was a "polly pseudonym" for several people interviewed. "The reason I keep parrots", said Mr Pretty, "is quite simple. It is the best way I know to make money bar none, and that includes the stock market, anything. It can pay the school fees. Even if they don't breed they more than keep pace with inflation. I know a bloke who makes £80,000 a year out of it, mostly exporting to the Continent".

The fact was that a few men did make large sums from parrots, either mutations or easy-to-breed expensive species such as the large macaws. But most parrot keepers only just covered their costs.

By the end of the twentieth century parrot prices had nose-dived and there was an excess of many species, especially inexpensive aviary birds. This was due to the activities of bird importers and due to the numbers being produced by small breeders. The trend towards fewer parrots in aviaries and more in homes made some aviary birds unsuitable as pets difficult to sell. The Swift Parakeet (*Lathamus discolor*), a threatened Australian species highly sought by breeders in the 1980s, was of little interest and could be bought for £50 each. (Aviculturists were not interested in "conserving" endangered species in captivity.) In the USA commercial breeders of the more expensive species such as macaws flooded the market, devaluing their young birds.

The most significant period

The last quarter of the century was the most significant period to date in the history of parrot keeping. It determined which species would be available to future aviculturists. Ironically, some species imported in large numbers had almost disappeared from aviculture by the end of the century while others were imported in lesser numbers yet were safely established in aviculture. The fate of a species was determined mainly by the ease of breeding it and the generation span. For example, easily bred species that matured quickly, and bred at one to two years old, such as many of the Australian parakeets, were quickly established in aviculture. Those that were more difficult to breed, and took four to eight years to reach sexual maturity, were established if they were also popular in the pet trade. Those that were more difficult to breed or were not in demand for the pet trade, survived only if a few keen breeders specialised in them.

A case in point was the little Red-capped Parrot (*Pionopsitta pileata*) from Brazil which was available from the wild only for a limited period. Numbers were not "topped up" by numerous importations. In the USA Tom Ireland had a number of pairs and bred this species with great success, yet ten years after his death none were to be found. In the UK there were two highly successful breeders who each maintained a number of pairs over a period of 30 years, John Scott in England and Geoff Tooth in Scotland. Both men were enchanted by these little birds that did so well with them, bred prolifically and died of old age after 25 years or so. Yet when John Scott sold the young they seldom lived long enough to breed. Almost invariably they were lost to the future gene pool. The fact is that no breeder with a single pair of one of the rarer species is likely to maintain it over the long term. It is only the specialists that succeed, partly because they secure a number of blood lines, and because they have a different philosophy to the breeder with one pair each of ten or twenty species.

Legislation and record keeping

During the 1980s so many parrots and other previously little-known birds were imported and bred in captivity that aviculture had the potential to make a major contribution to scientific knowledge. Major natural history museums throughout the world had few specimens or only those prepared a century previously of species that were discarded after death in hundreds by importers and breeders. The value of the published word was also ignored by the majority of breeders. Many kept no records of any kind. A few maintained excellent records and published ground-breaking articles but generally it was zoo personnel, rather than private aviculturists, who realised the importance of making observations and keeping records. They published the results in avicultural, scientific or zoological publications.

The lack of record keeping had serious consequences for a few breeders of endangered species. In an extreme case it even resulted in a prison sentence. Smuggling was suspected but without records and, incredibly, with closed-ringing of young being totally ignored, the breeder was unable to prove his declared innocence. To enjoy the privilege of keeping endangered species, which many parrot lovers will never even have the pleasure of seeing, let alone breeding, and to fail to fit closed rings to their young, is irresponsible. How can wise use be made of them if individuals cannot be identified?

■ *Swift Parakeet.*

Red-capped Parrot, immature male, captive-bred

When parrot breeding started in earnest, in the 1970s, there was a total lack of regulation in the UK. It applied not only to parrots and anyone could keep a tiger in their garden, if they so wished! You could import any species from anywhere. Quarantine regulations came into force in the early 1980s. By the end of the century all species recognised as endangered by trade, that is, on Appendix I of CITES, had to be registered and identified by a closed ring or micro-chip. Papers for the sale of young (or adult) birds would not be issued by the CITES authority (then the DOE, now DEFRA) in the absence of identification.

Regulations or international treaties such as CITES varied in their implementation from country to country. In the mid-1980s Spain was notoriously lax and a hot-bed of illegal international trade in parrots and other animals. Then suddenly in the early 1990s the treaty was implemented so rigorously in Spain that it was impossible to sell genuine closed-ringed captive-bred parrots until every bird in the collection had been documented and verified by officials. In the case of a large collection, such as that which I cared for in Gran Canaria, the work and its verification by officials, could take several years. During this period no young could be sold. To say that this created major space problems would be an understatement.

Further problems were created by loosely worded clauses in legislation that were interpreted differently by officials in different countries. Parrot breeding had evolved from a back-yard pastime to one that involved knowledge of international laws and contact with government officials. The legislation was necessary, especially in view of the smuggling that was threatening the future of some parrot species, but its implementation caused many problems. This was not the case at the century's end for breeders who kept good records and ringed or micro-chipped their young.

Susan Clubb recorded that, in the USA, "Aviculturists fear regulation on the national, state, or local level, which will limit their right to sell their birds. Confusion about the application of federal law to captive wildlife, and an ever-changing barrage of state laws and local ordinances fuel this fear. For example, in Florida an aviculturist must register in order to sell or exhibit birds in the state. Under the Sunshine Law, a freedom-of-information-styled law, these records are accessible to the public. Aviculturists fear that this makes their birds vulnerable to theft. Certainly the fear of theft or confiscation is a driving force in the development of paranoia among aviculturists, fed by the value of many species and the difficulty of tracing them once stolen" (Clubb, 1992).

The lighter side

Sometimes one needs to focus on the lighter side of parrot keeping. Advertisements in the British avicultural press could make you smile. One of my favourites read: "Three-legged rat (lost fight with Parrot). Free to approved home."

The unusual and the practical were combined by one breeder and his neighbour. The man was breeding Eclectus Parrots in the small garden of a south-east London suburb at a time (early 1970s) when these parrots were very uncommon. As the pair was prolific and he wanted the female to have a break from breeding, he removed the two eggs. However, they did not go in the bin. He gave them to his neighbour who fried them for breakfast!

3. THE WORLD OF ZOOS

I was fortunate to grow up near to the London/ Kent boundary, thus as a teenager London Zoo was easily accessible to me. The parrots were in cramped, over-heated accommodation – but in those days few people had seen these birds kept in any other way. Indeed, the Parrot House had not altered much in half a century or more. In 1879 C. W. Gedney had described it as "that room of horrors". He referred to the way the birds were kept. In the 1920s, the Rev. Farrar, vicar of Micklefield, near Leeds, wrote an entertaining book entitled *Through a Bird-Room Window*. He sometimes had cause to disagree with Gedney, but on one subject he was in full agreement. He described the Parrot House as that veritable avian 'Chamber of Horrors'".

It was reported in the *Avicultural Magazine* (1930, p80) that the building "will very soon either be demolished or used for some other purpose". It had been constructed at the time of the Great Exhibition of 1851 and paid for by the famous bird illustrator John Gould, in order to exhibit his unique collection of stuffed hummingbirds. The gate receipts went to Gould who made a huge profit. The new parrot house was opened in 1930, just after the start of the Depression, a bleak period in British history that brought hardship to those in industrialised towns. A visit to the Zoo would have been a rare treat for most families and the flamboyant macaws would have filled them with delight. For the more discerning, the rarities to be seen included a Racket-tailed Parrot (*Prioniturus*), of a genus whose species are noted for the intriguing tail formation. There was also a Red-cheeked Geoffroyus Parrot (*Geoffroyus geoffroyi cyanicollis*) from Halmahera in the Moluccas Islands. *Geoffroyus* are not rare in the wild but they have proved very difficult to maintain in captivity.

The Parrot House

Arthur Prestwich (*Avicultural Magazine*, 1930, page 215) wrote that at last a house worthy of the zoo's fine collection of parrots had been provided. (Prestwich later became secretary of the Avicultural Society. Between 1950 and 1954 he published seven volumes listing records of parrots bred in the UK.) An astute reader of the *Daily Mail* of June 26 1930, thought otherwise. "It is odious", he wrote, "that affectionate creatures like Lories and Caiques should be caged singly." How right he was! "Any doubter should give a minute to playing with the Brazilian 'Golden' Conure – he welcomes even a human friend in his solitary prison... Big birds are cramped; sociable birds are isolated; timid birds are, without possible retreat, at the mercy of teasing passers-by."

But this is how zoos were in that era. No thought was given to the psychological welfare of the occupants. "Environmental enrichment" was a long way in the future. Arthur Prestwich responded to the criticism by calling it a "hysterical outburst". He pointed out that one of the primary objects of the zoo was "the exhibition of the largest possible number of representative species, caged and housed in the best practical manner."

■ *Arthur Prestwich.*
Photograph courtesy of the Avicultural Society

This statement indicates how times have changed – and note the use of the word practical. By the end of the century the emphasis was on a few animals in an environment that was conducive to their well-being. There was also the widely held view, soon to be reinforced by law, that zoos must prove that they were involved in conservation or risk closure. Just showing animals was not enough.

In 1931 Sir Chalmers Mitchell wrote that London Zoo maintained "what is perhaps the finest living collection of parrots in the world". He described the Parrot House in *Guide to the Gardens and Aquarium, Regents Park*, as follows: "The large room facing the Flower Garden and formerly the dining room, has twelve aviaries on the northern side, suitable for lories and lorikeets, and down the centre and at the ends are stands and cages for parrots and macaws. The room to the west side, formerly a buffet and luncheon room, contains in the centre two rows of macaws on swings and has smaller parrots on stands round the sides. Not open to the visitors are rooms serving for quarantine of new arrivals, places for sick birds, and accommodation for keepers. The row of aviaries along the south side is for hardier birds and consists of shelters and large wired flights with turfed floors" (Chalmers Mitchell, 1931).

The number of species exhibited totalled 130 – a significant number in any era. Several had been there since 1907, including a Blue

and Yellow Macaw, a Ducorp's Cockatoo and a Greater Sulphur-crested Cockatoo. The macaws included a Spix's. Some of these cages were still in use in the 1960s. The rarest Amazon was the Imperial (*Amazona imperialis*). It arrived on loan from the Governor-General of the West Indies on April 17 1961 but died on October 27 of the same year. On arrival it weighed 965g. Twenty-eight days later its weight had increased to 1,180g, according to the zoo records. From the scant information available, 800–900g for an adult male would be the maximum for a healthy bird of this species. As Imperial Parrots were normally acquired by shooting, most captive birds had serious health problems.

This parrot is well named. It is indeed an imperious and aloof creature, quite unlike the friendly St Vincent whose temperament allows it to adapt more easily to captivity. A captive Imperial seems to be bewildered by an environment lacking in the majestic forests, mountains and waterfalls of Dominica (pronounced Dominíca), its island home in the Caribbean (not to be confused with the Dominican Republic). Extremely shy, it seldom encounters man, for it lives in the highest, almost inaccessible mountains. In this it differs from the Red-necked Amazon (*Amazona arausiaca*), Dominica's other parrot.

The Imperial was by no means the rarest occupant of the Parrot House through the years. This dubious title must go to the now extinct Glaucous Macaw (see Chapter 17). The Zoo's records indicate that a Glaucous arrived in May 1898 (when Queen Victoria was on the throne) and died in 1912 (when George V was king). Another entered the collection in 1906 and lived until 1916. These dates overlapped by six years. The sexes of these two macaws would have been unknown but one cannot help wondering whether they were kept together. If they were, they were almost certainly denied the opportunity to breed. They would have been correctly identified: Lear's Macaws were fairly well known at the time so it seems unlikely that a mistake was made. The two species are almost identical (see colour page 22) except in the shade of their blue plumage.

Unlike the Passenger Pigeon and the Carolina Parakeet, in which the deaths of the last zoo specimens were recorded down to the hour, there was no realisation that the Glaucous was

The Parrot House at London Zoo in 1969.

Photograph: Thomas Brosset

of special interest, or that it was rare. Nothing is known about its extinction in the wild; rumours, without evidence, persisted throughout the 20th century that it might have survived. The presence of the zoo's birds and another in the UK during the same era is not referred to in the historical literature.

There was little appreciation of the Glaucous, yet the arrival of a "rare and remarkable" Kakapo in 1907 was heralded: it was said to be a species on the verge of extinction. That it was the first to be exhibited at the zoo since 1875 made this "a matter of no small importance and satisfaction". It was considered satisfying to have captured a nearly extinct species. The bird was presented to the Zoo by the great natural history collector, the Hon. Walter Rothschild. He would have been fascinated by the flightless, nocturnal Kakapo, the heaviest of all parrots.

Because many parrots are long lived, the Parrot House collection was maintained, even through two world wars. By the early 1960s it exhibited one of the most comprehensive parrot collections in the world. To me, it was a veritable treasure trove. Nearly all the birds were housed singly; half a dozen lucky pairs had access to

The big parrot aviary at London Zoo in the 1970s.

Photograph: Thomas Brosset

■ *Female Vasa Parrot.*

outdoor aviaries. There was also a colony of Quaker Parakeets breeding in their nests of sticks.

It was in the Parrot House that I cut my teeth on parrot identification. I grew up being as familiar with Red-tailed Black-Cockatoos, Gang Gangs and Hyacinthine Macaws as with Grey Parrots and Senegals. I recall such Amazon rarities as a Black-billed Amazon and a Diademed (*Amazona autumnalis diadema*). I noted at the time that its cere and nostrils were feathered (unlike those of other *autumnalis* sub-species, although in *salvini* there can be a few feathers on

the cere). Extremely rare in captivity at the time was a tiny Double-eyed Fig Parrot (*Opopsitta diophthalmus*). It was presented to the Zoo in 1957 by the BBC, brought back by David Attenborough from his "Zoo Quest" expedition to New Guinea. This short-tailed parrot, only 5 ½ in (14cm) long, filled me with wonder. It lived for many years, until its plumage became mottled yellow with age. I was fascinated by the Greater Vasa Parrot, another BBC gift, this time from David Attenborough's journey to Madagascar. A female, she moulted her head feathers when she came into breeding condition – as is normal in this species. Furthermore the bare skin on the head turned bright yellow.

Some parrots were collected specifically for the zoo and carefully transported to England. Others were donated by individuals who had been living overseas. In contrast, by the century's end most parrots in zoos were bred in captivity or originated from big importations. There was no romantic "history" behind them as was so often the case in days gone by. The Parrot House even contained a parrot before it had been named to science. It hid under the name of the Mealy Amazon. A decade later Kawall's Amazon was described (see Chapter 16) and the mystery was solved.

■ *Parrot aviaries built at London Zoo in the 1990s. The big aviary illustrated on page 43 had been pulled down.*

In the early 1970s a Red-lored Amazon, whose beauty impressed me greatly with its great brown eyes, dark lashes and cheeks suffused with orange, was a fortunate bird for it lived in a big outdoor aviary. It liked to cling to the mesh to talk to passers-by. At the time the high aviary, devoid of landscaping, was probably the largest parrot aviary in a British zoo.

The Parrot House continued to fascinate parrot lovers until it closed in 1986. Most of the occupants were sent to other collections. The zoo had little interest in displaying parrots and by the year 2000 it kept only half a dozen species.

Elsewhere in England

During the 1970s and 1980s bird parks in the UK sprung up like mushrooms after rain. The life of some of them was not much longer. They failed to emulate the success of the first two, that opened in 1963. Rode Bird Gardens, near Bath, was the inspiration of Donald Risdon. The great attraction was seeing macaws flying free, gliding between the big ancient trees and even breeding at liberty within the garden's 17 acres. The woodland lake with its penguins, the flower gardens and the miniature railway made this an idyllic place to be on a summer's day. Many breeding successes occurred including

■ *Donald Risdon at Rode in 1964.*

the first UK breeding of the Endangered Red-tailed Amazon.

Birdland had some extremely rare species, such as Lear's Macaw and a Red and Blue Lory (*Eos histrio*), as well as uncommon ones such as Golden Conures and Hawk-headed Parrots. Among English bird gardens, the charm of Birdland in its Cotswold setting has, perhaps, never been equalled. The word garden was no euphemism. Lawns, ponds, and planting inside and outside the aviaries put the original Birdland (not to be confused with the current one close to the original site) in a class of its own. Budgerigars bred in holes in the trees, and macaws flew at liberty, their long tails floating in the wind before they circled and came in to land. Sometimes they descended to the lawns and paths where they could be observed busily chewing off dried up tulip heads or eating groundsel. The macaws were accompanied in flight by Grey Parrot, Juno. This bird was so tame that she would lie on her back in the hand of Birdland's jovial, loquacious owner, Len Hill; then he would bounce her up and down like a ball.

An eclectic selection of parrots included species that were then rare in aviculture: Palm Cockatoos and seldom-seen macaws including Hahn's (a breeding pair), Red-bellied and, rarest of all, a "pair" of Lear's. If only they had been a pair the history of this species in Europe might have been different. Those were the days before any form of sex determination, and the Lear's turned out to be two females. For many visitors, the tropical house, opened by the renowned conservationist and artist Peter Scott in 1965, was the highlight of Birdland. Inside one could see 70 birds of 33 species.

An aviary complex of historical interest was (and still is) Waddesdon Manor in Buckinghamshire. It had maintained its ornate Renaissance aviaries built by Baron Ferdinand de Rothschild in 1889 (see colour page 1). Outside the aviaries, macaws and cockatoos were placed on stands during the day and taken in at night. His descendant Lord Walter Rothschild, who died in 1937, was a great ornithologist and collector of zoological specimens. His contributions to ornithological literature ran into hundreds of papers. We do not know which species he kept in these aviaries but they almost certainly included parrots, in

Twenty-first birthday celebrations at Rode in 1985: Johnny Morris (left) and Terry Nutkin (right) of TV's "Animal Magic", Betty Risdon centre and, behind, Donald Risdon and Mike Curzon, curator.

Photograph (and preceding page) courtesy of Mike Curzon

visited the zoo in the mid-1970s I enjoyed seeing parrots bred on the colony system, especially the colourful and charismatic Red-masked Conures. Patagonian Conures had their own colony where they had increased from three to 17 individuals and in an aviary for Nanday Conures, the population had increased from four birds in 1968 to 30. Inside the parrot house a group of 15 Grey Parrots were thriving in one enclosure and two pairs were rearing young.

The largest colony was that for Cockatiels. George Mottershead, founder of the zoo and then in his eighties and as enthusiastic as ever, took me to see this aviary. A man after my own heart, he said I should not miss it because he liked to see large flocks. I have long believed that other zoos have missed out on what is always a wonderful attraction: a large group of one species flying together. Chester had another attraction for me: the last pair of the exquisite little Varied Lorikeet to be seen in the UK. Outside Australia, this species was available only to mainstream zoos.

Towards the end of the century the enormous expense of setting up a new zoo or bird park made this a very rare event. Few zoos, let alone

which he had a great interest. Three parrot sub-species were named in his honour but only that of the Fairy Lorikeet (*Charmosyna pulchella rothschildi*) is valid or truly distinctive. (It was Lord Rothschild who, in 1930, pointed out to his museum curator, Dr Ernst Hartert, the green band on the breast that distinguishes this form.)

The aviaries were restored in the early 1970s when free-flying macaws graced the magnificent grounds. Parrots could still be seen along with the pheasants and insectivorous birds at the end of the century.

For the last quarter of the century the biggest bird collection in any zoo in the UK was that of Chester – the North of England Zoological Society. The number of parrot species maintained was never large but unlike most zoos, Chester had and still has excellent breeding results. When I first

Left: Len Hill with Juno. Right: The charming gardens of Birdland.

■ *Birdland, Bourton-on-the-Water, in 1975 when macaws flew freely.*

Photograph: Thomas Brosset

programme at Jersey Wildlife Preservation Trust) could also be seen. By far the rarest were the Echo Parakeets (*Psittacula eques*), two males that were unsuitable for the captive-breeding programme for this Critically Endangered species on Mauritius (see colour page 11). Visitors might have passed by without realising it was one of the world's rarest parrots but believing it was one of the most common – the Indian Ringneck Parakeet! Jersey and Chester Zoos were the only other places where these parakeets could be seen. One of the highlights of Paradise Park was the 150ft (45m) long aviary, in which young macaws and cockatoos flew with other parrots bred there.

bird parks, could survive without adding family amusements. In 2001 the immensely popular UK bird park at Rode closed. It had refused to turn the gardens into an entertainment centre. There were few bird parks left.

The best parrot collection was found at Paradise Park in Cornwall, home of the World Parrot Trust. Set in attractively planted gardens, the aviaries contained rare as well as common species. The St Vincent Parrot had bred there and two male St Lucia Parrots (*Amazona versicolor*) (surplus to requirements from the breeding

■ *St Lucia Parrot at Paradise Park.*

European zoos

Holland and Germany have a long tradition of zoos with good bird collections. The Zoological Gardens of Wassenaar were situated 2 miles (nearly 3km) from The Hague, thus were the first stop for many zoo enthusiasts from Britain who took the ferry to Holland. Even in 1951 they exhibited more than 30 parrot species although many of these, such as the Kea, were single birds (de Goederen, 1951). Nearly 20 years later it was at Wassenaar that I saw for the first time parrots living in a flock in a large (very large) planted aviary. They were parrotlets (*Forpus*) and the thrill of seeing them kept this way has never left me. Whatever the weather, one could enjoy a visit to a huge heated planted indoor enclosure.

Because I knew so many parrots when I was young, I have no recollection of the first time I saw most species. My most vivid recollections in this respect relate to those that were not on show at London Zoo, for example, the Yellow-naped Macaw at Wassenaar and Crimson-bellied Conures (*Pyrrhura rhodogaster*, now *Pyrrhura perlata perlata*). It still seems strange to me when people who have kept parrots for some years tell me that they have just seen their first Hyacinthine Macaw or black cockatoo or Golden Conure. As a teenager these species were as familiar to me as the Cockatiel is to the man in the street. I was already squirreling away parrot facts and memories that would form the basis of two life-long passions: parrots and collecting information about them. While all birds fascinated me, I found parrots so compellingly beautiful and interesting that I wanted to know more – much more.

The middle decade of the century saw exciting new developments in European zoos. Private bird collections were fewer and less extensive but, said Jean Delacour and Lee Crandall in 1952, "... bird collections in the European zoos are often excellent, and much better exhibited than they used to be..." (*Avicultural Magazine*, page 5). It was in the 1950s that the first bird parks came into being, and these parks did not overlook the popularity of colourful parrots. One of the longest established, opened in 1949, was Avifauna at Alphen-on-the Rhine in Holland.

Founded in 1958 as the private collection of Wolfgang Brehm, a parrot collection was emerging as the finest in Europe. Vogelpark Walsrode put the small German town of Walsrode (between Bremen and Hannover) firmly on the map. At the end of the century it was still one of the world's most important bird collections. In 1981 it contained 4,000 birds of more than 900 species in 45 acres, 20 acres of which were set aside for breeding aviaries. The lovely grounds, situated within a pine forest,

were planted with thousands of rhododendrons, azaleas and 15,000 roses (see colour page 3). In 1978 it received a staggering 1.4 million visitors: an extraordinary number – especially as it opened only between March and November.

For me the highlight was the Lory Atrium, of pleasing design and fascinating exhibits, such as Striated (unusual for the vertical streaks on the breast), Musschenbroek's (with its deep red breast and under wing coverts) and Yellow and Green Lorikeets, and Cardinal Lories, all of which I saw there for the first time. It also housed an excellent collection of Fig Parrots.

The attractively designed parrot house, an octagonal pavilion, was opened in 1974. A huge painting on glass of Scarlet Macaws declared the theme. The house and the surrounding aviaries exhibited certain species seldom seen in captivity then, such as the Red-fronted Macaw (*Ara rubrogenys*) and the Red-throated Conure (*Aratinga holochlora rubritorquis*). Parrot fanatics would travel to Germany just to see the rare and handsome Blue-throated Macaws (*Ara glaucogularis*).

In its time the house saw even rarer parrots, including a Spix's Macaw and the Yellow-eared Parrot (*Ognorhynchus icterotis*), then called a conure, that had been imported into England a few years previously. (This unusual parrot from Colombia and Ecuador was almost extinct in the late 1990s – see Chapter 12). The single Imperial Parrot (see colour page 3 and illustration on page 45) provided the only opportunity to see this species outside Dominica. In addition, there was a pair off-exhibit. Hopes had run high when the female Imperial stayed in the nest-box for two months. When she emerged the anticlimax was enormous: the box was empty. No breeding was ever recorded there. Not only do times change but so do philosophies. Under no circumstances would a zoo acquire this critically endangered species today.

■ *The lory atrium at Vogelpark, Walsrode.*

Tropical house for small South American parrots at NiederRheinPark Plantaria.

Another avicultural rarity was a pair of Red-necked Amazons, also from Dominica. In superb condition, they chortled and shouted and flared their tails. This large parrot is mainly green, with the head and throat blue. According to the guidebook, these parrots had last been seen in Europe in 1900. This was incorrect as Sydney Porter had brought three to England in the late 1920s.

Another pair of large and magnificent Caribbean Amazon, the St Vincent, or Guilding's Amazon, was perhaps the most admired of the parrots for its friendly personality and unusual plumage – different in every individual. One bird, for example, had white on the forehead, crown and lores, a subtle mixture of yellow, blue and green on the rest of the head, tawny orange, brown and green body, blue primaries and blue tail broadly banded with yellow. This is a large, broad, parrot, almost equal to the Imperial (the largest of the short-tailed parrots excluding the Kakapo) in size and bulk. Off-exhibit were two more pairs, one female of which had laid but the eggs were infertile. At the time captive-breeding was often cited as the way to save this parrot from extinction. This proved not to be the case.

Four ranges of aviaries extended between the Parrot House and the Lory Atrium. Unusually a pair each of two unrelated species was kept in each aviary; for example, *Pyrrhura* conures would share their spacious aviary with a pair of different sub-species of Crimson-wing (including the Timor) and King Parakeets (Parrots). The fabulous dark red, long-tailed Shining Parrots from Fiji were represented by two specimens from Vanua Levu (*Prosopeia tabuensis atrogularis*).

The aviaries were, and still are, set along a rose-lined path. It borders a wide expanse of meticulously groomed lawn and a fountain whose elegant jets of water almost equal in height the tall fir trees behind. By the century's end, the parrot collection was much reduced. As in most bird parks, it had been necessary to include other forms of amusement in order to maintain visitor numbers.

In Walsrode's hey-day, off-exhibit breeding facilities for parrots in zoos were non-existent or meagre. The opposite was the case here. Completed in 1978 was a large, light, airy building with a wide passage, flanked on each side by 24 aviaries. At the touch of a button the roof lifted up and would operate automatically according to the temperature at which the mechanism was set. The building was heated by boilers. Stainless steel feeding hatches in parrot aviaries were almost unheard of then – and the envy of any aviculturist who saw them. Constructed from glass bricks, the food preparation kitchen was equally impressive. At 7am daily it was presided over by Klaus Trogisch, the ebullient head parrot keeper. He had an awesome knowledge of the parrots, obtained as a result of long hours in their company and many trips to the tropics to bring back birds.

In Europe a few small bird parks had come into existence during the last decade of the century when most mainstream zoos had few parrots in their collections. In 1998 a new bird park opened in Germany and the emphasis was heavily on parrots. Located in the west, not far from the borders with Belgium and the Netherlands, the design of the aviaries at NiederRheinPark Plantaria was outstanding. There was meticulous attention to detail and it was easy to tell that an experienced aviculturist was behind it. Director Werner Neumann had kept parrots for decades and most of those on show came from his extensive private collection. The arrangement was geographical. The aviaries for the smaller neotropical species were within a large tropical house with a glass-panelled roof. Here birds, plants and fish combined to create a jungle atmosphere as plants climbed over the tops of aviaries. Banana palms, cordylines, ginger plants and heliconias gave more than a hint of the tropics. On a rainy day this hall was the perfect retreat. The outdoor aviaries were an integral part of this innovative building. Viewed from outside, the tropical house had a modern look with the two-tiered roof of glass panels above the red-brown roof which sloped down to the aviaries. Lovers of flowers delighted in Plantaria. Before it opened, 500 trees, 28,000 shrubs and nearly 100,000 spring flowers were planted.

In the USA

The preferences or passions of a zoo's curator often played a strong role in the species exhibited in zoos. At Chicago's Brookfield Zoo of the 1950s curator Karl Plath was very interested in parrots and pigeons. It had one of the finest parrot collections in the country and recorded a number of first captive breedings for the continent, including Goldie's Lorikeet. Between 1938, the year that parrot breeding commenced there, and 1951, impressive (for the era) numbers of some species had been reared. These included 35 Swainson's Lorikeets, 109 "Shell Parakeets" (Budgerigars), 27 Princess of Wales Parakeets, 36 King Parrots and 21 Bourke's Parakeets (Plath, 1951).

Wonderful as the European collections of the 1980s were, I yearned to visit what was, at the time, the world's most comprehensive parrot collection. Blessed with the wonderful climate of southern California, the visitors had poured into San Diego Zoo since 1916, enabling it to obtain rare and beautiful creatures from all corners of the planet. Director Belle Benchley had a passion for parrots, thus started San Diego's long association with these birds.

A generation on, under the curatorship of Kenton C. Lint in the 1960s, the parrot collection had become second to none and recorded many first captive breeding successes. These included the Thick-billed Parrot (*Rhynchopsitta pachyrhyncha*) from Mexico and the Blue-crowned Lory (*Vini australis*) from the Pacific islands. If London Zoo was my school, it was San Diego Zoo that was my inspiration. By 1975 I was married to another parrot enthusiast, Bob Grantham. There could be only one destination for our first trip outside Europe: San Diego Zoo. On arrival we met K. C., a most kind and hospitable man, courteous and softly spoken and one of the truly great men of the zoo world. We were to remain friends until his death. Over lunch on that first day I began to appreciate the depth of his knowledge, his immense practical experience and the extent of his travels in search of birds. He had seen Patagonian Conures eating pumpkin seeds in Patagonia and Vasa Parrots drinking coconut milk in Madagascar. (Some knowledge of how the birds in your care live in the wild is, in my opinion, essential to good husbandry.)

He had built up the bird collection from 40 species in 1936 to more than 400 species. The collection lived up to my expectations – and more! For me the focal point was a large aviary containing hand-reared young lories. If you entered, you could not escape having half a dozen species (some of which, as a lory enthusiast, I could only dream about) climbing over you,

*K. C. Lint, **left**, and Art Risser, successive bird curators at San Diego Zoo.*

tasting your face and hair. I was enchanted by this riot of fun and colour! Furthermore, K. C. showed me how to hand-rear lory chicks. The vastness of the zoo, with its cable car high above the enclosures, the sub-tropical planting and the California sunshine would lift anyone's spirits. For me, savouring the new-found friendship of K. C., the friendliness of all the zoo staff and the plethora of parrot species, this was nirvana!

Then at its zenith, within a few months of K. C.'s retirement in 1976 the parrot collection was reduced to a shadow of its former glory. In 1986 the Curator of Birds was Art Risser – one of a new breed of curators emerging in that era. Exhibiting as many species as possible was no longer fashionable; concentrating on a few important birds was the aim. Parrots that had been breeding at the zoo for years, including prolific pairs that had supplied other collections, were dispersed in many directions and soon some were virtually lost from US aviculture.

Some years later Art Risser returned from a three-week collecting trip in New Guinea with two parrots unknown to aviculture. One of these was a species of Tiger Parrot (*Psittacella*). The name alone sounds mysterious. There are four species of these little parrots, only 6in (14cm) to 10in (24cm) in length and characterised by the brown and yellow stripes in different areas of the plumage. It had probably never before or since been seen outside New Guinea. Sadly it, and the tiny Whiskered Lorikeets, did not survive long. In the 1990s a few Whiskered Lorikeets reached Europe but proved to be difficult to establish in captivity. (Only Loro Parque and two or three private breeders were consistently successful.)

On the east coast of America there was a very different bird collection. Parrot Jungle in South Miami was famous for its macaws. Many of them were free-flying for most of their lives in the attractive 20 acres of gardens. I suspect that Parrot Jungle was the inspiration behind many bird parks that opened worldwide in the coming decades. No location worldwide had more generations of captive-bred macaws. A Military, imported in 1936 for the opening of the park, died in 1992, aged at least 57 years. The first two macaws hatched there (hybrids) were christened King and Queen. Queen died aged 49 and King lived for a few years more. The owner, Franz Scherr, had a dream of producing a golden macaw, which he nearly achieved by hybridising.

When the Scherrs retired in the 1980s, Parrot Jungle was bought by a former bird

Birthday celebrations for King and Queen.

Photograph: Parrot Jungle

King aged 52 years in 1992.

importer, Bern Levine. In 1992 Miami was hit by Hurricane Andrew. When the hurricane warning was issued staff worked for many hours to move all the birds to a safer location. Not one was lost. Few trees had been left standing in their former condition – a tragedy for this oasis of Florida hardwoods which had been famous for its lush vegetation. In 2005 it was moved to a new location just off the coast, and changed its name to Parrot Jungle Island.

Loro Parque's supremacy

In the 1980s Wolfgang Kiessling usurped Walsrode's premier position among parrot collections, in a climate conducive to attracting a high attendance. Kiessling realised Tenerife's future in tourism before the Canary Islands had become a major holiday destination. He knew nothing about parrots but could envisage their potential. Never a man with small ambitions, he decided to build up the finest parrot collection in existence. Loro Parque opened in 1972 in the warm and often cloudy climate of northern Tenerife. It was destined to become more than a parrot park (see colour page 2).

Wolfgang Kiessling

Since the 1980s Loro Parque has been renowned for the finest parrot collection worldwide that is open to the public and the most comprehensive that has ever existed. It is also a botanical garden where palms, including the native dragon tree, pines and cacti flourish side by side. Estrelitzia, lilies and many other attractive and showy flowers are blooming. Low hedges of the red-flowering crown of thorns provide neat barriers in front of some aviaries. Trees of impressive size, including a giant fig, occur throughout the park which is always clean and immaculately kept.

As soon as the collection became large, well before my first visit in 1984, the parrots were arranged zoogeographically, making comparison of different species easy. I worked and lived there from 1987 to 1989. It was a privilege to observe so many interesting species on a daily basis. Among my favourites were a small group of exquisite little Orange-breasted Fig Parrots (*Opopsitta gulielmitertii*) and the drab-coloured and behaviourally unique Vasa Parrots (*Coracopsis*). Even now the excitement I feel as I enter Loro Parque never leaves me. With so many parrot species to observe, the day ahead can only be fascinating. This is partly because of the opportunities to observe and learn. The geographical arrangement has great appeal for me. It is like seeing *Parrots of the World* (Joseph Forshaw's classic work that describes every species in detail) come to life. Perhaps if the species were scattered around randomly, the lure of this park would not be so strong. It is unique and an experience that no parrot keeper should miss.

In the three decades since its inception there has been a major shift in the way birds are exhibited in zoos, with increasing emphasis on maintaining them in more natural conditions, in large enclosures. It seems likely that eventually Loro Parque must acknowledge this trend.

Since the mid-1980s breeding parrots at Loro Parque assumed great importance. The large breeding centre near the dolphinarium opened in 1987 when I was curator. It provided additional off-exhibit accommodation for pairs besides that in the original breeding centre opened in 1983 with one hundred aviaries. Dozens of trees were planted for shade and hundreds of suspended aviaries were built. There was also a range of 59ft (18m) long aviaries with solid

Orange-breasted Fig Parrots at Loro Parque in 1988.

superbly landscaped enclosure.

At the start of the 1990s there were approximately 800 parrots of about 220 species (of the 350 or so in existence) and up to 60 more sub-species in the collection. Thirty-five staff cared for the birds and five people worked in the hand-rearing room in two shifts. Approximately 700 chicks were reared every year of 130 species and sub-species. The public could watch the chicks being fed through large windows in an attractive curved building entitled the "baby station". In my day we had two small rooms, one of which had a small show window. Two girls worked there (in two shifts) and I worked the weekends.

By 2001 the annual total reared had grown to 1,150 young of 160 species and sub-species. Chicks hatched in nest-boxes with their parents spent three weeks in a quarantine room before joining the incubator-hatched chicks. Every day

walls where, among others, the Spix's Macaws (see colour page 18) were kept.

During the 1990s the park was redeveloped and improved to an extraordinary degree. Only the famous curving range of lory aviaries remained to remind me of how it used to be – and those aviaries were replaced in 2002. By then the generous, often dense, planting between aviaries, provided a barrier between each pair of parrots. Admittedly for many visitors the parrots were of lesser interest than the dolphins, the sealions or the bachelor group of gorillas in their

The original curving range of lory aviaries.

8,000 feeding dishes were washed. Every other Saturday two tons of casuarinas branches were delivered, to be distributed among the aviaries. How parrots loved those branches!

In 1997 there was a huge development: the opening of the first phase of the new breeding centre for 2,000 parrots, a few kilometres from the park. It was acquired as a 4,000 sq metre banana plantation in 1995. Mr Kiessling, the park's founder, told me: "My aim is to make this the best parrot breeding centre in the world. The emphasis is on keeping parrots under the best possible conditions." Furthermore, the parrots were now the property of Loro Parque Fundacion, the important conservation organisation founded in 1994 (see Chapter 13).

Loro Parque's collection had grown from 150 parrots in 1972, in an area of 13,000 sq metres (4.6 acres), to more than 3000 parrots of 340 species and sub-species by the end of the century. Its area had increased four-fold. The park collaborated in 23 of the 24 European breeding programmes for endangered parrot species (EEPs) and kept the studbooks for five of these. The 1.5 million visitors per annum included 25,000 schoolchildren. There was close collaboration with educational authorities and school videos had been produced in four languages. The park was voted the regional model for educational school activities. It had become the supreme example of a zoo that was fulfilling its conservation and educational commitments. In addition it had raised the profile of parrots and given millions of visitors to Tenerife a day to remember.

Asia

North America and northern Europe had led the world for outstanding bird collections in zoos. Asia was up-and-coming, with one of the world's best bird collections. Jurong BirdPark in Singapore was a bird lover's paradise. The visitor needed two full days to see everything. Some of the aviaries in the Parrot Paradise section were notable for their painted backgrounds depicting the species' natural habitat. However, it was watching parrots in the enormous planted aviaries, behaving as they would in the wild, that gave the greatest satisfaction.

In the huge Waterfall aviary one could watch dozens of lories (see colour page 4), often moving in a flock, shrieking and squabbling

▌*Jurong's parrot aviaries were notable for backgrounds depicting the species' natural habitat.*

and whizzing at ear level past the unsuspecting visitor. They were a riot of colour in a tropical setting, the intense hues of their plumage dominated by the scarlet of the Red and Yellow-bibbed Lories and the deep red Cardinals. Red Lories sat together in a row, their black and blue wing markings saving them from being garish. The surrounding trees were filled with lories, mock-threatening their neighbours, wing-whirring and hissing. Their calls filled my ears.** Their hues were like those of a child trying to use all the brightest colours in the paint-box. The Waterfall Aviary, covering two hectares and at one time the largest aviary in the world, contained the highest man-made waterfall. Yet even that 100ft (30m) construction feat seemed dull and lifeless compared with the scene painted by the lories' colours.

At appointed times, three keepers brought big jugs containing liquid food. The lories appeared ten to 15 minutes before (parrots know the time as surely as humans) in eager expectation. When the keepers arrived one little Obi Lory (*Eos squamata obiensis*) beat the system by flying down to a jug and helping himself to nectar-soaked bread.

On a lower path Yellow-backed Lories fed from papaya spiked on to a tree branch and elsewhere birds were feeding on the bananas that grew in the aviary. It also contained 80 species of African and South American birds most of which were not as conspicuous (and certainly not as loud) as the lories!

In South-east Asia, in areas where tourism was booming in the 1990s, other bird parks were springing up with the potential to become some of the best in the world. In Australia a number of bird parks, some of them privately-owned, were operating by the end of the decade. The accent was heavily on native species due to the bird import ban (lifted only briefly during the 1990s). Macaws were considered the most prestigious parrots to exhibit but the native black cockatoos were also greatly admired.

Australia

Adelaide Zoo, in South Australia, had an especially fine and representative collection of native parrots in the first half of the century,

■ *Ronald Minchin.*
Courtesy of the Royal Zoological Society of South Australia Inc.

mainly due to the enthusiasm of Ronald Minchin, who was the third generation of his family to hold the position of Director. He is credited with the first captive breedings worldwide of the Moustache Parakeet (*Psittacula alexandri*) and the Green Conure (*Aratinga leucopthalmus*). The zoo's report for 1936 showed that it kept 48 of the 59 species of parrots known in Australia. That year had been successful for Queen Alexandra's (Princess of Wales) Parakeets, with 13 young reared from two pairs. Unusually, the zoo maintained 29 parakeet breeding aviaries, each one designed for a single pair. By 1940 the number of Australian species kept was fifty. They included the very rarely kept Ground Parrot (see colour page 3). The zoo's annual report stated: "It is the ambition of the Council to acquire the remaining species to attempt to breed them in captivity and thus learn something of their habits before they finally become extinct."

** In 2004 the lories were moved to an enormous, purpose-built exhibit entitled Lory Loft.

■ *Castle block aviaries, Adelaide Zoo, 1929.*

Courtesy of the Royal Zoological Society of South Australia Inc.

Towards the end of the century its off-exhibit aviaries were successful in producing the critically endangered Orange-bellied Parakeets (Parrots).

For the overseas visitor the interest was in the native parrots that did not exist in collections elsewhere. It was the Glossy Cockatoo (*Calyptorhynchus lathami*) that totally captivated me. In appearance it is not unlike a small Red-tailed Black Cockatoo but possesses an even greater ability to tug at the heartstrings. John Courtney, a good friend from New South Wales, wrote that hand-reared males were "the ultimate experience in bird ownership. They possess an extraordinary rapport with their human owners ... they are the 'dolphins of the bird world'".

The black cockatoos (genus *Calyptorhynchus*) are, with the macaws, probably the most imposing of all parrots. They are large (24–26in – 61 to 66cm) except the Glossy at 19in (49cm), with very appealing personalities. Their mainly black plumage is delicately spotted and/or barred in contrasting red, yellow or white. Confined to Australia, with no export permitted, few exist overseas. Not surprisingly, they are targets for smugglers (see Chapter 6). In contrast the small endemic lorikeets, Little, Purple-crowned and Varied,

are beautiful gems but they appeal to a minority of aviculturists. This is partly because large parrots are more prestigious than small ones.

On Queensland's Gold Coast, at Palm Beach, Currumbin Bird Sanctuary was famous for the wild Rainbow Lorikeets that came twice daily to be fed. It was an amazing spectacle – and its origins had nothing to do with tourism. Alexander Griffiths, the founder, operated a flower farm in the 1940s. His 12,000 gladioli blooms attracted huge flocks of lorikeets that fed on the nectar. To entice the colourful invaders away from his flowers he fed them on a mixture of honey (produced by his bees) and water. Soon more people were coming to view the lorikeets than to buy flowers. The Gold Coast's major tourist attraction was born!

Currumbin's appearance on countless television channels sparked off the fashion (to become widespread in zoos), of walk-through aviaries where the public could feed these fearless and inquisitive birds. Visitors bought (to supplement the zoo's income) tiny paper cups half-filled with nectar and waited for a group of lories to clamber all over them in their eagerness to reach the sweet liquid (and probably deposit some liquid droppings as a memento!).

South and Central America

In South America zoos I have seen many sad sights that are best left undescribed. The problem is partly lack of money and partly lack of understanding of the birds' needs. For example, in Santa Cruz Zoo in Bolivia parrots were crowded together in small cages, as though numbers made the biggest impact. Nearby a huge planted walk-through aviary seemed almost bare of occupants and could have provided a wonderful home for many of those in cramped and dirty conditions. In Lima Zoo in Peru, in 2003, a huge face-lift was taking place due to a large cash injection from an oil company. The assistance of big business could be the way forward for some of the zoos of the neotropics.

With increasing tourism it is likely that more privately-owned bird parks, like the one at Iguaçu Falls, will be created. Parque das Aves opened in 1994 in a small way. By 2003 it had more than 800 birds, most of which originated in Brazil.

South Africa

South Africa is not an easy place in which to run a bird park, due to economic and political problems. One of the best established, Umgeni Bird Park in KwaZuluNatal, was forced to close in 2002 after a series of thefts. By the end of the century the largest was World of Birds at Hout Bay. It exhibited 3,000 birds of 500 species, including many parrots.

Zoo collection planning

Between 1993 and 1997 the EEP (European Endangered Species Programme) Parrot Taxon Advisory Group (TAG) surveyed European zoos to define how many parrots were kept. Not all zoos responded but from those that did valuable information was gained. The TAG then decided which species should be included in collection planning, based on their conservation status and, in some cases, the availability of confiscated birds. TAG could also recommend which species should be the subjects of ESBs (European studbooks) and EEPs.

The TAG survey indicated that, to cite lories and lorikeets as an example, 1,229 birds of 30 species and 14 sub-species were reported. Only four species were represented by more than 50 individuals; the majority of species were unlikely to be sustained in zoos because so few birds were kept. Six species were recommended for ESBs – but no studbook keeper could be found for three of these species. Nine other species of lories and

■ *Glossy Cockatoos (only in Australia)...*

lorikeets were recommended for studbooks but stocks of captive-bred birds were too low for these studbooks to be implemented. The species for which studbooks were compiled were Mindanao (Mount Apo) Lorikeet (*Trichoglossus johnstoniae*), Red and Blue Lory (*Eos histrio*), and Purple-naped Lory (*Lorius domicellus*).

■ *Purple-naped Lory.*

Ultimately, collection planning will mean that zoo-goers see mainly ESB parrot species in mainstream zoos. Already parrot collections in most zoos (which do not allocate many aviaries to parrots) are beginning to look remarkably similar.

TAGS and EEPs for mammals, for example, make sense but in the case of parrots, where the populations of nearly all species are greater in private collections than in zoos, one cannot help wondering how valid they are. On the other hand, species kept in the private sector are at the whim of fashion. In the mid- to late 1990s most private lory collections in the UK disappeared, along with the birds, many of which were exported. By the end of the century zoos were at last making a concerted effort to maintain some of the threatened and endangered parrot species over the long term.

They also took on the responsibility for confiscated birds of threatened species, such as the Lilacine Amazon (*Amazona autumnalis lilacina*). During the early 1980s approximately one hundred were confiscated by Customs

officials in the UK and 50 in Germany. Always rare in aviculture, the Lilacine is found only in a small region of lowland coastal forests in western Ecuador. In the UK the confiscated birds were distributed to zoos and private breeders. The regional studbooks for the UK and Germany were brought together in an EEP. The recommendations made were that all the birds should be sexed, ringed and/or micro-chipped and screened for certain diseases. It was then possible to transfer birds between collections to establish breeding pairs. When the EEP was established in 1993 there were 66 wild-caught founder birds; five years later the number traced had increased to 101. By 1998 the number of young hatched by these birds was 129 but only 64 were still living. In other words, the total of known birds was only just higher than the numbers imported nine years previously. Inevitably, private breeders lost interest when they discovered this Amazon did not have pet potential despite its beauty. Both the private sector and zoos were failing to maintain it.

In North America collection planning was under the auspices of the American Zoo and Aquarium Association (AZA). Emphasis was placed on involving the private sector in many of the programmes. SSPs (Species Survival Plans) had then been established for the Palm Cockatoo (from confiscated imported birds), Thick-billed Parrot (*Rhynchopsitta pachyrhyncha*) and St Vincent Parrot. A fourth species, the Red-browed Amazon (*Amazona rhodocorytha*) was added to that list in 1998.

Overall, most zoo breeding programmes are for popular birds like cockatoos, macaws and Amazons. Most exist in large numbers in private aviculture. I may be a cynic but I find it difficult to foresee the day when zoos will initiate EEPs for endangered Cuban (see colour page 13) and Hispaniolan Conures (*Aratinga euops* and *A. chloroptera*). These birds are small and, at first glance, plain green yet concerned zoos and aviculturists should be working with them. Macaws are unlikely to die out in captivity. They have charisma!

Worldwide many zoos participated in the International Species Inventory System (ISIS). This aided the location of species, found zoos that need surplus animals and assessed captive stocks. In 1989, 343 were zoos were participating; the most numerous parrot in their

Graphics at San Diego Zoo in 1992 educate visitors about the plight of the Thick-billed Parrot.

collections was the Blue and Yellow Macaw. A total of 415 were held in 116 zoos. In that year only 43 chicks bred by these zoos survived beyond 30 days. This low breeding rate for a commonly bred species is typical of zoos, partly because many parrots are exhibited in mixed aviaries with no facilities for breeding. Clearly zoos, except the rare specialist collection like Loro Parque, were not playing a role in the continuing existence of endangered parrots in captivity.

Educational opportunities

Many zoos were making contributions to the conservation of parrots in the wild. This occurred either in partnership with organisations such as Loro Parque Foundation (for example, Chester Zoo in the UK was helping to fund the Philippine Cockatoo project) or by selecting a project to sponsor directly. By the end of the century conservation was high on the list of priorities of many zoos worldwide. In the form of collecting boxes, zoos presented another opportunity: that for the general public to contribute directly to parrot conservation.

In the UK a 2002 law made it compulsory for zoos to offer educational programmes. Some zoos had been operating such programmes for many years. At Chester Zoo more than 20,000 children (mostly from primary schools) attended one of 60 specialist classes held every week. At Bristol Zoo's Conservation Education Centre that figure is exceeded. For children, parrots are always a highlight of such a day out. They help to instil in them awe and reverence for the animal kingdom.

The contrast between zoos at the start of the 20th century and those at the end was truly extraordinary. This not only applied to the experience of visiting but to the philosophy for the very existence of zoos. David Waugh, Director of Loro Parque Fundación, commented that "Man, through an inexorable process of urbanisation, is becoming less and less connected to the natural world, and that which he does not know, he will not understand and he will not care for... The responsible zoo not only maintains and breeds species of threatened fauna, but also offers an 'open classroom' to the tourists which pass through its gates. In being able to capture the attention of the visitors, the zoological park has the opportunity to make aware, educate and promote positive attitudes towards fauna, flora and the environment..." (Waugh, 2005).

Another view was held by William Conway, one of the most esteemed men in the whole of the zoo world. He wrote that zoos should no longer argue that "... exciting children in New York or Tokyo about the plight of gorillas in Cameroon or Congo is responsive conservation. It is too indirect, too far away and too unlikely to affect the real issues" (Conway, 2000).

But both men made valid points.

4. The Big Collections

During the first half of the 20th century specialist parrot collections did not exist, partly due to the limited availability of species. In Britain during that era the most comprehensive parrot collections were those in zoos, such as London, and the private collection of Herbert Whitley, the forerunner of Paignton Zoo. Most private owners did not specialise although some kept an interesting range of parrot species.

There were only a few aviculturists between 1930 and 1950 who could devote time or money, during a period of austerity, to the apparently frivolous pursuit of keeping parrots. In those days, making money from parrots was never considered. While most keepers depended heavily on Australian species, the Duke of Bedford kept a more eclectic mixture. This included an Imperial Amazon, one of the rarest parrots in existence, which he exhibited at the 1930 Crystal Palace bird show (the premier event). It took the award for the best parrot. Crystal Palace was a huge glass building constructed for the Great Exhibition in Hyde Park in 1851 and later moved to South London.

At Paignton, in Devon, a popular seaside resort, Herbert Whitley kept many kinds of domesticated animals at Primley. He cultivated rare plants in greenhouses extending over several acres and maintained a pigeon loft that was said to be unequalled anywhere in the world. In 1930 the more striking parrots in his collection included Spix's, Lear's and Hyacinthine Macaws, Red Spectacled and Hispaniolan Amazons, also "Yellow-bellied" (probably Yellow-faced) Amazons, Short-tailed

Parrots and three forms of Shining Parrots from Fiji (Red, Tabuan and Koro). These striking Fijian parrots of the genus *Prosopeia* might be described as something like long-tailed Eclectus but with crimson or maroon head and underparts. They are extremely handsome birds with a lovely quality of feather, and they have always been very rare in captivity.

Other rarities included the beautiful 6in (14cm) Golden-backed Hanging Parrot (*Loriculus philippensis chrysonotus*) from the island of Cebu in the Philippines (see colour page 19). Some years later it was believed to be extinct but it might have survived in minute numbers. There is no record of it in captivity during the second half of the century. The Hanging Parrots are truly avian gems, the scarlet rump making a stunning contrast to the vibrant green of the body plumage. The Cebu Golden-backed exceeded them all in its beauty. The male's entire neck and upper back was golden yellow and his forehead and throat were scarlet, the rest of the plumage being green with tinges of blue. If this exquisite creature has indeed been lost forever, it would be a tragedy. If it survives, for how much longer will it exist on the denuded island that has already lost half of its 14 endemic species and sub-species?

After the middle of the century private aviaries grew, resulting in some memorable collections, such as that of Reg Partridge in Worcestershire, in the UK. Situated in the Vale of Evesham, his aviaries were so numerous that it took three hours to walk round them! At the entrance resided a pair of Hyacinthine Macaws, in an enclosure nearly as large as the average man's garden. A labyrinth of paths was lined with aviaries and birdrooms. The huge selection of Australian parakeets was housed in 20ft (6m) flights with tiled roofs. I recall a magnificent pair of Leadbeater's Cockatoos in a 30ft (9m) flight and a delightfully tame pair of Dusky Pionus (*Pionus fuscus*), a little-known species then.

In Bedfordshire Alfredo Marques had a famous collection (see photograph on preceding page). Five blocks of aviaries, comprising 78 lengthy flights, included one range of 18 parakeet enclosures that were 45ft (13.5m) long. The floor covering was of clean, well-raked gravel. Every available species was present and it was there, in 1968, that I saw Rock Grass Parakeets (*Neophema petrophila*) for the first time. No expense was spared. The Rosellas were offered gentles (maggots) and ate about a gallon a week!

For me, the most unforgettable bird in his collection was a St Vincent Parrot, the first to be imported into Britain for many years. The second largest of the Amazons, from the Caribbean island of the same name, the species is unique among parrots for its plumage variations. This bird, mainly brown and green with blue and white on the head, was eventually bought by a lady in Ireland and resided with her in a cage for about 30 years. When it must have been nearing 40 years of age it was bought by a breeder in the east of England who joined the St Vincent Parrot Consortium (a group set up to co-ordinate the few captive birds) and was thus able to acquire a mate for it!

In most collections the emphasis was still heavily Australian, with just a few aviaries devoted to other species. Good collections were accessible mainly to an elite band of wealthy bird keepers. A few generous owners, such as Reg Partridge, regularly admitted coach-loads of visitors, members of cage bird societies.

The first collection I ever visited where the emphasis was not on Australian parakeets was a revelation and an absolute joy to me. Near Wolverhampton in the Midlands, was a treasure trove containing the kinds of parrots that were closest to my heart. The collection belonged to Nell Howard who, with her husband Rob, ran a famous kennel of Springer spaniels. She also owned a pet shop and imported parrots, of

▌ *Reg Partridge (above) had countless parrot aviaries, also birdrooms where he bred parakeets. His curator was Peter Brown (below), who went on to work in Australia in parrot conservation.*

Photographs: Thomas Brosset

which she kept the rarest for herself. She had attractive aviaries and gardens, with ponds and rockeries and shrub-covered arches.

In her aviaries I saw Illiger's Macaws, Queen of Bavaria's Conures, Cuban Conures, Lilacine, Festive and Yellow-shouldered Amazons, Bronze-winged Pionus, Goffin's Cockatoos and other little-known parrots. I fell in love with a Black Lory, a species (in the form of the Rajah, *Chalcopsitta atra insignis*) that still captivates me on a daily basis. She inspired me to keep lories, which were just a small part of her fabulous collection. A bird whose character and appearance captivated me was a Slender-billed Conure (*Enicognathus leptorhynchus*), the only one in the country. On Mrs Howard's death he came to me. Later I was to have breeding pairs in my own collection and at Palmitos Park – and my fondness for this sociable species never left me.

In 1959 *Parrots and Related Birds* by Henry Bates and Robert Busenbark was published in the USA. Apart from the Duke of Bedford's book (an expensive collector's item), it was the only book available that described all the parrots in aviculture. It became the most used volume in my possession. The tattered cellophane that I used to protect the dust jacket is now yellow with age. I used the page margins to note where I had seen the species described, and the date. These notes included: Blue-tailed (Red and Blue) Lory, Mrs Howard 3/65; Philippine Cockatoo, Wendy Duggan 5/65; Blue-eyed Cockatoo, Kelling Park Aviaries, Norfolk 8/68; and Pesquet's Parrot, John Wilson, Norwich, 8/69. I recall hearing the harsh calls of the single Pesquet's well before I saw it. Little did I know that this would become my favourite parrot species, that its strangely un-psittacine head and glossy scarlet and black plumage would become so beloved. An even rarer bird was John Wilson's Ponapé Lorikeet (*Trichoglossus rubiginosus*), a little known species from the Pohnpei, one of the eastern Caroline Islands in the Pacific. Three birds were imported into England during the 1960s, and perhaps never before or since.

In the 1970s emerged a few stalwarts whose life-long interest became breeding and observing parrots. In Cambridgeshire veterinarian George Smith wrote hundreds of thousands of words on the subject, often amusing and sometimes questionable! He hand-fed a wide range of species (see colour page 4). In Worcestershire Ken Dolton bred Thick-billed Parrots (colour page 11) and maintained that his success was due to keeping several pairs in the same locality. In Essex Fred Brookes had a fine collection of the larger parrots, such as Queen of Bavaria's Conures. In Oxfordshire Jim Hayward, a talented parrot artist and producer of his own parrot magazine, *The Parrot Breeder*, was the only commercial breeder to maintain his interest in parrots. He started to breed Amboina King Parrots (*Alisterus amboinensis*) in the late 1970s and by the end of the century had produced countless generations. He was a rare example of an aviculturist whose efforts were primarily responsible for establishing a species in captivity.

In Europe

During the 1970s large parrot collections were being built up in Western Europe, especially in Holland and Germany. The emphasis was on Australian parakeets and, later, on mutations. Denmark emerged as a country where enthusiasm for parrot breeding was, and still is, high. It was in this decade that the ordinary person started to travel to "the Continent", usually by train or car, and ferry. Many friendships (some of which lasted for three decades) were forged between British and Western European parrot breeders. In this way new mutations reached England.

Isolated from Western European aviculture, Czechoslovakia had hundreds of parrot breeders and that interest was strongly maintained in the Czech Republic and in Slovakia. These countries had private breeders with valuable parrot collections. The Mediterranean countries, with their strong traditions of keeping Canaries and finches, were late starters at parrot breeding but by the 1990s they had some sizeable but little-known collections.

Specialists

Most breeders kept a wide range of parrot species or Australian parakeets and their mutations. Few specialised in one genus or group of parrots. Some that did were outstandingly successful, reflecting the enthusiasm and knowledge of their founders. They included John and Pat Stoodley in Hampshire. In the 1970s they bred more Pionus parrots than anyone had previously

From left to right: George Smith, Rick Jordan and John Stoodley at the Third International Parrot Convention in 1994.

done in Europe and went on to do the same with Amazon Parrots. In 1980 they kept and bred 12 species of *Amazona* and six sub-species and later increased this number substantially. They broke new ground with their feeding and incubation methods. The Stoodleys were unusual in their dedication to neotropical species. This was rare, their predecessor having been Ramon Noegel in Florida who was one of the most successful breeder of Amazon parrots worldwide.

In Holland, Mrs Spenkelink van Schaik of Soesterberg was notable for her successes with small neotropical parrots such as *Pyrrhura* conures (she bred 97 of seven species in 1980) before these parakeets became fashionable. She pioneered the keeping and breeding of lesser-known tiny *Bolborhynchus*, such as the Mountain Parakeet (*B. aurifrons*) and wrote fascinating articles about this species which was particularly difficult to establish in captivity. By the end of the century many people were specialising in breeding Grey Parrots – or attempting to, often with limited success. The get-rich-quick fraternity tried to cash in on its popularity, setting up dozens or even hundreds of breeding pairs. As some of these people had no previous experience with parrots, the result was dismal failure.

In the sunshine

If one asks the question why big collections flourished in California, Florida, South Africa, the Philippines and in the Canary and Balearic islands, the factor they have in common soon becomes obvious: year-round sunshine and a climate that facilitates parrot-keeping. During the 1980s some excellent parrot collections were growing up in the Canary Islands and in Majorca. Many Europeans, tired of the grey skies of their native lands, started to move to sunnier climes. The Canary Islands were an obvious choice, especially among enterprising German people.

Wolfgang Kiessling, who created Loro Parque in Tenerife, had not been the only one to start his own bird park. On the neighbouring island of Gran Canaria the spectacular mountains of the central area go unseen by most visitors. The informed visitor, strolling on the fine beaches and dunes of Maspalomas, could look up towards the mountains and point out a very special rock. It was here, in this one-acre kingdom, sealed from the rest of the world by its electrically operated gates, that Klaus Paulmann built up his parrot collection. When first he set eyes on this rock it took two days to reach it on donkeys. A decade later it was only 20 minutes by road from Maspalomas.

Lower down in the mountains in 1972 he opened Palmitos Park with his partner Carlos Böttscher. Soon Europeans travelling to the Canary Islands in their millions for the year-round sun, needed a diversion from the beach. In Palmitos Park the enclosures were set along a path that wound through the mountains in this little oasis of palm trees – a beautiful setting. With his love of everything that grew and with his artistic flair, Klaus Paulmann created a very special place for lovers of birds and plants. One of the attractions was the multitude of free-flying lovebirds, Quaker and Ringneck Parakeets and even toucans. In his private collection Klaus Paulmann was breeding Cuban, Hispaniolan, Yellow-shouldered, Green-cheeked and Tucuman Amazons.

Amazon parrots have always been *very* near to my heart; they have so much personality and they are so beautiful. Not long after I first visited Klaus Paulmann, in 1989 I left Loro Parque to look after his collection, living in a house among the aviaries. There were at least 400 parrots at the time, about 85% of which were neotropical species. The others were cockatoos, including Palms, about eight pairs of Leadbeater's, and a few Australian parakeets.

■ *Klaus Paulmann with a Hyacinthine Macaw reared by the author.*

In addition were my other favourites, lories and lorikeets – of 14 species. Within a few months the collection had increased to more than 80 parrot species and, in time, to more than 700 birds. Producing *parent-reared* Palm Cockatoos were among the most notable achievements.

It was probably the best private collection of Amazon parrots in Europe, with 20 species and seven sub-species. It was a privilege to work with these birds. By the time I left, 5 ½ years later, all the Amazon species had bred with the exception of the notoriously difficult Blue-cheeked (*Amazona dufresniana*) from which a chick had been produced, and the Red-tailed (*brasiliensis*) which were extremely nervous birds. It would be difficult to chose a favourite Amazon but the little Yellow-lored (*A. xantholora*) and the vibrantly-coloured Pretre's or Red-spectacled (*A. pretrei*) were wonderful birds to work with – both then almost unknown in other collections.

Other neotropical favourites of mine were the Hawk-headed and Purple-bellied Parrots. The Hawk-heads were adorable to hand-rear and the young birds made a wonderful exhibit in a large aviary in the park. However, when hand-reared Hawk-heads are closely confined, either in a breeding aviary or (unwisely) as pet birds, they become "the birds from hell" at maturity, attacking people without provocation. The young birds are irresistibly sweet, making this Jeykell and Hyde transformation all the harder to comprehend.

Purple-bellied Parrots (*Triclaria malachitacea*) are unlike any other species in aviculture, in appearance and in behaviour. They are dark green, with quite a long, broad tail, big dark eyes and ivory-coloured beak. Very skilful in flight, they fly with light buoyancy, unlike most parrots and more like a softbill. They also sing like thrushes! (I was fortunate to have this rare parrot in my care in four locations and over a period that spanned 36 years. I bought my first pair from a well-known English aviculturist, Herbert Murray, who maintained a huge planted aviary alongside the mainline Essex railway. When he advertised the pair for £30 I was the only person to answer the advertisement!)

Another neotropical favourite of mine in Klaus Paulmann's collection was the Queen of Bavaria's or Golden Conure (*Guaruba guarouba*) (see colour page 21). The contrast between its green wing coverts and flight feathers and the rest of its plumage is as clear-cut as between a daffodil and its leaves. No other parrot has so much yellow plumage and of such purity of colour. The young ones I hand-reared were adorable – with golden personalities to match their plumage. Ever curious and seldom shy, they are noisy extroverts, often giving you a quizzical look with the head tilted sideways. We had several pairs of these comical, endearing birds. Sadly they are endangered by habitat loss in Brazil.

One species that I feasted my eyes on every day was Pesquet's (*Psittrichas fulgidus*). This is my favourite of all the parrots. A big bird measuring about 20in (50cm) and weighing about 900g, only some macaws and the Kakapo are consistently heavier. Despite its amazing scarlet and black plumage, many people consider it to be ugly. Its elongated beak is less curved (especially in young birds) than that of other parrots and the almost bare skin on forehead and face is black. In the wild Pesquet's eats figs and other soft fruits; their faces would become sticky if feathered.

I was extraordinarily fortunate that Loro Parque had a breeding pair when I arrived there.

11 Breeding pair of Pesquet's Parrots *(Psittrichas fulgidus)* at Palmitos Park, Gran Canaria (CHAPTER 3). **12** Blue-crowned Racket-tailed Parrot *(Prioniturus discurus)* at **Loro Parque**, Tenerife (CHAPTER 3).

13 Plum-crowned Pionus *(Pionus t.tumultuosus)* and **14** a family of Mount Apo Lorikeets *(Trichoglossus johnstoniae)* at **Loro Parque**, Tenerife (CHAPTER 4).

15 The Moluccan Cockatoo has great dignity and beauty. It is shameful that trade reduces this bird, also a female Eclectus Parrot **17** on Seram (photographs by Stewart Metz MD), to objects of sadness and pity (CHAPTER 7). **16** Note the body of the Red-cheeked Parrot on the cockatoo's cage. Few birds of this species survive in captivity (CHAPTER 7).

Photo: WorldParrotTrust.org

18 Patagonian Conures waiting to go to the European Union – torn away from their colony in Argentina and soon probably separated forever from other members of their species. The tragedy is that no one will want these wild-caught birds as pets. They are too noisy (CHAPTER 7). **Different continents, same problem.** **19** Trapping Blue-fronted Amazons in Argentina and **20** Grey Parrots in Cameroon (CHAPTER 7).

Photo: WorldParrotTrust.org

Photo: Lolo Williams

▌ *Palm log nest of the Pesquet's Parrots.*

Palmitos Park acquired this species soon after my arrival. Of course they were wild-caught and newly imported from Singapore, probably trapped in the Indonesian part of New Guinea. It was heartbreaking to watch three of the four birds die from salmonellosis soon after. Even though I consider working with Pesquet's to have been the highlight of my career, I would rather the birds had never been trapped than perhaps seven or eight caught to supply us with one female. Such loss of life can never be justified, especially in a species found in low densities and traditionally hunted for its feathers. I knew of a male in Switzerland, imported in 1973. It is probably the most long-lived bird of its species ever in captivity. It was still alive in 2005, making it at least 32 years old. The pair (colour page 5) was a constant source of worry to me. I feared the male would kill the female. He had already injured her once when I asked the keepers to make a partition with a door that separated the aviary into two parts. Then I installed a CCTV camera in the aviary and a monitor in my house. This saved the female's life on more than one occasion. If I saw on the monitor that the male was behaving aggressively I would rush to the aviary, usher the male into the other part and close the door. When the two birds were clinging on the wire, obviously wanting to be together again, I would open the door.

These extraordinary parrots are a challenge. Although they have been bred using a nest-box, it is the stimulus of excavating a palm log that encourages most pairs. Offer a log with a small indentation and a pair will hollow it out. It can take months of work. They carry out the wood chips tucked in their plumage, shake the feathers and unload the chips over the aviary floor. The resulting excavation is amazing; it looks as though it has been machine-turned – it is so smooth.

The female Pesquet's Parrot would lay two eggs. At best one chick hatched. Much as I longed for a parent-reared youngster (we had one at Loro Parque) it always happened that either I had to remove eggs to prevent the male eating them or I had to remove the chick after a few days. The first Pesquet's I reared there (from the egg), a female, was the most unforgettable

▌ *The young female Pesquet's Parrot at six months old.*

parrot in my life. She has never forgotten me either and on the rare occasions I have seen her (first at Palmitos Park and, since 2005, at Loro Parque), I am always extraordinarily touched by her behaviour towards me. There have been periods when she has not seen me for up to seven years but it makes no difference. The moment she sets eyes on me she flies to the front of the aviary, and climbs down for me to rub her head through the wire. It might be considered to be unprofessional for a curator to be emotionally involved with the birds in his or her care. In my opinion compassion for the birds is essential in a good curator – and compassion leads to a strong attachment sooner or later.

On another holiday isle, that of Majorca, another large private parrot collection was flourishing. No one could have foreseen the tragic circumstances that led to its closure during the 1990s. The owner, his young son and a young woman who was working in the hand-rearing room were gunned down one day.

American collections

During the 1980s there were some knowledgeable breeders of the old school (pleasure, not profit) who were passionate about parrots. Extremely hospitable and welcoming, they made my visits to the USA memorable. As well as Ramon Noegel in Florida, there was the popular Tom Ireland (neotropical parrots), Bob Berry (cockatoos and macaws) and Ray Jerome (Lories) in Texas and Ed Shoemaker and Paul Schneider in California. Jim Dolan of San Diego Zoo, one of the most knowledgeable zoo men who ever existed, bred parrots and Arab horses.

In the late 1970s parrot breeding became popular in the USA, especially in California. Suddenly it was big business and people were giving up their jobs to become breeders. They took an enormous risk – but many were successful. At this time there emerged some huge commercial breeding stations. Probably the largest went under the strange name of Behavioral Studies of Birds and Animals Ltd. It was set up in 1978 by Gerald L. Schulman. His aim was to make a significant contribution towards meeting the demand for exotic birds, mainly parrots. Emphasis was on quality stock, with good health care. There were two centres of operation: a finch-breeding

unit in the San Fernando valley, and a much larger establishment mainly for parrots, with a few toucans and other softbills, in North Los Angeles County. The largest operation of its kind in the USA, it boasted 11 buildings containing nearly one thousand aviaries. When I visited it in 1981 the facilities were impressive. They included a hospital with infectious and non-infectious disease wards, food preparation rooms combined with seed gardens and houses for sprouting foods, and an administration building including library and classroom.

❚ *Dale Thompson.*

Curator Dale Thompson was an ideas man who questioned established techniques and embarked on many trials of his own. He showed me 60 pairs of large macaws, cockatoos on a similar scale, 300 pairs of Cockatiels of various mutations, countless lovebirds, Australian parakeets, Amazon parrots, Eclectus, conures and others. At the time it was surely the largest parrot collection in existence. However, privately owned facilities are at the whim of one man and his finances. If the bank balance crashes, the birds have to go. And this is what happened a few years later.

Schulman set up the International Foundation for the Conservation of Birds. It gave grants to bird conservation projects but, alas, did not survive any longer than Behavioral Studies. It hosted a wonderful four-day symposium in 1983 at which more than 50 specialists from

❚ *Dick Schubot (foreground), Tom Ireland and Mike Gammond.*

around the world, myself included, spoke on aviculture and conservation. It was a remarkable meeting at which many friendships were made that would be sustained for decades. It brought together people with similar interests who would never otherwise have had an opportunity to meet.

Also in 1983 Dick Schubot discovered parrots. Being wealthy enough to start in a big way, with the best consultants, he soon built up one of the most important private parrot collections. His aviaries and his expertise grew at an incredible speed. Located in Loxahatchee, Florida, his breeding centre was soon known worldwide by the initials ABRC (Avian Breeding and Research Center). Unashamedly sentimental about his parrots, advertisements for his birds in the avicultural press showed him holding his Palm Cockatoo, called "Love" after he rescued it from death's door. He called himself "Love's father".

The value of the collection was soon so high that few visitors were allowed and security precautions rivalled anything dreamed up for a James Bond film! I visited in 1988 with some friends from Florida. After the security guards let us in they radioed news of our arrival to Mr Schubot who met us driving a golf cart. This was the most convenient form of transport on his property – so large that he was able to plant groves of eucalyptus, pandanus and papaya for food. His gigantic refrigerated storerooms would have been the envy of the smartest hotel in the most exclusive Florida resort. They contained cases of the finest fruits, such as blueberries and pomegranates. Most of the breeding cages were small but there was one unforgettable enormous aviary. Galahs were reared there in a colony. None of the nest-boxes were immediately evident; they were reached through tunnels of wire mesh hidden behind vegetation.

Dick Schubot was a benefactor to avian medicine. He funded the Schubot Exotic Bird Health Center at Texas A&M University, donating one million dollars. After his death the collection was kept on by his son for some time, before being disbanded in 2002. By then one of the largest collections of parrots in the USA was another private one, this time in Dripping Springs, Texas. Well-known aviculturist Rick Jordan and his partner Mark Moore managed 650 pairs of more than 75 species, in addition to 50 pairs of non-psittacine species.

In Brazil

Some interesting private collections existed in Brazil during the 1980s, only one of which was known outside Brazil. It belonged to Nelson Kawall, after whom Kawall's or the White-faced Amazon (*Amazona kawalli*) was named (see Chapter 16). In 1988 I saw many species of macaws, conures and Amazons in his aviaries, and numerous colour mutations of the latter two groups. He also kept Lear's Macaws. The bird that made the most impression on me was a Yellow-tailed Caique (*Pionites leucogaster xanthurus*) the first I had ever seen – and the only one. It is surely the most remarkable of all the caiques, with its entirely yellow tail. Later he acquired a wild-caught Blue and Yellow Macaw of a very unusual mutation, sometimes called "mosaic". A striking bird, it was mainly yellow with blue and yellow markings on the wings in a pattern reminiscent of an opaline Budgerigar.

João Alberto de Camargo Cardoso started to keep parrots in 1980. By 1983 he had approximately 100 enclosures containing South American parrots. Three hundred Amazons included all the rare ones, such as the Diademed and the Red-tailed. The Pionus included Massena's and Plum-crowned (*Pionus tumultuosus seniloides* and *P. t. tumultuosus*) from the Andes. Both have always been rare in captivity. But for the occasional importation of one or two birds, the species would now be unknown in aviculture. The Plum-crowned (see colour page 6) has always been sought for its unusual and beautiful head coloration. The northern form, Massena's, with its mottled grey head, attracted little interest: another example of how aviculturists are greatly influenced by colour.

In Sao Paulo, Pedro Callado's private bird park contained 700 aviaries. Three Spix's Macaws were among the occupants. This was not unusual in that era as practically all the wealthy Brazilian collectors kept this species. They contributed to the fact that within 20 years it was to be extinct in the wild. As these men were collectors, not breeders, all these Spix's, except one pair, died without breeding. If only a couple of collectors had realised the importance of breeding, the captive Spix's population would probably be much more secure than it is today (see Chapter 13).

In the Philippines

This macaw's position in aviculture was rescued from near-oblivion in the largest parrot collection that has ever existed, Birds International Inc., in the Philippines. Owned by Antonio de Dios, he was a businessman with a passion for birds. At the end of the century his aviaries contained about 9,000 parrots, with 140 people taking care of them. In 1979 he had acquired a young pair of Spix's Macaws. In 1988, when this species was prematurely believed to be extinct in the wild, and had a captive population numbering about 20 birds, this pair produced their first young. He announced this important event to me in a telex in June. (A telex was a message received via a teleprinter connected to a telephone line. I can still recall the sound of the printer tapping out messages in the office at Loro Parque! Electronic mail was in the future!)

At that time, no other captive birds were breeding and this was the first hatching outside Brazil. Two chicks were hand-reared, the first of many in this very efficient breeding complex. In 1992 negotiations were carried out between Birds International and the Brazilian Government to donate one of the females bred there to join the last Spix's Macaw left in the wild. Sadly, it never happened.

By then this collection was famed throughout the world as the largest parrot collection in existence, with approximately 6,000 individuals.

■ *The first Spix's Macaw chicks hatched at Birds International Inc. in 1988.*
Photograph: Birds International Inc.

Located in a suburb of Quezon City, it covered 15 acres (six hectares). The young produced there were sent to every country where aviculture was practised, often via an agent in Germany. In 1992 a new breeding centre for lories was completed with more than 100 breeding cages. In the next six months 19 species and sub-species produced young. These included Rajah and Red and Blue Lories (*Eos histrio*) and the native Mindanao or Mount Apo Lorikeet, a very pretty little bird with unusual pink coloration on the face. However, when lories lost their popularity, nearly a decade later, breeding lories ceased. At the same time great success was being achieved in the parent-rearing of Fig Parrots, such as Edwards', including all three species in the genus *Psittaculirostris*. These small parrots are some of the most beautiful in existence – but few consistent breeding successes have been achieved elsewhere. A probable world first captive breeding was gained with a native species, unknown in aviculture outside the Philippines, the Guaiabero (*Bolbopsittacus lunulatus*). This little green bird proved to be most difficult to breed.

Also in the "difficult" category were the Racket-tailed Parrots, pairs of which had almost never been seen in aviculture. Consistent breeding success was achieved with the native Blue-crowned (*Prioniturus discurus*), with parent-rearing and hand-rearing. Two hand-reared birds sent to Loro Parque in 1994 (see colour page 5) enchanted visitors. This 11in (27cm) white-beaked parrot is mainly green, darker above, with the crown and nape blue. Among the white cockatoos the highest priority was and is given to the native and Critically Endangered Philippine or Red-vented (*Cacatua haematuropygia*). The young reared there gave a boost to dwindling numbers in Europe and the USA.

In 1993 a new centre was built for hand-reared birds. The popular pet species were weaned and handled in a way that would maximise their pet potential. Parrots produced as future breeding stock, especially endangered species, were discouraged from becoming too attached to people. They were familiarised with their own species as soon as possible after weaning, in large flight aviaries. At the end of the century Birds International Inc. (BII) maintained its position as the world's biggest producer of parrots (Loro Parque is close behind but is not a commercial breeding operation.) In the 2001 breeding season the following were reared at BII:

parrots	917
macaws	874
conures	731 (including 64 Queen of Bavaria's)
cockatoos	383
Amazons	214
parakeets	52

Great success was achieved with macaws. In that year 130 Hyacinthines, 50 Buffon's (Great Green) and three Spix's were reared, among others. Upon the request of the purchaser, parrots were sexed and tested for the most important infectious diseases. During the 1990s two highly unusual mutations of the Blue and Yellow Macaw were developed there. One was the blue (blue and white) and the other was mainly yellow with blue markings on the wings.

Australia

The large parrot collections in Australia were maintained by men who started in a small way and slowly built up their pairs. They had enormous enthusiasm and were very knowledgeable. The emphasis was on native species and their mutations, especially parakeets (called parrots there). There were some fine specialist collections and even one that had almost every species and sub-species of Australian parakeet and no mutations. Mark Schmidt near Adelaide must have been unique in this respect. When I visited him in 1989 he was already 20 years into his aim of building up a comprehensive collection of Australian parrots. He had kept 49 species plus 12 sub-species and had reared young from almost all of them. His birds were pure, untouched by mutants or even by crossing different sub-species. They were parent-reared, except in rare circumstances.

He told me: "It is sad that people buy parrots as a money-making exercise with no thought to the survival of the species." When, for example, there was a big demand for Red-vented Blue-bonnet Parakeets, many inferior birds were sold, some of which were hybrids between the Yellow-vented and the Red-vented (*Psephotus h. haematogaster* and *P. h. haematorrhous*). His Red-vented Blue-bonnets were magnificent in the extent and the depth of the red in their plumage. His maxim was that breeders should be known for the *quality* of the birds they breed, not the *quantity*. He was also very successful with black cockatoos (*Calyptorhynchus*). The Yellow-tailed was the most difficult. In his experience weaning ages for the young were six to eight months for Red-tailed, eight to ten months for White-tailed and ten to 12 months for Yellow-tailed Black Cockatoos. The latter two species consumed 100 to 200 mealworms per day when rearing young.

Other breeders, with fewer aviaries, specialised in cockatoos or lorikeets. By the end of the century Ringneck Parakeet mutations were extremely popular. The Smyth brothers specialised in *Psittacula* (Asiatic) parakeets. Theirs was one of the best-known collections in the country.

What pleased me most about visiting Australian breeders were the large aviaries. Except perhaps among the younger generation, all-wire suspended cages were not popular. Many of the older breeders had a lifetime in breeding parrots, mainly on a hobby basis, and the tradition of walk-in aviaries was very strong. Large planted aviaries were always popular there and it was a delight to see small lorikeets such as Purple-crowned breeding in a mixed

Little fluff balls – chicks of Yellow-tailed and Red-tailed Black Cockatoos bred by Neville and Enid Connors.

collection of finches or in a colony of their own species. This was something that could not be seen anywhere else in the world.

Among the most impressive collections were those that concentrated on the black cockatoos such as the Red-tailed, the most frequently bred. To visit such aviaries when chicks were being hand-reared was an unforgettable treat. The chicks are big balls of the longest, densest bright yellow or white (depending on the species) fluff – so unlike other parrot chicks which have sparse natal down. The young of these species melt the heart – especially the Glossy Cockatoo.

Big business in South Africa

In South Africa parrot breeding became big business during the late 1980s and 1990s. Countless "breeding farms" produced birds that were exported to Europe and elsewhere. Many of these farms were short-lived. They ceased to be viable by the end of the 1990s due to over-production, falling demand overseas and a ban on export due to avian influenza.

When I visited South Africa in 1996 it had the finest lory collections in the world. I had seen a number of specialist lory collections in the USA and was saddened at the way the birds were kept, mostly in small wire cages, even in barns or warehouses. Quality of life for these poor birds was nil. How different were the lory collections in South Africa! The aviaries were outdoors and spacious or under cover in a good environment. Several keepers were vying with each other to maintain the largest number of lory species, with totals in the low forties. Apart from the small Australian lorikeets, every species of lory and lorikeet in aviculture could be found in three collections!

Willem Grobler was a diary farmer turned "parrot farmer". His varied collection was enormous. Most of his pairs were kept in suspended cages, except the white cockatoos; they lived in aviaries 28ft (9m) long. Each range of cages was covered in black shade cloth to protect the birds from the Transvaal sun. The bird kitchen was fascinating. Storage containers like small silos and enormous stainless steel apparatus for cooking "mash" dominated the space. Parrot farmers had a different way of

One of Willem Grobler's lovebird aviaries.

▌ *Gill du Venage with her Blue-throated Macaws.*

feeding their birds. The morning feed consisted of cooked maize, peas, carrots, soya beans, wheat and sweet potatoes, made into a mash. In the afternoon the parrots received sprouted and dry seeds. Oranges and sweet potatoes were grown on the premises and were thrown whole on to the cage floors. I was amazed to see a little Goldie's Lorikeet eating sweet potato!

Willem Grobler produced hundreds of lovebirds on the colony system. At a time when Black-cheeked and Nyasas (*Agapornis nigrigenis* and *A. lilianae*) were not common in the UK, he had separate colony aviaries for Fischer's, Black-cheeked, Nyasas and Lutino Peach-faced. Three or four rows of nest-boxes covered the back wall of each aviary – and every box was occupied.

At this time perhaps the largest macaw collection in the world, outside of the Philippines, was located 100km north-west of Johannesburg. Gill du Venage was possibly more besotted with macaws than anyone I ever met. It was an absolute pleasure to watch her visit her aviaries carrying a tray of nuts and calling out "Hi, guys" to the occupants of each one. I suspected that the Blue-throateds were her particular favourites (as, indeed, they were mine, when I hand-reared them at Loro Parque). Gill's ambitions were lofty indeed: 15 to 20 pairs of each species as an insurance against catastrophe overcoming

wild populations. If that sounds like the voice of a commercial breeder, it was not. Gill rarely sold her young but bred Grey Parrots for the pet trade to help fund the macaw enterprise.

Apart from the Hyacinthine, the blue macaws species were, of course, absent in the collection, but there were between seven and 20 pairs of all other macaws except the Blue-headed (then virtually unknown). Her aim was to have 50% of the young parent-reared. I was impressed that Gill left young Hyacinthines with their parents for 18 months. Here was someone who recognised how long it takes this species to grow out of the baby stage. There were five well thought out areas for hand-rearing: one each for newly hatched chicks, young chicks, older chicks, a weaning room and outdoor flights. A staff of three cared for the young macaws. About four years later Gill and her husband had sold their farm for health reasons and moved out of the area. I felt for her since it would have broken her heart to part with all those macaws, so lovingly reared and cared for.

Mutation breeders

In many countries large collections of a different kind were flourishing. They belonged to the mutation breeders. These started in the 1970s in the USA with Cockatiels, to be followed by lovebirds. Then mutations caught on in Europe where former favourites had been ousted by mutations of Australian parakeets by the end of the century. Some breeders had dozens of pairs and the smaller species were bred in cages like Budgerigars. In Europe and the USA some large collections specialised in mutations of lovebirds and Ringneck Parakeets. The prices for new colours reached unbelievable levels, creating a few wealthy breeders overnight. Some of these specialists had hundreds of pairs as this increased their chances of producing that elusive new mutation. Sudden popularity of a mutation or species was inevitably followed by a price crash and breeders selling-up. These were business ventures, not parrot keeping for the love of it.

Mutation lovebirds were smuggled into Australia during the late 1970s. The few breeders made truly enormous sums from selling the young. Then it was the Ringneck Parakeet mutations that reigned supreme. They started to lose this supremacy at the end of the century when many new mutations of conures and lorikeets occurred. The large-scale production of mutations can apply only to species that mature early and produce a new generation every year – along with devaluation of the latest mutation. However, for me the term "large collection" conjures up a picture of many different parrot species – not one species in an array of colours.

The last of the big collectors?

Towards the end of the 20th century newcomers to parrot keeping with sizeable and interesting collections were rare. One of them was a young man from Kent called Lee Gardiner. He was in his early twenties when I first met him. Quietly-spoken and serious, his passion for parrots, which started in childhood, was all-consuming. He dreamed of owning some of the rarest and most fascinating species. Ten years later he had achieved this dream, with an amazing collection that included pairs of Pesquet's Parrots, nearly all the rarer Amazons, the most

expensive cockatoos such as Gang Gang, Red-tailed and Yellow-tailed, Leadbeater's and Blue-eyed – and several pairs of each in some cases. He lived for his birds. He ordered the finest fruits and vegetables (including unusual exotic kinds) and employed a girl to carry out the feeding. He ordered high-priced parrots from the Philippines, some costing as much as £20,000 per pair. His spending had become a talking point. It seemed that he had an indulgent benefactor somewhere.

▌ *Lee Gardiner.*

The truth, when it emerged in 2002, was shocking. A bank employee in a position of trust, for four years he had been transferring money from 38 customers' accounts into his own. The total sum of his thefts amounted to nearly £2.2 million. He allegedly spent £700,000 on parrots. In 2003 he was sentenced to nine years in prison. All his parrots were sold in an attempt to repay the money. This was a very sad case in which a passion for parrots had led to ruination: career, reputation and birds – all gone.

It was extremely unusual for someone as young as 32 to keep a large and choice collection of parrots. The reason is obvious. It is an expensive commitment, even if less rare species are acquired. Most people with money prefer to spend it on holiday villas in the sun, fast cars or seagoing yachts. The writing is on the wall. Big parrot collections will soon be history. They are just too time-consuming and there is no longer big money to be made.

Patronized by their Royal Highnesses The Prince and Princess of Wales, &c.

CROSS,
KING of WILD BEAST MERCHANTS,
LIVERPOOL.

500 GREY AFRICAN PARROTS.
10,000 Pairs of Small Birds. *Fresh Arrivals Daily.*
The Highest Price given for Birds, Beasts, Shells, Curiosities, Skins, & other Stock.
Speciality—Splendid African Grey Parrots with Crimson Tails.

5. TRADE THROUGHOUT THE CENTURY

By the beginning of the 20th century, trade in wild-caught birds, British and foreign, was extensive. Nightingales, Choughs, and Woodlarks were among the species offered for sale and Skylarks could be purchased for 9d (about 4p) each. The importation of wild-caught birds from overseas was very well established. In 1879 C. W. Gedney wrote, in Foreign Cage Birds, volume 1:

The importation of foreign birds into this country has grown to such vast proportions of late years that one is almost at a loss to imagine where a market can be found in which to dispose of the hundreds of thousands of specimens which annually pass through the hands of our great bird importers. The explanation is very simple. Some three or four men in this country have, by a system of agency, secured a monopoly of the trade, and from these men the continental as well as English bird dealers, obtain their stock. It is, therefore, no uncommon thing for one of these "merchants" to receive and dispose of a thousand foreign birds in one week; sending consignments to most of the chief cities in Europe.

One of the major importers in England, John D. Hamlyn of London, claimed in his advertisement to be "absolutely the only dealer who attends shipping at London, Southampton,

Plymouth, Antwerp, Bordeaux, Havre, and Marseilles".

According to Dr G. Cresswell, FZS, writing in 1905, enormous numbers of parrots were imported annually into England – 80,000 by one man alone. He wrote of African birds that "Vast numbers, both adult and immature, are trapped by the natives for export, the young ones being easily taken by hand when they first leave the nest. Overcrowded in wicker cages while still in the trappers' hands, subjected on the voyage to every discomfort associated with filth, and therefore obliged to eat and drink under the foulest conditions, it is no wonder the majority of the poor creatures succumb, either during the voyage or soon after landing, to a disease produced and fostered by an environment to which their race has hitherto been a stranger" (*Bird Notes*, June 1905.)

British rule in Malawi (then Nyasaland), Zambia (Northern Rhodesia) and Zimbabwe (Southern Rhodesia) commenced about 1890. By the early years of the 20th century white people residing in these countries had built up large bird export trades. There was no attempt to regulate numbers. Lovebirds were trapped until their populations had been virtually depleted. The Black-cheeked Lovebird (*Agapornis nigrigenis*), found in a relatively small area, never recovered from this heavy exploitation that continued

▮ *Black-cheeked Lovebirds.*

at least into the 1920s. However, decreasing rainfall leading to desiccation of habitat since about 1950 was a contributory factor.

Trade in living birds was a subject of regret in correspondence by bird lovers in *Bird Notes* and in *The Avicultural Magazine*. One contributor to the latter (May 1907) suggested that a committee should be appointed to visit bird shops. The names of the shops most suitable for purchasing birds would then be published. In the same issue, another contributor recorded his disgust on seeing, in a shop window in Regent Street, London, a hat decorated with the heads of fifteen Blossom-headed Parakeets. E. Hartley wrote: "This sounds like an exaggeration but it is not, I counted them many times, I tortured myself by counting them." A hat decorated with parakeet heads was acceptable in an era when millions of birds (such as egrets) were slaughtered annually for the millinery trade. What kind of lady would wear such a hat? Probably the average woman who had not yet learned to regard birds with compassion.

The demand for Grey Parrots

Then the Grey Parrot, called African Grey, was one of the most sought after species. In early reports of them kept as pets, mention is often made of their "docility". This infers that wild-caught adults were not usually exported, a fact confirmed by Wolfgang de Grahl in his book *The Grey Parrot*, written in 1982. He stated:

> ...even a century ago the birds were brought into ports to be sold. In those days young birds were usually taken from nests, reared,

and sold, because they commanded the highest prices. Furthermore, Grey Parrots are extremely shy and wary, and in earliest times it was hardly possible to capture them with nets or snares.

It was much easier to find fledged youngsters that only occasionally flew to and from their nest holes, or to climb up the tree at night to fasten a net or sack in front of the hole... The adults were usually released (in earlier times), because they were too wild to tame. The natives captured birds only to be sold; they did not keep them as pets. It was often possible to see whole rows of tame birds with clipped flights sitting on the roofs of huts.

In some areas, though, adults were captured. Young or old, they were transported in cylindrical containers, 20in (50cm) long and 8in (20cm) in diameter, made of reeds. In the late 19th century the price fluctuated between four shillings (20p) and 15 shillings (75p) per bird. In 1890 a good supply resulted in the price dropping to one shilling and six pence (7p) each. (Note that in 1900 one pound had the same purchasing power as about £53 in 2000.) Buyers travelled along the coast and inland to acquire birds from trappers. Most Greys were shipped from Accra (Ghana) and Nigeria to Liverpool, Antwerp, Rotterdam and Hamburg.

The steamers and sailing ships were met by the bird dealers who paid more for parrots from the sailing ships. Experience had taught them that mortality was lower because the parrots had been kept in better accommodation and given better care. Due to the belief that water should be withheld from parrots, many of these poor birds died, with swollen livers and constipation; others apparently had tuberculosis. They had been fed only on bread and cooked rice (de Grahl, 1987). By 1900, Greys were transported only on steamships; they took five weeks to reach Europe. Conditions had improved in that they were kept in small rooms – but chained to wooden perches.

In Liverpool in the 1920s there was a famous animal dealer by the name of Cross who imported thousands of Grey Parrots every year (see 1902 advertisement above chapter heading). The well informed knew better than to buy from him. The

▌ *Grey Parrots.*

The Royal Natural History

Rev. Farrar recorded his sad experience. He read the "seductive advertisement" offering black-eyed baby Greys and "sure livers" and sent his 15s with confidence. The poor bird soon arrived by train in a small wooden box – "one of the most pitiable objects human eyes ever lighted on". It was too weak to protest at being removed from the box, but clung to the perch, swaying weakly. It drunk so much the water was removed. Next morning its corpse was found to be "as thin as paper and as light as a cork". The body was returned to the seller requesting a replacement. This one lived for two days (Farrar, undated). No doubt these unfortunate Greys were starving. All the dealer gave them was boiled corn and if they could not eat that they died.

From the first years of the century to the last: in 1999 Grey Parrots were the cause of a feud between local people. The village of Ikodi, in Nigeria, on the south-eastern coast, is known as parrots' paradise, one of their last refuges in Nigeria. Several thousand Grey Parrots were known to live in the tall palm trees. The villagers valued their Greys. They never caught them or harmed them; they even banned firearms in the village. They were farmers and fishermen who went into the forest and collected their feathers, to sell for the equivalent of about 10p (15c) each for use in traditional spiritual practices. They were used not only for ornamental purposes but also for making local drugs that were believed to cure various ills. Easy accessibility to the parrots' feathers had, it was said, reduced poverty in Ikodi. The people were forbidden by an age-old custom from killing birds or from felling the trees in which they live. Bush burning near the parrots' habitat was also prohibited. "We want this settlement to be made a tourist attraction in conjunction with the community," said Chief Aleme, while Chief Okpaadi stated:

"We have no oil in the village. Our only resource is the parrots."

Then the poachers came. They hired young men from neighbouring villages to raid the forests to trap the parrots. Violent clashes between the trappers and the villagers left two Ikodi youths dead. Efforts by the Ikodis to get justice were unsuccessful as local authorities were unwilling to become involved. So the villagers set up their own vigilante groups. If poachers were caught they faced a severe beating or imprisonment in the village. This led to retaliation. A group of armed poachers raided the village – not for the birds but for captive poachers. The Ikodi people were critical of the government for doing little to support the law, so a single forestry officer was sent to the village.

Unscrupulous local officials were bribed to provide the necessary clearance papers. The Greys were probably smuggled out via the airport at the northern city of Kano. Mike Pugh, of the London-based World Society of the Protection of Animals saw a man there carrying a large crate to be prepared for export. It contained five chimps, one gorilla and 250 Grey Parrots.

During the entire century not much changed regarding the trade in Grey Parrots except that planes replaced ships as the method of transport. By the time of air transport, parrots were exported in shallow wooden boxes with the front made of wire netting or welded mesh. In the year 2000, it was reported that 40,000 were exported from Africa (see Chapter 7). This parrot, so intelligent and sensitive, has probably suffered more than any other at the hand of man. In the UK imported wild-caught Greys were an invariable feature of dealer's stands at bird selling shows during the 1990s. Most people who attended these shows were totally insensitive to their suffering. Not all, however. One lady wrote after attending her first show: "Being a complete novice, I was totally unprepared for the horrific screams that reverberated around the hall. Upon closer inspection I realised this to be the sound of wild-caught African greys crammed into tiny cages... The torment and fear in their eyes made me sick to my stomach..."

Trapping Australian cockatoos

In Australia, it was the cockatoos that suffered most. In the early years of the century trapping was carried out to protect farmers' crops. Of course it failed to do so because cockatoo numbers were, and still are, so high. Trappers put up their nets at night. Before first light they rose to await the dawn and the arrival of the Galahs. No sooner did the sky flush rose-pink – the colour of the Galah's breast – than the birds started to appear. One witness, Charles Barrett, wrote:

> In twos and threes at first they came, flying swiftly from the trees along the creek, then in flocks of thirty or forty. It was wonderful to see this assembling over the wheat of a host of beautiful birds. As they wheeled and dived, the sunlight, feeble as yet, shone softly on grey and rose-tinged plumage. Once or twice, some magical touch of the sun transformed a bird into a living form of silver, which seemed to float in the blue. But the harsh cries of the cockatoos put all one's dreams to flight.
>
> For a while none of the Galahs came near a net. Then the call-birds became vocal, and the trappers crouched lower, intent, keen-eyed, and ready to act. From the shelter I watched a flock alter its line of flight, and steer for the net, attracted by the notes of the call-birds. The wild, free, Galahs

■ *Sailor and Grey.*

A trapper in Riverina with a tame Galah – the decoy bird.

species that are considered to be agricultural pests, such as some white cockatoos.

Greater Sulphur-crested Cockatoos used to be removed from the nest in large numbers for the pet trade. This habit ceased when it was realised that psittacine beak and feather disease (PBFD) was rife in wild nests. Previously no breeder would give aviary space to such a common and inexpensive bird, but the demand for the pet trade was soon being partly met by breeders.

answered their captive fellows, hesitated for a moment, then dropped down on to the unseen net. Instantly the rope controlling the release was pulled by a trapper, and a babel of bird-voices arose. Ten of about thirty Galahs were caught... Over eighty birds altogether were captured; hundreds escaped the nets.

In 1921 Australia prohibited the export of native birds. This law must have been rescinded quite soon because in 1929 the press was again reporting an end to bird exports. The prime mover in this decision had been the Minister of Customs, Mr Gullett, who had visited London. There he saw finches exported from Australia "shivering in the cold and in such a neglected state" that he resolved to stop the trade. People were still permitted to leave Australia with their pets, and zoos to exchange birds bred in their aviaries. In reporting this, the editor of *The Avicultural Magazine*, David Seth-Smith, commented that the treatment of Australian finches in dealers' shops was "nothing short of scandalous" and that the Minister had acted in the best interest of his country and of its avifauna.

So! The debate on the importation of wild-caught birds had started – and was set to run for the rest of the century. In Australia in the 1980s and 1990s some people pressed for the export of the "pest" species of cockatoos. But the government wisely took a firm stand. There would be no exceptions. Capture is allowed under licence on certain occasions for

UK import ban and private initiative

Back in Britain the importation of parrots was prohibited for health reasons. The Minister of Health ordered that from May 20 1930, under the Parrots (Prohibition of Import) Regulations no more parrots should be imported. This was due to consignments of Amazon parrots that had been accused of transmitting psittacosis. Fourteen people in the British population of over ten million had died as a result. The editor of *The Avicultural Magazine*, David Seth-Smith, was angry. "Why make Australia and India suffer for the sins of South America?" he asked.

In 1952 the "parrot ban", as it was widely known, was lifted. There had been no significant recurrence of psittacosis in the UK since the outbreak that had led to the ban. By then the volume of trade in live birds coming through Heathrow Airport (some were in transit) was enormous. In 1952 the RSPCA opened an animal reception centre there to care for consignments of birds and animals that needed attention. In 1976 new premises were built. Jeff Trollope worked there from 1952 until 1994 and described the enormous volume of trade in birds and animals in the early years. Sometimes a DC4 or a large air freighter would be filled with living cargo and an attendant would travel with the animals. Except in special cases (such as racehorses) the use of attendants became rare by the mid-1960s, as consignments became smaller.

∎ *Goldie's Lorikeets.*

By the mid-1960s importation of parrots into Britain was occurring on a large scale. There were few controls and no quarantine so it was not only dealers who were bringing in parrots. The more enterprising private keepers also took the risk. One of these was Jim Hayward in Oxfordshire, who was to become well known as a parrot artist and expert on the genetics of the many mutations that became popular. He imported Scarlet Macaws from Colombia at the list price of £12.50 each and Blue and Yellow Macaws at £7.50 each, plus freight charges of £3.75 per bird.

In the mid-1960s £1 had ten times the purchasing power of today and £12.50 was the equivalent of a week's wage for many people. Jim Hayward recalled how the macaws were transported in flimsy containers; the frames were made from tea chests covered in chicken wire, with an outer layer of white muslin stretched around the sides. Why, he asked, did they not shred these containers during the flight? They would have been in the dark hold during the journey, probably too stressed and frightened to do anything.

Meanwhile in the UK of the 1970s enterprising bird keepers started to import parrots after sending to Singapore for trade lists and discovering how cheap parrots were. One friend imported Lesser Sulphur-crested Cockatoos and lories from Singapore. The cockatoos (now critically endangered due to over-trapping) cost about £5 each. Amazing species that until then had been only pictures in books (taken for granted now) were appearing on the lists of dealers in Guyana and Singapore. A very adventurous friend, Stephanie Belford, went out to Georgetown, and came back with Sun Conures, Queen of Bavaria's (Golden) Conures and Hawk-heads. The Sun Conures were not the first in the UK. Two of these striking orange, yellow and green parakeets imported by a dealer in July 1971 caused a sensation, probably being the first in living memory. How familiarity breeds not contempt but certainly a lack of appreciation!

Stephanie Belford brought in parrots from Singapore in advance of the professional importers. Driving over to her house in Welwyn, sometimes with the expectation of seeing a species I had never seen before, was exhilarating. In 1977, before anyone had seen

∎ *Salvadori's Fig Parrot.*

Goldie's Lorikeets in the UK, she had a cage containing thirty. It took about six months to sell them all and she lost not a single bird. In this same house in the same year I saw my first Salvadori's Fig Parrots, enchanting stocky little parrots, with a jerky way of moving. Soon Goldie's and Fig Parrots were gracing my own aviaries. When she opened up a box and saw her first Palm Cockatoo (and the size of its beak) she panicked and sold it instantly by picking up the phone! Later she imported more of these gentle giants and loved to demonstrate their lack of malice by placing your finger in the cockatoo's beak! She even brought in Pesquet's Parrots! (See Chapter 4.) They were amazing days, never to be repeated.

Advertising wild-caught birds

Parrot selling shows that were established events by the end of the century did not exist then. In the UK the most effective way to sell wild-caught parrots was through advertisements in the weekly magazine *Cage and Aviary Birds* which was fiercely defensive of its advertisers. In 1938, when the magazine was called *Cage Birds*, a contributor to the *Avicultural Magazine* had complained that the editor of *Cage Birds* refused to publish any letters or articles that "might upset traders who advertise". This tradition was still firmly upheld at the end of the century. In 1991 the weekly newspaper refused to publish an advertisement from the World Parrot Trust.

■ *Gordon Cooke.*

The director, Mike Reynolds was told that the Trust was a "protectionist" organisation and was therefore excluded from mention. The publishing director and the editor objected to one of the aims: that which advocated "effective controls on the international trade in wild-caught parrots, and its replacement by captive-bred birds". This was seen as a threat to the advertisers of wild-caught birds. Subsequently the World Parrot Trust was instructed that it should cease to show unpleasant pictures of birds in transit if it wished to advertise. The Trust, of course, refused to censor its publications or re-write its objectives.

A regular advertiser for many years was Gordon Cooke of Leicester. He told me: "My family have been involved in birds since 1878. From 1950 to 1980 I was a leading UK importer and exporter of birds and I have travelled the world many times collecting birds for shipment. I have seen the appalling cruelty in the keeping of trapped birds before shipment and I have also seen the casualties – dead birds thrown out of holding pens each morning onto rubbish piles.

"Even during that period of my life I had grave reservations about what I was involved in. I can personally vouch for some horrendous losses in some of my consignments – the most tragic were large losses of Hyacinth Macaws, Red-

■ *Skulls of three Hyacinthine Macaws. Only one bird in this consignment of 35 Hyacinthines could be saved.*

Photograph: Gordon Cooke

vented Cockatoos and Green-winged Kings. In my travels overseas I have seen parrots and parakeets in their natural environment and, of course, that is where they should be left. When I was collecting in India I found conditions so bad that I set up my own holding facilities. I also had my own quarantine station in Singapore.

"The spurious claims put forward by some people in favour of wild imports, such as new blood, are ludicrous. These people have absolutely no idea what is involved in the trade. Now I am retired I ought to look back on a lifetime of working with birds but, unfortunately, this is not the case. I remember only too well being involved in a wicked occupation."

He recalled consignments with 100% mortality, such as 600 birds, mostly parakeets, from India; every single bird died a slow, lingering death from Newcastle disease. They had been *en route* to Canada. On another occasion, 83 Green-winged King Parakeets (*Alisterus chloropterus*), gorgeous long-tailed red, green and blue birds, were three days in transit. Only one survived.

Trapping adults

The worst aspect of the trade in wild-caught parrots is the trapping of adults. In the first half of the century this was rare in many countries. But as parrot numbers declined due to over-trapping and deforestation, trappers caught anything they could get. A chick taken from the nest and hand-reared has no memory of life in the wild and usually adapts well to captivity – depending on the species. But the trapping of adults is another matter entirely. Look into the eyes of a recently trapped adult parrot and you see only fear and bewilderment. Many are unable to adapt to confinement and the close presence of humans. Their entire lives are lived in fear and stress. They have lost their mates, their homeland and their freedom and all too often they are caged in lonely solitude in a totally alien environment with nothing at all to relieve the tedium of the day. The suffering of large intelligent birds like macaws and cockatoos must be intolerable. It is no wonder that they pluck their feathers or even mutilate their own flesh. It is cruel beyond words. The best that can happen to many of these birds is that they die quickly.

Various methods are used to trap macaws. In 1983 a dealer in Beni, Bolivia, described to me how Blue and Yellow, and Green-winged Macaws were caught. He wrote: "A tall straight tree is selected in the feeding area. All the branches are stripped off and traps are fixed to the sides in place of branches. Then a macaw of the same species, either tame or wild-caught, is positioned in the tree. This bird will call the others. They alight on a trap and a trigger mechanism releases a strong elastic band that grasps the foot. It is possible to trap several in one day in this way. As the trapper is paid the equivalent of two weeks' wages per macaw, this pastime is very popular and vast numbers of macaws are caught in this way every year.

"In our back garden we have an aviary of assorted wing-clipped parrots. Quite often pairs of Yellow-collared Macaws will visit the garden. We would simply open the aviary door and often one of a pair would enter while the other kept watch. Using a piece of string we would close the door from a distance, then clip the wings of the trapped bird. Often when we opened the door we would trap the other one, either the same day or three or four days later, because the pair bond is so strong."

In Brazil, Hyacinthine Macaws were so easy to trap on the ground that whole populations could be removed from one area. During one period so many were imported into the UK that dealers could not sell them and many died. Most of these birds were adults. It was the height of irresponsibility and a scandal that more than 10,000 Hyacinthine Macaws were removed from the wild in a short period up to the 1990s. Yes, *ten thousand*! That figure was believed to be twice as many as existed in the wild at the century's end. Dealers did not care that only a handful of people had adequate facilities to look after these huge birds. Sadly, the illegal trade in this slow-breeding macaw continues. A pair nests perhaps every two years and rears one, more rarely two, young. This charismatic species is a magnet to the unscrupulous.

Internal trade in Amazon parrots

For some species the capture of birds for the internal (domestic) trade is a serious threat. This is the case with the Yellow-naped Amazon (*Amazona auropalliata*) on the Pacific coast of Mexico and Central America. Because of its beauty and its exceptional ability to mimic, it was deemed the most desirable of Amazons. In Honduras, where parrot export was not permitted, trappers demanded between US$25 and US$60 per bird – a large sum where the average daily wage was only $2. Parrots were sold to foreigners to be exported illegally. In November 2002 this Amazon was placed on Appendix I of CITES because excessive trade had threatened its survival.

▌*Yellow-naped Amazon.*

In Venezuela, Amazons and other parrots have been traded for centuries. However, after the devaluation of the national currency in 1983, international trade increased many times in magnitude even although export of parrots was banned in 1970. A law forbidding hunting, trading or transporting non-game birds was usually ignored. Trappers who were caught were fined ridiculously low sums, the equivalent of the local cost of one pair of Amazons.

Most neotropical countries banned legal export of parrots well before the end of the century. The years in which this occurred are given below.

Brazil	1967
Costa Rica	1970
Venezuela	1970
Colombia	1973
Paraguay	1975
Ecuador	1981
Belize	1981
Mexico	1982
Bolivia	1984
French Guiana	1986
Guatemala	1986
Honduras	1990

However, illegal export and internal trade are so strong that many parrots from these countries (especially Mexico which recommenced export in 2002) are now endangered by trade.

Importation and Australia

When Australia banned the export of birds from 1960, it also banned their importation in order to protect native birds and poultry from disease. This action encouraged smuggling of exotic parrots. Species that were unknown in aviculture worldwide until the 1980s mysteriously appeared in Australia. Of course the claim was made that they were already there along with a few other species of non-native parrots that had been maintained by breeding.

In 1980 proposals were made for the importation of birds to recommence – but they were dropped due to strong objection by the poultry industry. The situation changed in 1990 when the Australian Quarantine and Inspection Service permitted the first shipment of legally imported live birds into the country since 1948. They were racing pigeons. Thirty-four of the 159 pigeons were dead on arrival. They had suffocated after apparently having been stacked in the hold of the aircraft in a manner that had restricted airflow. Unfortunately, this is the kind of hazard that birds in transit must face. The second consignment of live birds entered the quarantine station soon after. They were Budgerigars, 500 of them. It is ironic that this species should be imported, like coals to Newcastle, but of course these were exhibition birds of a "quality" sought by breeders. With the aim of reducing smuggling, the choice of species was dictated by levels of illegal importation.

Subsequent shipments consisted of more racing pigeons, Budgerigars, and zoo birds. Exotic parrots included only species that already existed in captivity in Australia, to augment breeding stocks. Such species as Black-capped Lories and Green-winged and Blue and Yellow Macaws were brought in. These importations, considered ill-advised by many, were very short lived and few in number. They were also expensive. Using the quarantine facility cost more than $1,150 per week per consignment. Nevertheless, wealthier Australian aviculturists could purchase species they had only dreamed about in the past – at the expense of some British macaw owners whose birds had been stolen to fulfil the orders. After importation ceased, smuggling of exotic parrots (in the form of eggs) thrived, so legal importation failed to end smuggling.

CITES

Meanwhile worldwide trade had escalated. The legislation already in place under the Convention on Trade in Endangered Species (CITES) was designed to protect species from being endangered by excessive trade. It failed. This is the only global treaty that monitors and regulates trade in fauna and flora and their products (feathers, skins, ivory, etc). The Treaty was initiated in 1973 and was signed by 21 nations. By 1990 nearly 100 nations were signatories; by the end of the century the total was 130. Parrots came under discussion at virtually every CITES meeting of participating countries. Representatives from non-governmental organisations could attend and contribute their views.

All parrot species, with the exception of two, are listed in the CITES Appendices. Appendix I includes the highest level of threatened species, in which commercial trade of wild-caught specimens is not allowed. The trade of Appendix II and III species is supposedly regulated by the Convention and by EU legislation.

- Appendix I: species threatened with extinction on which trade would have a catastrophic effect.
- Appendix II: species that could be threatened if export was not regulated effectively. Trade in these species is permitted if it is sustainable and the specimens were obtained legally. Also permitted are the offspring – but not those of the first generation – of species on Appendix I.
- Appendix III: Budgerigars and Cockatiels.

On June 6 1981 nearly all members of the parrot family, excluding those listed in Appendices I and III, were placed on Appendix II. This was the first time that an entire group of birds, rather than named species, had been listed. Countless parrot species on Appendix II had been threatened by trade by the end of the century, thus CITES had not halted their export. It had even encouraged it because dealers instructed trappers to catch huge numbers of species like Moluccan Cockatoos when the intention to list it on Appendix I became known.

Unfortunately, some countries that trade in enormous numbers of wild-caught parrots are not signatories and many countries that are signatories still have a large legal import trade. This includes the UK.

There are several ways in which CITES is rendered ineffective. Annual export quotas are set by some countries but the quota system does not work because CITES documents accompanying bird exports are frequently forged or used on more than one occasion. Another method is to list wild-caught birds as captive-bred. In 1985 a huge consignment of 3,148 Brazilian Jendaya Conures were exported from Argentina as captive-bred. Captive breeding of this species is small-scale. These birds were imported into the United States resulting in a State Department's wildlife investigator travelling to Argentina where, of course, he found no breeding facility.

■ *Jendaya Conure.*

(A lot of time and money would have been saved if the documentation had been questioned before importation occurred.) Argentina's Wildlife Department then stated that no further export of this species would be allowed.

Another way to circumvent the treaty was (and is) to smuggle parrots into neighbouring countries that are not signatories to CITES and to export them from that country. This is common practice. During the 1980s, Bolivia was banned by CITES from exporting due to its failure to comply with the Convention. Bolivian officials had falsified numerous CITES permits, many for rare and endangered species. Dealers from neighbouring countries had smuggled large numbers of parrots into Bolivia where they were exported with illegal documents. Another problem was that Bolivia and other South American countries were sending birds to Honduras and Mexico (not members of CITES at that time) where they would be sent on to importing countries in other continents. Massive bribery of officials allowed illegal trade to flourish.

Another loophole concerned "ranched" specimens. This designation was created for crocodiles and similar species when they were moved from Appendix I to Appendix II to allow ranched animals to be traded. Certain countries used this term for parrots. If they had admitted that they were wild-caught some airlines would have refused to carry them so they described them as "ranched". Apparently no one questioned what this term might mean in relation to parrots. The assumption might be that ranched parrots were those reared from eggs or chicks taken sustainably from wild nests.

Parrots on Appendix II of CITES could be exported if trade was deemed to be sustainable, i.e., wild populations were not being depleted. In a typical year, take 2000, 89 parrot species were legally trapped and exported. No research had been carried out on most species and it was not known whether trade was sustainable. The assumption could be made that it was not as almost all parrot species had by then suffered serious declines due to loss of habitat and/or trapping.

Other regulations flouted

In addition to CITES, some countries had other regulations that pertain to parrots. For example, Bahrain did not permit the importation of parrots from Indonesia. However, because of a trade agreement with Jordan, which pre-dates CITES, wild-caught cockatoos could enter Bahrain from Jordan and other Arab states. Importation was eventually mainly confined to the winter months of December to February. Previously, parrots imported during the hotter months seldom survived for more than a few days because they could not tolerate the extreme heat.

Bahrain imported hundreds of Ring-necked Parakeets from Pakistan, chicks that were still being hand-fed. They arrived packed into wooden crates, like day-old chicks (poultry) and were landed at Bahrain airport. To circumvent the law, which did not allow importation of birds from Pakistan for health reasons, they were then driven across the border to Saudi Arabia. There a veterinary certificate stating that they were free of Newcastle's disease was obtained, and they were immediately driven back to Bahrain, a round trip of about five hours.

Eighties import boom in the USA

During the 1980s the United States imported approximately half the parrots in international trade. Note that not all of these would have been wild-caught birds. Of parrots in trade worldwide during 1982 to 1988 the USA imported 47.6%, the European Economic Community (EEC), 29.8%, Japan 5.2% and other countries 17.4% *.

The spread of Exotic Newcastle Disease (END) from parrots to poultry was of major concern to the US government. In 1973 it introduced a 30-day quarantine period for all exotic birds entering the country. Birds found free of the disease were released from quarantine; infected birds were destroyed or sent back to the exporting country. From October 1979 to June 1980 END was detected in birds imported from South and Central America. The U. S. Department of Agriculture imposed restrictions

---

* Compiled by TRAFFIC International from CITES Annual Reports.

■ *Iguaçu National Park – devoid of macaws.*

try to shut out their suffering. I had never encountered a sight like it and I wondered that there were so many people insensitive enough to actually work in these places. One hundred and fifty years earlier the evil trade in human slaves was flourishing: now it was parrots.

I had no objection, at that time, to small importations in which parrots were (as I thought) humanely treated, but consignments consisting of hundreds of birds of one species left me sick to the stomach. In those in which Newcastle Disease was found, every bird would be killed. This applied in 1985 for example, in the following single consignments of parrots imported into the USA: 637 Blue-fronted Amazons from Argentina, 55 critically endangered Philippine Cockatoos, 1000 Ringneck Parakeets exported from India and 1582 threatened Red-masked Conures exported from Peru (Nilsson, 1989).

In one Florida quarantine station there were hundreds of Blue-fronted Amazons, for example; many were blind or had lost an eye due to avian pox. It was true that a vet was treating them – but a vet cannot restore them to the forests and mountains where they belong and to the other members of their flock. If they were young and they had no such memories, and were fortunate enough to be bought by caring people, their lives would be tolerable or good, but the vast majority would die of disease or ignorance on the part of their owners after a few years (usually not many) of a miserable existence. Trade went on for more than a decade like this, which would have been unlikely if the mortality rate had been low.

A few men made big fortunes. The mark-ups were huge. During 1986–87, 73% of US bird imports were controlled by five conglomerates. Some of the smaller dealers in Florida were also heavily involved in the illegal trade in birds, reptiles and other animals. They went to prison as a result.

The scale of the trade in parrots needs to be shown in context with that of other birds. In 1985, for example, 418 species were imported

on imports from Bolivia, El Salvador, Honduras, Panama, Paraguay and Peru for this reason, for limited periods.

The early 1980s saw an enormous increase in the importation of South American parrots. Between 1980 and 1984, the number of macaws imported in the USA totalled 77,908. Researcher Charles Munn concluded, after studying macaw populations in Peru, that 100 pairs of large macaws might fledge as few as 15 to 25 young annually. With such a low reproduction rate it was not surprising that by the early 1980s some areas (such as the Iguaçu National Park on the border of Brazil and Argentina) were devoid of macaws.

Imports of birds (mainly parrots) into the USA from Indonesia also increased significantly – from only 3,134 in 1980 to 29,849 in 1985.

Florida and California were the hotbeds of parrot importers. The first time I visited one of these warehouses where parrots were stacked in cages in rows by their thousands, I had to into the USA, of which 163 were parrots. By volume, parrots accounted for almost half this trade: 303,400 were imported of a total of 738,712. It is worth noting that some of the parrots imported were of species that had never or almost never been kept alive in captivity outside their country of origin. These included:

except under certain circumstances and stopped the importation of most parrots. Poaching (illegal taking of parrots from the wild) was significantly lower in the neotropics after the act was passed. In the subsequent three years, 75% of all parrots legally imported worldwide (some would have been captive-bred) entered the EEU

Species	Imported	Died in quarantine
Guiaibero		
(*Bolbopsittacus lunulatus*)	43	43 (Newcastle disease)
Golden-mantled Racket-tail		
(*Prioniturus platurus*)	3	3
Racket-tailed Parrots		
(unspecified)	24	24 (Newcastle disease)
Rose-faced Parrot		
(*Pionopsitta pulchra*)	1	1
Black-winged Parrot		
(*Hapalopsitta melanotis*)	14	14
Source: Nilsson 1985		

These species would have proved difficult subjects for even the most caring and experienced aviculturists. In a US quarantine station they had no chance.

EC ban of Indonesian species

In 1987 the European Community banned the importation of Indonesia parrots known to be threatened by excessive trade, including many lories, all the fig parrots and most cockatoos. This probably had little or no impact on the totals trapped. The USA then had no conscience about depleting populations of threatened species (but this was set to change). It imported 4,431 Moluccan Cockatoos in 1988 and 5,037 in 1989 (despite the fact that the Indonesian capture quota for 1989 was only 3,000 birds). By this time it was feared that this cockatoo was approaching extinction due to excessive trapping.

Import bans and world trade

In 1992 the USA took a giant step in the direction of a more humane attitude and passed the Wild Bird Conservation Act (see Chapter 7). This regulated the importation of wild-caught birds

(European Economic Union). This seemed to indicate that worldwide the number of legally exported parrots was hardly affected by the USA's initiative.

During this period Japan and Taiwan were important importers of parrots. Previously, in 1976, for example, Japan imported more than 344,000 parrots, but these were mainly from Hong Kong, also from Thailand, Taiwan and the Netherlands. One should note that most people in Japan live in apartments; very few have aviaries.

Despite the controls on the importation of wild-caught birds imposed by many countries, I believe that trapping and exporting of certain species will not cease until there are none left to trap.

In the course of one hundred years, during which time man had reached the moon and made other astounding technological achievements, he had done little to stop the suffering of countless millions of parrots shifted around the world with no more compassion than bags of sugar. Some governments imposed restrictions, then lifted them and perhaps imposed them again, but overall little progress had been made.

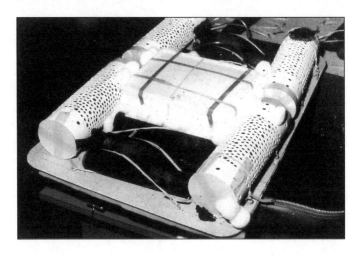

6. SMUGGLERS AND THIEVES

While visiting Indonesia in 1994 a man from Belgium bought seven Black-capped Lories (*Lorius lory lory*) in a market. These beautiful nectar-feeding parrots, with their red, blue and green plumage, were popular pets there. They have such character and they are clever mimics. He planned to take them back to Europe where it was illegal to import this species, so he drugged them and stuffed them into lemonade bottles. He was apprehended when he arrived at Schipol Airport in the Netherlands. All the lories were dead. Sadly, there was nothing unusual about this incident.

This chapter illustrates the worst sides of human nature: greed, avariciousness, deceit and, perhaps worst of all, inhumane treatment of innocent and defenceless creatures. Exploitation of endangered birds is another serious factor. Many parrot lovers will find that this chapter makes unpleasant reading, but a history of parrots in the twentieth century would be incomplete without it. Parrots, of course, are only a part of the illegal wildlife trade which, in 1995 was estimated by the World Wildlife Fund to net $20 billion per year. It was exceeded only by the drugs trade, with the smuggling of arms in third place.

Bizarre as it might seem, the combination of parrots and drugs was extremely lucrative – and cruel. In Bolivia and Argentina some parrots in shipments to the USA would be killed just prior to export. Sealed plastic tubes containing heroin were inserted into the mouths of the dead parrots and pushed down into their crops. The bodies were then packed in shipments with live parrots. A few dead ones at the other end aroused no suspicion when the crates were examined by Customs' officers.

Some smugglers didn't miss a trick. In California U. S. Fish and Wildlife Service officers investigated the illegal importation of parrots from Mexico. It was noticed that often the smugglers would load the vehicle with guns before driving to the Mexican border. It took a while for the realisation to dawn that the guns never came back. The men smuggled guns out and parrots in (Nichol, 1987).

In every country where parrots are found, people make a living by trafficking in them illegally. Wildlife smuggling was often big business, and tied up with drugs. Gangsters in China, Japan, Russia and Sicily were heavily involved. In Colombia the drug cartel participated, even using regional fishing fleets to smuggle drugs and animals through the Caribbean to the United States and Europe.

Why does the smuggling of parrots occur and who are the smugglers? Professionals are only one part of the problem. They will deal in anything that is profitable. Because some parrot species are worth substantial sums or because smugglers could illegally import large consignments (perhaps even chartering an aircraft for the purpose), there was (and still is) big money to be made. Large illegal consignments would enter Florida, for example, where they were quickly sold, perhaps to unsuspecting purchasers along with legally imported parrots.

In 1987 Mario Tabraue of Miami illegally imported parrots and endangered species such as leopards. He was convicted on 61 drug racketeering charges, bribing the police and killing a federal informant. In the same year Anna Marie Stevenson of Fort Lauderdale was arrested for operating a cocaine factory. Two years earlier she had illegally imported 104 Palm Cockatoos from Indonesia, a species that is threatened by trade and never found in large numbers in the wild.

Another category of smuggling concerned the trade in small numbers of an endangered species, such as Lear's Macaw. Because there were reportedly only about 200 birds left in the wild, some unscrupulous but wealthy collectors were determined to acquire a pair of these blue beauties that might be described as a smaller version of the better-known Hyacinthine Macaw. They would have to hide them forever because they could not have been legally acquired. But this fact did not deter them. It was possession that counted. For some collectors the blue macaws were the ultimate prize. The Glaucous was extinct, the Spix's extinct in the wild and the

Hyacinthine highly desirable but no longer very rare in captivity. Lear's became the "must have" species for the very wealthy few.

In Indonesia a chain of vendors and smugglers of illegal wildlife extended across the far-flung archipelago. The trade in cockatoos, lories and other parrots thrived despite Indonesia's membership of CITES because no one enforced the law and because the profits were so high. Bribery and corruption operated at every stage of the export procedure: forestry officials, airport customs and animal quarantine centres. The case of the Black-capped Lories related at the beginning of the chapter might fall into the category of opportunistic smuggling by ignorant people. This Indonesian species was neither expensive nor rare in Europe and aviary-bred birds were available.

During one investigation, ProFauna Indonesia exposed that some smuggled birds ended up in Germany. The most popular were Black-capped Lories, cockatoos and Eclectus. ProFauna's investigator penetrated the criminal network of the illegal wildlife trade and discovered that traders from Pramuka bird market in Jakarta constructed secret compartments in the bottom of each animal crate. It seemingly contained only dogs, reptiles or monkeys. In a crate large

∎ *Black-capped Lories*

enough to contain one Doberman, up to 25 Black-capped Lories or cockatoos could be jammed together in a hidden bottom drawer. They had their mandibles taped together to prevent them from making any sound on the long flight. "It is an outrage to see how cruel the trade is and how much the animals suffer," said one investigator. "It's no surprise that 40% die before reaching the markets."

The conditions where they were kept before export were appallingly cramped and dirty. Animals were treated inhumanely with no understanding about their welfare or basic needs. Traders in Pramuka regularly smuggled protected species to Kuwait and South Korea. For shipments to Korea they crated dogs with hidden compartments to hide the birds. Indonesian customs and airport authorities at Sukarno-Hatta International airport were bribed by the traders to allow the cargo to be loaded onto the aircrafts.

Cockatoos from Australia

The inadequate punishment handed out by the courts for wildlife crimes is perfectly illustrated in the case of one of the cruellest acts of smuggling ever perpetrated. Martin Barber from Cannock in the UK, jammed eleven cockatoos (one was a Galah) into mailing tubes, ALIVE, put the tubes into a box and mailed them to England by express post. He was arrested in Australia following the detection of the parcel in the post. Of course all the cockatoos were dead and some had suffered terrible injuries. In their panic they had attacked each other. His sentence for this unspeakable inhumane crime was three six months' terms of imprisonment, to run concurrently. Customs officials in the UK discovered that Barber and his associate Christopher Turner had attempted to export three Grey Parrots to Australia by the same method. These parrots also died. Turner, who funded this evil venture, was fined a mere £1,000 and a six months' sentence suspended for two years. Never was there a better example of parrots being treated as mere merchandise. Totally inadequate punishment was not unusual at that time.

In Australia in the late 1980s, the trade in illegal Australian wildlife was worth $40 million to smugglers *every year*, according to the World Wildlife Fund. (It would have been difficult to substantiate this figure.) One smuggler went to extreme lengths but wildlife crime officers outwitted him. He eventually entered a travel agency and booked a flight to Asia. The officers hid in the false ceiling of Sydney airport to wait for him to check in, then ordered the removal of his bag from the conveyor belt. Inside were plastic irrigation tubes with a model aeroplane engine and propeller driven by a battery (see photograph above chapter heading). This acted as an air-conditioning unit when a bag of dry ice was placed in front of the propeller. The case was lined with insulating wool. Inside were a number of wooden sections, each one containing a Major Mitchell's (Leadbeater's) Cockatoo (see colour page 10). The smuggler was taken to court. He was fined only $800. These beautiful pink- and yellow-crested cockatoos were reputedly worth AUD$15,000 (about £6,500) each on the international market in 1988.

Seventy-four Major Mitchell's Cockatoos were confiscated by police that year from a man apprehended near St George in western Queensland. This area is known for its cockatoos. They had been forced, 20 at a time, into small wire cages. Three were badly injured and the fortunate survivors were released.

▌*During the mid-1960s smuggling methods were crude. Cockatoos were injected with luminal and stuffed into wire tubes inside a suitcase. None survived.*

Photograph: Michael Schooley

▌*Eastern Slender-billed Cockatoo.*

The activities of a single miscreant pale into insignificance beside that of international smuggling rings. A concerned motorist in the Cairns area of Queensland reported to police hearing parrots squawking from a NSW-registered truck in a disused section of the road. The police traced the truck to a motel in Sydney and to two Austrians and an Australian man. When the vehicle was opened Galahs (Roseate Cockatoos) and Sulphur-crested Cockatoos were found inside. More than eight hundred! The Austrian's house and place of work were searched and plastic tubes for smuggling birds were found. Information from overseas indicated that, in addition, there were 200 rare parrots hidden away in New South Wales. The three men were charged under the Queensland Fauna Conservation Act. They hired three of Sydney's leading barristers. A "not guilty" verdict was returned (Schooley, undated).

In New Zealand the National Flora and Fauna Investigations Unit was set up in 1990 with just one member of staff. There were nine by 1994. One of the unit's most celebrated operations involved a chartered aircraft, found with a cargo of about 100 birds, some of which were said to be worth NZ$10,000 each (about £3,300). Among the dead birds located as they were being smuggled out were the big native mountain parrots, the Keas, which were rare in captivity worldwide. Because of New Zealand's proximity to Australia, Australian parrots – or more probably, their eggs – were smuggled in.

Breeders could legally export the young they reared, such as Eastern Slender-billed Cockatoos and Musk Lorikeets, because they were not native species. To close this loophole it was intended that exporters would in future be asked to prove the origin of their birds by DNA-testing of young and of the birds claimed to be their parents.

In 1992 enforcement agencies in the United States, Australia and New Zealand co-operated to smash a smuggling ring. In the US alone 100 law enforcement agents were involved, with 45 more in New Zealand. They seized smuggled wildlife (mainly parrots) exported with false documents and by means of complex laundering schemes.

Black Cockatoos

As detection of smuggled parrots became more frequent, smugglers turned their attention to eggs. This became a big, lucrative business for a few individuals, especially those who specialised in smuggling cockatoo eggs from Australia to Europe. Most of the *Calyptorhynchus* (black) cockatoos in Europe originate from these operations. These magnificent birds, the largest of all Australia's parrots, cannot be exported legally, except to zoos. Because there had been no legal bird export since 1958, and the imposing black cockatoos, such as the Red-

▌*Young Red-tailed Black Cockatoo.*

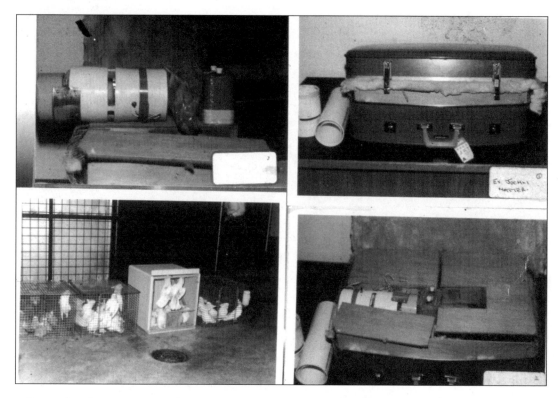

■ *Smugglers' equipment and, bottom left, Major Mitchell's Cockatoos and Galahs recovered before illegal export occurred.*

Photograph: Michael Schooley

tailed, were highly sought and difficult to breed, they were the main targets. Egg smugglers wore vests with pockets in rows in which the eggs were held. Their body warmth effectively incubated the eggs in transit.

In the Netherlands, CITES enfor-cement officers spent more than one year investigating such crimes. In May 1994 two Dutch men were charged with smuggling eggs of black cockatoos. An organised network had been in operation. The eggs were incubated in the Netherlands and the young were sold for huge profits. In April 1993, 86 black cockatoos had been seized. Jan van der Gulik and Kenny Dekker were arrested but when the case came to trial it was dismissed due to lack of evidence. The Dutch authorities appealed to a higher court and in May 1994 the men received prison sentences, of 12 and 18 months respectively. Twenty-two black cockatoos were confiscated from van der Gulik and placed in zoos.

Also in 1994 John Barth in Las Vegas was charged with importing the eggs of Australian cockatoos. He admitted that the value of the birds reared from these eggs was between $500,000 and $800,000. The sentence for such a crime was a maximum of five years in prison plus a fine of $250,000 or twice the gross gain! Those convicted of wildlife crimes in the USA did not receive the lenient sentences of their European counterparts.

Australia followed suit in imposing harsh punishments on smugglers. In 1996 William Wegner of New York was sentenced to five years imprisonment. He had recruited former high school friends to rob cockatoo nests and to take the eggs to the United States. So many young people from a certain town wanted their share of this lucrative business that competing smuggling groups were organised. This went on for eight years before the operation was uncovered. Wegner's article about "breeding" the White-tailed Black Cockatoo was even published in a leading avicultural magazine.

In 1994 police and Customs and Excise officers were involved in the first seizure of its kind in the UK. Nineteen black cockatoos were confiscated in South Wales. Five people were arrested, including the retired vet and well-known aviculturist, Alan Griffiths. Crawford Allan, a TRAFFIC[1] International Enforcement officer, said: "This seizure and pending prosecution will send shock waves through the avicultural community in the United Kingdom and elsewhere, setting a precedent which signals to smugglers that illegal practices will not be tolerated." He added that international co-operation between enforcement bodies, combined with the increasing use of technology, such as DNA testing and microchips, were major obstacles to illegal wildlife trading.

Griffiths was sentenced to eight months in prison and ordered to repay £29,000 plus £2,500 prosecution costs. He had made at least £54,000 from the sale of cockatoos hatched from the poached eggs. These illegal activities had thrown the avicultural world into disrepute; it was shocking because a former member of a respected profession was involved. He was not the first person in the UK to smuggle in the eggs of black cockatoos; others had escaped detection. Griffiths' prison sentence sent out a warning to would-be smugglers. The temptation was great because the rewards were so high. A pair of black cockatoos would fetch a sum that exceeded the annual income of many households.

Two-way traffic

The traffic in smuggling eggs was often two-way. Smugglers from Europe took eggs of lories out to Australia. The demand was high due to a prohibition on importation and limited stocks of exotic lories. It was claimed that these birds had been in Australia for many years despite the fact that some species were unknown when legal importation ceased! The eggs of other parrots, such as Amazons and Greys and rare mutations, were also of interest to egg smugglers.

Grey Parrots

Although countless Grey Parrots were legally imported into Europe and elsewhere, smuggling (thereby evading quarantine) made it possible to offer these parrots at relatively low prices and still make a big profit. One African national would smuggle 20 or so birds on one trip, after buying the birds for small sums. But he did not confine these forays to a single trip. Why would anyone buy smuggled birds of common species like Grey Parrots? The answer is simple. They are much cheaper than captive-bred birds. For many ignorant buyers, price is the major consideration.

A cruel act was perpetrated by a Nigerian man in June 1993. Twenty-eight African Grey Parrots were found in his luggage when he arrived at Istanbul airport. Thirteen were already dead. On June 14 of that year 33 more were smuggled in using the same method: the birds were packed in tiny wire cages with their beaks taped up. Seven were dead on arrival. The surviving birds were placed in a zoo's quarantine – but about half of them did not survive.

It seemed that one person (and/or his associates) was making weekly trips to different countries. On June 22 1993 customs officers at Schipol Airport in the Netherlands arrested a Nigerian, *en route* to Istanbul with 33 Grey Parrots in his luggage; four were dead on arrival. On June 30 a Nigerian was apprehended at Rome airport, also travelling from Lagos, also with Greys – totalling 40 – in small cages with their beaks taped. Obviously it was not the first time; he told Customs officers that controls in Italy were more stringent than previously, and that next time he would go to Switzerland where he had never been stopped.

In 1994 a Miami parrot importer was accused of bringing more than 4,000 Grey Parrots into the country using false papers. Adolf Pare imported the Greys between 1985 and 1991 with a total value of between US$3 million and US$5 million. The forged export documents stated that the Greys came from African nations with legitimate captive populations. In fact the parrots were poached from wilderness areas of Zaire (now the Democratic Republic of Congo), which country banned their export in 1984. The maximum jail sentence that could have been imposed on this man was four years and the maximum fine $1.86 million. (No information was available on his sentence.)

In 2000 Zimbabwe's Society for the Prevention of Cruelty to Animals accused the army there (11,000 troops) of illegally trafficking in Grey Parrots. It claimed that officers flew hundreds of

---

[1] The trade monitoring programme of The Worldwide Fund for Nature.

▍ *Young Hyacinthine Macaw.*

Greys from the Democratic Republic of Congo to an air base near Harare, and thence to Tripoli in Lebanon. Military security made it impossible to gain access to the air base – but there was no reason to disbelieve the SPCA's findings.

Macaws

The biggest parrot smuggling scandal in history threw suspicion and infamy on the whole avicultural community. Tony Silva, an American of Cuban descent, was well known as a speaker at parrot conventions and author of articles in various avicultural magazines. He purported to abhor smuggling and other illegal practices, while carrying them out on a huge scale. Interested in the rarest birds that Brazil had to offer, in 1995 he was charged with smuggling into the USA 186 Hyacinthine Macaws. The total retail value was US$1,386,900. Over a period of six and a half years he masterminded several different smuggling schemes, all involving endangered or protected parrot species.

Many well-known aviculturists in the USA bought these smuggled birds. Silva was charged after an investigation that took nearly four years.

His offences included tax evasion and perjury. The charges were made as part of Operation Renegade. Using undercover criminal investigators and confidential informants, the US Fish and Wildlife Service had penetrated bird smuggling operations in which parrots had been smuggled from South America, Mexico, Africa, Australia and New Zealand. James Burn, the prosecuting attorney said: "It is disgraceful that Mr Silva, who obviously understands the value of these rare birds, had engaged in activity that proved directly fatal to many Hyacinth Macaws and other highly endangered species that were smuggled illicitly. It is unconscionable that a person of Mr Silva's stature in the avicultural community would contribute, ultimately, to the illicit process that threatens these exquisite creatures with extinction."

The Assistant Attorney General added that Silva and the other defendants (his mother included) were involved "in nothing less than plundering the national treasures of other countries. These crimes threaten not only our ability but that of the international community to protect endangered species and global biodiversity."

Silva was sentenced to 82 months in jail, without parole, the longest prison term ever handed out for bird smuggling. He was also fined $100,000 and ordered to carry out 200 hours of community service during the supervised three-year release period following the prison term.

While this man was motivated entirely by avariciousness, Britain's best-known parrot smuggler had different motives. Harry Sissen was by far the most successful commercial breeder of large macaws in the UK. When he saw Red-fronted Macaws (*Ara rubrogenys*) at a dealer's premises in Europe he bought them and tried to smuggle them into the UK in his car. At that time he was probably the world's most successful breeder of this endangered species and he believed that these macaws would be better off with him. He was caught – and jailed. Export of this macaw was legal at the time the species was introduced to aviculture in 1973 but became illegal when the macaw was placed on Appendix I of CITES in 1983.

The Critically Endangered Lear's Macaw resembles the Hyacinthine apart from its smaller size. A few years after the Red-fronted Macaw fiasco, Harry Sissen legally acquired two Lear's Macaws that had been many years in captivity. ("Legal" means legally imported; no birds of this species have been legally exported.) They pre-dated the time when the origin of the wild birds in Brazil was discovered (as late as 1978). The only captive pair in Europe, they were stolen from his aviary, along with nine other parrots, in 1996. The Lear's were never recovered. His next mission was to smuggle three Lear's Macaws into the UK from the Czech Republic (along with six Blue-headed Macaws, *Ara couloni*). He was jailed again, this time for 18 months. Harry Sissen apparently believed that he could save Lear's Macaw from extinction by captive breeding but had somehow overlooked the fact that it was facing extinction due to the activities of illegal trappers fuelled by collectors like himself. Most of his huge collection of parrots was confiscated as he had failed to keep records and was unable to prove their origins, although many were legally obtained.

When there was only one Spix's Macaw left in the wild, Lear's Macaws were the prime target of wealthy collectors. They were the subject of another scandal in 1996. At Charles de Gaulle airport in France customs officers asked a Singaporean serviceman, in transit from Brazil, to open his carry-on bag. Inside they found two young Lear's. The birds were confiscated but the man was allowed to leave. He had used faked CITES documentation. Reputedly from Chile, it was written in Portuguese! In 2000, after long drawn-out legal action in Singapore, Lawrence Kuah Kok Choon was convicted of smuggling, jailed for one year and fined Singapore $10,000. The two Lear's Macaws were kept in a zoo before being returned to Brazil, to Sao Paulo Zoo. This man, still very young, kept a large collection of rare parrots in his parents' apartment: cage after cage of rare lories, fig parrots, cockatoos and even birds of paradise.

Richard Hartley visited the habitat of Lear's Macaw in 2000. Its total population was believed to number 181 birds. In Bahía, in the north-eastern part of the country, he met sixty-year-old José Cardoso de Macedo. The cliffs in which the Lear's nested had been in his family since the turn of the century. "There used to be 200, maybe 300, birds flying overhead every day. Then the gringo came".

The "gringo" (foreigner) was respected ornithologist Helmut Sick. His Lear's Macaw mission was to discover from where it originated – but he had not envisaged the disastrous consequences. Suddenly there were people visiting the area from all over the world.

▌*Lear's Macaw chick illegally removed from a wild nest.*

Macedo said: "That's when the traffickers came" and the Lear's population started to decline.

Eurivaldo Macedo Alvez was paid by Fundacao Biodiversitas to guard the Lear's area against poachers. In 1999 he apprehended two men who were to be paid $1,000 each to obtain Lear's. He handed them over to the authorities – but nothing happened. Former poacher Carlos Araujo Lima was paid by another foundation, BioBrasil, to provide it with information on traffickers. One day in his absence, an intern to the project watched helplessly as two mean captured a pair of Lear's and took them away (Hartley, 2001).

The world's most notorious smuggler of Lear's was the infamous Carlinhos from Petrolina. Five feet six inches tall, with gold chains dangling from his neck, he openly boasted that he received US$13,000 in cash and a new car for one of the first pairs he sold. After he had poached and sold 40 to 50 Lear's he was arrested and spent seven months in jail. Apparently seven months was considered an appropriate sentence for trapping at least 20% of the population of one of the world's most endangered birds. While he was in jail he was approached by one of the foundations. They would pay him a monthly salary; his knowledge and contacts could help to save the Lear's...

The thefts continued. By 2001 it was believed that about one quarter of all nests were poached every year. Conservation organisations were (and, in 2006, still are) working to try to ensure a future for this charismatic macaw. The difficulties in protecting it are many.

In recent years worldwide threats from terrorism have resulted in body searches of passengers boarding planes becoming almost routine. Yet still this does not deter some smugglers. They carry eggs sewn into pockets in their vest. In 2003 a 31-year-old Portuguese man was arrested at Recife airport in Brazil, attempting to smuggle out 58 eggs. Most of the rare and endangered Brazilian parrots that enter Europe do so via Portugal. It has been suggested that during the 2001–2002 breeding season, as many as 200 eggs were illegally collected from Hyacinthine Macaw nests in the Pantanal region of Brazil. It seemed that illegal egg collecting continued to be a major threat to the survival of some endangered parrots.

From Mexico to the USA

In the middle years of the century it was forbidden to import parrots into the USA because of the risk Newcastle disease[2] presented to the multi-million dollar poultry industry. Sheldon Dingle recalled of members of the American Avicultural Society:

"This did not stop many of our fellow bird friends. Many ladies would wear the fashionable full skirts with many petticoats under them and walk into Mexico and return hours later with dozens of birds wrapped in cheesecloth bags. Some of the wealthier members of the Society would take their private boats (yachts) to many exotic locations and smuggle as many birds as they could catch and place under the floorboards of their boat. I remember one story about my friend David West's dad being caught with Cockatoos from Australia" (Dingle, 2003).

Countless parrots were smuggled across the Mexican border at Tijuana into California, some at the hands of private individuals who did not take these controls very seriously. There was no stigma attached to small-scale smuggling. Published in 1971, a book entitled *A Bird in my Bed* related the story of a small parakeet, an Orange-fronted or Petz's Conure (*Aratinga canicularis*). It was bought in a market in Mexico by the author, Anne Dunbar Graham. Apparently her intention was to release him but when she discovered he could not fly, she smuggled him into California. That kind of naïve purchase by members of the public who have little knowledge of birds is of course illegal but in a different category to smuggling by aviculturists. Their smuggled birds were putting at risk the collections into which they were introduced.

In 1994 an American was apprehended in Texas with 70 young Yellow-naped Amazons in the rear of his van. Customs agents discovered

[2] A highly infectious viral disease found in many bird species.

Amazons smuggled into Europe

When smugglers were apprehended in the UK they were fined insignificant sums, even although the case had cost thousands of pounds to bring to court. In 1989 David Deans of Mansfield applied to import Blue-cheeked Amazons (*Amazona dufresniana*) (colour page 9) from Guyana. The request was refused because Guyana had a nil export quota for this species. In February 1980 Deans imported them anyway, and was apprehended as he tried to bring them through Heathrow Airport. (Six of these 11 Amazons subsequently died of psittacosis.)

The investigation and prosecution brought by Customs and Excise took more than one year, involved detective work in the UK and in Guyana, and cost more than £12,500. Yet Deans, when found guilty, was fined only £250 with £250 costs despite the fact that there was no ceiling on what the court could have imposed. The fine was a mere fraction of what he would have received for selling the birds. Furthermore, his company could continue trading in parrots because at the time there was no provision to withhold import licences from convicted smugglers! The law was an ass!

One Amazon has long been the victim of sea-faring smugglers. Almost the entire European population of the Cuban Amazon (*Amazona l. leucocephala*) was smuggled out of Cuba to Russia over a number of years. As a result it was one of the most common Amazons in aviculture in former Eastern Bloc countries, such as the Czech Republic. In the Canary Islands it was often seen as a pet after Russian ships *en route* to Europe docked with their cargoes. From the early 1990s, when Spain began to take their CITES commitments more seriously, these Amazons were confiscated at ports and given (usually a dozen or so at a time) to zoos who were obliged to take them. Some zoos there had aviaries full of Cubans! Strange as it may seem to Western Europeans, who still regard this beautiful Amazon as desirable (and expensive), these confiscated birds were not necessarily welcome additions to the collections. They took up much-needed aviary space, had to be fed for years without recompense and they could never be given away or exchanged. Furthermore, their acquisition could have constituted a disease risk.

▌ *Chicks of Yellow-naped Amazons were smuggled across the Mexican border.*

that the man had been involved in large-scale smuggling of parrots from Mexico. He claimed that the birds he sold were hatched at his state-of-the-art breeding facility. Sentenced to five years in prison and three years supervised release, he was also fined US$10,000.

In 1985 the U. S. Fish & Wildlife Service estimated that 50,000 parrots per year were smuggled across the Mexican border; in 1990 the World Wildlife Fund's (WWF) Trade Record of Analysis of Flora and Fauna in Commerce estimated this figure as approximately 100,000 annually. An Amazon that would cost less than $10 from a native trapper sold for hundreds of dollars once across the border into Texas or California. Profits were huge even though mortality was said to be as high as 80%. Some people made fortunes. One pet shop in California ordered parrots from Argentina and Singapore to be shipped to the airport in Mexico City, to be collected by a corrupt veterinarian. He sent them to Tijuana, from where they illegally entered the USA.

In March 1982 the United States Department of Agriculture (USDA) brought in legislation to prevent parrots being shipped out of California until they had been examined by a veterinarian and fitted with an approved USDA band (ring). However, there were only four offices in the entire state of California that could handle this procedure. Some parrot breeders who wanted to ship young birds outside the state had to wait so long that they lost sales.

■ *Cuban Amazon.*

Beautiful as Cuban Amazons are, with their pink and white faces, it is the Antillean Amazons that are most attractive to the collectors – and smugglers took big risks to get them. In the late 1990s two sought-after species that could not be exported legally, the St Vincent Parrot and the St Lucia Parrot (both from the islands after which they are named) turned up in the Czech Republic. These large colourful Amazons might have been smuggled in as eggs or chicks.

Smuggling within Europe

Smuggling across European borders was commonplace. There were two reasons for this. Before birds from EU countries could move freely without going into quarantine, people brought in birds illegally to avoid the expenses of a five-week quarantine period. They also did so, from the middle of the century to the 1980s, because some countries permitted the importation of parrots and others did not. In 1940 John Yealland, who became Curator of Birds at London Zoo, wrote that the ban on the importation of parrots into Britain had been in force for about ten years. During that period there had been a great increase in the keeping of parakeets but prices of all psittacine birds had risen to "absurd levels". In Belgium, where there was no such ban, prices went down and "all sorts of very interesting Psittacine birds turned up". In Holland the ban was removed in 1939. Before then, parrots were smuggled across the frontier from Belgium at a spot where "owing to the marshy nature of the ground and the foggy state of the atmosphere, the Customs officials, for reasons of health, did not care to linger in the night air".

Parrots were smuggled into Germany concealed in crates containing lions! With a nice touch of humour, Yealland wrote: "... it would be inconvenient if every time you wanted to send someone a parrot, you were obliged to get a lion to go with it" (Yealland, 1940).

In *The Animal Smugglers* John Nichol described how a dealer demonstrated another routine. In the 1980s Germany did not permit parrot importation yet an animal dealer in Germany obtained parrots with comparative ease. At sunset he drove towards the Dutch border, arriving an hour after midnight. Then he parked in a small wood, walked for one mile, waded a ditch, struggled through a wire fence and finally crossed fields to reach a narrow road. Then he was in Holland. His contact was waiting. At his house he selected the parrots. Each one had its beak closed with tape and was then inserted head first into a pair of tights and taped up to prevent it moving. Then he trekked back to the car with the parrots strung around his neck (Nichol, 1987).

CITES Task Force

In 1992 HM Customs and Excise set up the CITES Task Force in the UK to help combat the illegal trade in wildlife. Located at Heathrow Airport, which probably handles more wildlife traffic than any other airport worldwide, it commenced with a staff of three. By 2003 this number had trebled. Charles MacKay; head of the Task Force, said that as smugglers became more sophisticated, intelligence gathering became more important. Law enforcement, of course, and education were other important aspects of its work. A library of photographs of parrot species and sub-species was built up to assist in identification.

In half a century the attitude to smuggling has undergone an important change with the advent of prison sentences, very large fines and a lot of publicity. Nevertheless, by the end of the century it seemed that there was no country in the world, even the most remote aviculturally, that was not involved in this activity, albeit on a small scale. Parrots were smuggled from Singapore into countries like Serbia and Montenegro, which were not signatories to CITES. Some then went into Bulgaria and Macedonia and on to Western Europe. An alternative smuggling route was from Turkey, through Bulgaria and Macedonia, and thence to Serbia. Macedonia joined CITES in 2002 but it remains to be seen whether this will reduce smuggling. Bringing in parrots legally was difficult as customs officers did not recognise CITES and veterinary certificates.

Some people believe that if trade in wild-caught parrots was banned, smuggling would increase. This is extremely unlikely because the illegal trade depends heavily on forged import and export licences for its existence.

The con men

Over the years unsuspecting aviculturists have provided rich pickings for con men and fraudsters, for smugglers and thieves. All kinds of scams have been dreamed up by unscrupulous bird importers. Unfortunately, bird dealers have never been known for their honesty, even faking and dying to get the desired appearance regarding species or gender. For example, when only wild-caught Turquoisine Parakeets were available, in the 1920s, females were scarce, as was apparently the case with most Australian parakeets. Some importers had a remedy for this. With Turquoisines, they pulled out the male's red wing feathers and destroyed the blue face markings with "caustic" (presumably caustic soda), which changed the colour to a dull brown, leaving only the forehead blue. They then had an imitation of a female that would have deceived some people.

In Mexico bird dealers regularly bleached Green-cheeked and Finsch's Amazons to resemble the more desirable Double Yellow-head, much sought-after for its talking ability. They also used peroxide to bleach the head colours of Amazons and conures to make them look different. In Brazil, cheats dyed or painted the common White-eyed Conure (*Aratinga leucophthalmus*) yellow, leaving the wings green, then sold them for the high-priced Golden Conure (*Guaruba guarouba*).

More recently, in the 1980s, Queen of Bavaria's (Golden) Conures could be imported into the UK, despite the fact that they are found only in Brazil, which country had not permitted the export of its native fauna since 1967. One part-time dealer imported high-priced Cuban Amazons and Queen of Bavaria's Conures under licence. He realised that he could have sold them many times over. But why would he go to the expense and trouble of importing more when he could cheat? He photocopied the licence and changed the date of importation. Armed with this forged document he proceeded to take orders from a few wealthy aviculturists for the birds he claimed to be importing in the near future.

"I want 50% of the payment now and 50% when the birds are in quarantine," he told those gullible enough to part with considerable sums of money. The fictitious birds never arrived – but he stacked up a pile of cash. One parrot breeder who had been tricked sought revenge, so the story goes. Flanked by two "heavies", he confronted the bogus importer as he opened up his shop, early one morning. Under threat and menacing behaviour, the importer was forced to visit the bank and withdraw the appropriate sum of which the parrot breeder had been fleeced. The breeder received no Golden Conures – but he engineered a cash refund and a satisfying revenge!

In Australia one well-known breeder, now deceased, was heavily involved in smuggling, exchanging parrots he trapped or bred for those smuggled from Europe. Reputedly he even took money in advance for birds he claimed were being smuggled in – then told his "customers" that Customs had taken the birds!

Thieves

By the early 1980s the rarer parrots and the large macaws commanded very high prices. Then the thieves swung into action. They visited private aviaries, posing as buyers, and a few nights later the birds would be stolen. Access was easy in those days. Breeders were not suspicious and willingly showed their birds to other people who were apparently parrot lovers. In the UK there were no selling shows and surplus stock was advertised in the weekly magazine *Cage & Aviary Birds*. Parrot theft was not yet big business and it was very easy to dispose of stolen birds. They could be driven on to a ferry that night and be sold in a different country the next morning. The police had no interest in parrot thefts.

Zoos were also targets, especially those with macaws. These birds are large and loud, and therefore not the easiest parrots to remove illicitly. In 1989 a very tame Scarlet Macaw called Mickey was stolen from Glasgow Zoo. By then police were more aware of the value of parrots and they publicised the theft widely; if the thief was local, the macaw would become too hot to handle, especially as Mickey could be identified by one missing claw. This tactic paid off. Four weeks later Mickey was offered to a local pet dealer – and he was soon back in the zoo.

In 1991 four macaws were stolen from Birdworld at Farnham, Surrey in the UK. One of them had been a pet of the Harvey family, owners of Birdworld, for 22 years. The birds were recovered in the following month and two men were charged. A sad theft occurred at a well-known bird park in Cornwall. One of the original birds, an Umbrella Cockatoo called Susie, a special pet of the owners, was stolen after 25 years. Nothing can replace such a treasured pet. Years after the owners still wonder: "Where is Susie now? Is she still alive?"

The theft of valuable parrots attracted the hardened criminal element. In 1993 two precious breeding pairs of very valuable species, Palm Cockatoos and Buffon's Macaws, plus a single Hyacinthine Macaw, were stolen from Paradise Park in Cornwall. It was a tragedy: one member of each pair died as the result of the rough handling they received. The man convicted of their theft had already served a four-year prison sentence for child cruelty and a three-year sentence for kidnapping and other offences. For the parrot thefts he received another four years.

Hyacinthine Macaws, the most expensive of the parrots usually available, were particularly attractive to thieves. When the pair at London Zoo was stolen, the publicity regarding the theft made the unfortunate birds unsaleable. They were dumped in a phone box, one of them already dead when discovered. It was a tragedy for the birds concerned. Often long-time pairs were broken up by thieves, and sold as pets. The small-time thief usually operated by word of mouth in a pub. The birds were always passed on at prices that were far below market value – a clear indication that they were stolen.

The more organised, knowledgeable thieves stole to order. A breeder foiled what would have been a lucrative haul of nearly £20,000. He received a telephone call from a man who asked him if he wanted to buy a pair each of Palm Cockatoos, Leadbeater's Cockatoos and Hyacinthine Macaws. Realising that the birds would be stolen, and anticipating an opportunity to expose the thieves, he expressed an interest in them. The *modus operandi* of the more cunning thieves was to arrange a rendezvous at a motorway service station in the early hours, so that the birds were moved on immediately. A time and a place were mentioned for the following day. This was too soon so the breeder invented a business meeting, and defined the date for the following week. The thieves were naïve: the location and the species were immediate clues to the origin of the birds to be targeted. The breeder wasted no time. He informed the bird garden and the police. There was much information, even the registration number of the car to be used in the heist (essential knowledge for the rendezvous). It turned out to be a "street car" – one that is available to a gang of thieves for their illicit jobs.

It should have been so easy to catch the thieves in the act – but the police could spare only one officer. On the night, half a dozen other men, equipped with walkie-talkies, were ready and waiting. The thieves arrived, set off the alarm, and then waited an hour before entering. Alas! What followed was a complete fiasco, like something out of a *Carry On* farce. The thieves escaped – but the birds were safe.

▮ *Leadbeater's Cockatoos.*

▌ Ramon Noegel with his Cuban Amazons.

One day I visited Chester Zoo. Some rare species were exhibited in the aviaries outside the parrot house – but it was a pair of Blue and Yellow Macaws that caught my attention. They were so compatible – so obviously devoted to each other. A prolific pair, they had been together for nearly 30 years, as General Curator Roger Wilkinson told me. Next day I was shocked to learn that one of the pair had been stolen. The theft occurred in broad daylight (no mean feat) and while I was in the zoo. My heart went out to the pair, now separated after decades together. Local television and press gave much coverage to the story. The following day a woman telephoned the zoo, claiming to have bought the macaw in a pub for £550 on the previous evening. The happy outcome was that the macaws were reunited.

One of the most unlikely parrot thefts ever to occur was that of the Critically Endangered Puerto Rican Parrot (*Amazona vittata*). An undisclosed number of birds were taken from the breeding facility of the U. S. Fish and Wildlife Service on Puerto Rico. They were never recovered. As all the captive birds of this species are government-owned on Puerto Rico, the stolen birds could not be offered for sale on the international parrot market. The probable explanation is that they were stolen to order for a collector who cared more for the acquisition of endangered parrots than he did for their survival in the wild. Such a collector is not a genuine parrot lover because he can see no further than the end of his aviaries. His greed and selfishness blacken the name of aviculture.

By the 1990s in the UK every issue of an avicultural or parrot magazine carried a list of the latest thefts. Ex-police officer John Hayward set up a bureau entitled the National Theft Register to help people recover stolen and lost parrots. He visited individuals and bird clubs, giving advice on security and crime prevention – but all too often people sought advice *after* the event. Not until 2005 was there some form of deterrent for illegally trading in Appendix I species (the main targets of some thieves); they could then face six months' imprisonment if sentenced at a Magistrates' Court or *five years* if sentenced at a Crown Court.

Florida breeders lived in fear

In the USA in 1998 breeders in Florida lived in fear. There was a spate of thefts by people so callous and cruel that I will spare readers the details. In eight robberies alone 232 parrots valued at more than $312,000 were stolen. No one was ever charged. One of the victims was Ramon Noegel whose 35 years of breeding Cuban Amazons was almost wiped out overnight. He had a unique and intimate knowledge of his birds. He was able to buy back some of his young Cubans from other breeders to start again. Several years later he and his partner Greg Moss visited a breeder offering Cuban Amazons for sale. Ramon Noegel recognised some of his stolen birds and bought them on the spot. They were quiet on the journey back but as they neared the place where they had been hatched, they started to call and chortle. They knew they had come home!

Even pets are targets

It is not always rare parrots or big collections that are the targets of thieves. In the UK in 1995 a Blue-fronted Amazon named "Silver" was taken from his owner's home in Sale, Cheshire. Julie Rollings was so upset that she contacted the local newspaper to make an appeal for his return. Nine days later a woman phoned, claiming the usual story – she had bought the parrot from a stranger in a pub. She told Mrs Rollings to be in the car park of a certain pub that night. As Mrs Rollings waited, a black taxi drew up. Inside was Silver, sitting alone on the back seat. "It was like something out of a spy movie!" she said. She paid the fare and the driver left without speaking. She was so happy to be reunited with her parrot that she burst out crying. To be reunited with her Amazon was sheer happiness...

7. BAN THE TRADE!

Gerald Durrell was a high-profile figure in the world of conservation. He founded the first zoo (in Jersey) to specialise in breeding endangered animals and to lack popular creatures such as lions and tigers. This was considered to be financial suicide – and it nearly was. The zoo was financed by the popularity of his books. In 1992 he felt strongly enough about the trade to write (in his book *The Aye-Aye and I*):

"Between 1980 and 1981 over 30,000 wild-caught parrots passed through Amsterdam airport. Most of them either died on their journey or shortly afterwards because to save costs they are squashed together as slaves used to be. If they survive they are sold to 'bird lovers' in different parts of the world."

Mortality *was* high but could be documented only for parrots that died in transit or in quarantine. Official figures for exotic birds (not only parrots) showing numbers dead on arrival (DOA) to the UK and those that died in quarantine (a period of five weeks) in 1989 and 1991 were as follows:

Just consider that figure: during two years 40,000 birds died in transit to Britain or soon after in quarantine. An unknown number (probably higher) had died before export. And the people who bought the survivors could maintain them for a period that would have ranged from a few days to perhaps a few years. Most were of species that would have been financially viable to breed in captivity if the importation rate had not lowered their value.

In January 1997, just prior to the general election, a Labour Party spokesman announced that if Labour were elected there would be a ban on the importation of wild-caught birds. Labour was elected. What happened? The trade continued unabated. During the period 1997 to 2001, the total number of wild-caught parrots legally imported into Britain and other EU countries was 588,975 of 113 species. The pre-export mortality was estimated as 35%, giving a total in the region of 795,000 trapped in the wild. Mortality of survivors during the 12 months after export has been estimated

Year	Total imported	DOA	Died Qteen	% mortality
1989	184,577	4,732	20,619	13.7
1991	129,000	19,000		14.7

DOA = dead on arrival
Qteen = quarantine

(possibly conservatively) at 25%, to give the total of estimated deaths as 323,936. In the same period, 2,480,186 non-psittacine birds of CITES-listed species were imported into the EU. No records were kept of non-CITES species.

In the USA
Thomas Ryan worked in a United States Department of Agriculture quarantine station in 1979. He reported that the mortality rate varied with shipments and according to the species. "It was not unusual to get a shipment of 500 Greys and only have 250 come out. The most common causes of death were salmonellosis and aspergillosis. The same holds true for the Hyacinth Macaw. Many of these died simply because they gave up and stopped eating. Others, such as the Green Wing Macaw or the Amazons, had a mortality of less than 3%" (Ryan, 1980).

Official figures for the USA show even higher mortality rates than those in the UK. In the year 1985, for example, the mortality of birds (not only parrots) in quarantine with the ten largest importers showed mortality (including dead on arrival) of 18%. This varied between importers from 53% to only 2%. One of the problems, in both countries, was the high numbers permitted in any one importation. For example, in 1985, a UK importer could bring in 750 parrots in one consignment.

When Durrell lamented the trade in 1992 press reports had highlighted deaths of parrots in transit, and the ethics of trade in wild creatures. When parrots became freely available in the late 1960s and 1970s buyers were totally ignorant about all aspects of the trade. I look back and wonder that I never questioned the ethics of removing birds from the wild. The moral climate (partly due to ignorance of what trade involved) was different then in relation to animals.

Not until the 1980s did some facts became known about the bad conditions many parrots suffered during transport and in holding stations, and the high mortality rate prior to export. These were revealed during investigations carried out by British and American researchers in the country of origin or exporting countries. Papers were published about the wastefulness and cruelty of the trade.

I bought no wild-caught birds after 1978, with the exception of two species of conures (*Enicognathus*) in the early 1980s to make up pairs with two individuals already in my aviaries. I never patronised the big dealers but bought my birds from private importers whose small shipments were usually carefully tended.

In 1992 the RSPB (Royal Society for the Protection of Birds) contributed their position statement on trade to *PsittaScene*, the magazine of the World Parrot Trust. Mike Everett wrote (May 1992, p10) that recent investigations by the RSPB, RSPCA and the EIA (Environmental Investigations Agency), in Africa, South America and South-east Asia, showed that "the problems of cruelty and of widespread abuse (and downright flouting) of existing laws are even worse than originally believed. Corruption is rife in some quarters and the enforcement of existing legislation either non-existent or wholly ineffective. Above all, perhaps, the studies have revealed the full conservation implications of an uncontrolled trade which has little or nothing to do with the sustainable exploitation of a natural resource, nor, in reality, in providing a livelihood for local people. Instead, it has directly affected the survival of over 40 species – 30 of them, all faced with extinction, are parrots..."

He went on that the European Community was the largest consumer of wild-caught birds in the world; approximately three million were imported annually. Such was the mortality rate that this number probably represented only half the number originally trapped. Concerned about mortality, some airlines banned trade in wild-caught birds at the end of the 1980s. At least one country found a way to circumvent this. Nicaragua described the parrots it exported as "ranched" – not wild-caught.

In 1989 ICBP, the leading British avian conservation organisation, with partners in 60 countries worldwide, launched a campaign called Protect the Parrots. Its aim was to ban trade in all parrots at risk of extinction and to encourage the purchase of captive-bred birds. The campaign was short-lived and it failed.

In my books and articles I repeatedly appealed to people to buy captive-bred parrots. These pleas fell mainly on deaf ears. People who did not educate themselves by reading before they acquired a parrot were those most likely to buy wild-caught birds. Some did not know their origin and others genuinely believed that such birds were no longer imported. Others simply did not care – until the deaths hit their pockets. Anecdotal evidence suggested that mortality was very high. One man I spoke to bought 14 Senegal and Grey Parrots at the UK's biggest parrot selling event in October 2000. All but two died within the first six weeks. For the majority, price was the over-riding factor – and wild-caught parrots were always cheaper than those bred in captivity.

Extinction will result from trade

Many keepers in the UK react strongly to the suggestion that importation should stop. They counter this with: "Well, you had wild-caught birds – why shouldn't we?" Here is the answer. During the late 1970s and 1980s mass parrot importation followed small-scale trade, and the number of available species increased greatly. There was no information on the status of parrots. Joseph Forshaw, renowned author of *Parrots of the World*, attended the 1980 meeting on neotropical parrots of the Parrot Working Group of ICBP. Forshaw wrote: "I doubt that at the time there was full appreciation of the seriousness of the situation, and certainly there was no adequate forewarning of the critical problems that we would be addressing a decade later" (Forshaw, in Beissinger and Snyder, 1992).

CITES Article IV stipulates that exporting countries must establish that the export quotas will not be detrimental to the survival of the species, yet this was not scientifically proven for any of the parrot species traded during the 20th century.

In 1980 almost no fieldwork had been carried out (except on the Critically Endangered Puerto Rican Amazon) and there were no organisations to look after the survival of parrots. CITES existed – but by permitting trade without information on parrot status it was failing in its mission. In the mid-1980s a few parrot field projects started to show how damaging was the current scale of trade. During the next decade parrot field projects escalated. In 2000, when *Threatened Birds of the World* was published, it stated (page 19): "More parrots are globally threatened with extinction than any other family, with 57% of threatened parrots impacted by trapping." The book listed 113 species of

globally threatened birds for which trade was a significant threat. Of these 113, forty-eight were parrots. This puts into perspective the danger that trade presented to parrots in comparison with other bird groups. The next most threatened group was pigeons and doves – with eight species.

There is no doubt that excessive trade in some species will cause their extinction. Some were already close to that point at the end of the century. These species are listed at the end of this chapter. Two examples are the Blue-throated Macaw (see Chapter 12) and the Red-masked Conure (*Aratinga erythrogenys*). When Walter Goodfellow journeyed through the Andes of Colombia and Ecuador in 1899 he found these conures to be "exceedingly common". They were offered for sale at 5d (2p) each. In Carmen, Colombia, he saw "immense clouds". Carmen could boast of little vegetation other than bamboo, which grew in great thickets. He noted that "... every branch of these giant grasses was literally weighed down" with these conures (Goodfellow, *Avicultural Magazine*, vol vi, page 69 (1900).

At a meeting in 1990, the eminent ornithologist Robert Ridgely mentioned their catastrophic decline due to trade. He said that in 1977 there were thousands passing over Guayaquil every morning and evening; it was a common and widespread species. "Now you really have to look for the odd dozen or two, perhaps 50 in remote canyons with relatively

■ *Joseph Forshaw.*

■ *Red-masked Conures, once common, suffered massive declines.*

low human population density... it's devastating to me that this has been happening. It shows what concerted efforts to trap and export birds over a decade can do to a population" (James, ed, *in* Beissinger and Snyder, 1992).

By 2000 one in three of all parrots had been placed in a threat category. These statistics alone should have been sufficient to stop the importation of wild-caught parrots into the UK. But this was not the case.

Capture of adult parrots

Other factors indicated how changing times affected the parrot trade. Once young birds were the focus of the trade but greed had overtaken common sense and any parrot that could be trapped was taken. Parrots caught as adults are normally unsuitable as pets. In the 1980s there was a big demand for parrots as aviary birds; these wild-caught parrots could exist in aviaries – and many did breed. By the end of the century there had been a significant shift in emphasis towards keeping the larger parrots as pets rather than in aviaries. Fewer people kept them outdoors due to increased incidence of theft, and new houses with small gardens and close neighbours who would not tolerate the noise. These wild-caught adults, bought by

ignorant people as pets, soon became unwanted, and even abused. There were outdoor aviaries available for only a few. After months or years of insensitive handling, their suffering would, in some cases, be ended by euthanasia.

By the end of the century parrots were being bred in the UK and elsewhere on a very large scale. There was an excess of many species and the *need* to import parrots no longer existed. In the early 1980s few large parrots were hatched. In contrast, small prolific species such as lovebirds and Australian parakeets (which were not imported) were produced in big numbers.

Diseases brought in with imported birds did enormous damage to existing parrot stocks. Viral diseases killed thousands of parrots with whom unquarantined birds come into contact. In the 1970s and 1980s quarantine procedures were very strict then, in the 1990s, parrots could be brought into the UK from Europe with only a health certificate. Although certificates were signed by veterinarians many imported parrots had not been quarantined after coming from the wild. Nevertheless there were always buyers for them as most people were ignorant of the disease risks.

An end to U. S. imports?

In the USA the import of wild-caught parrots was effectively stopped in 1993 when the Wild Bird Conservation Act became law. It put the onus on exporters to show that the harvest of the species to be exported was sustainable. This was impossible to prove in most cases, and in others it was known that species had declined significantly due to trade. Annual quotas, such as those established by the governments of Guyana and Argentina, were not based on research and, in the case of the Blue-fronted Amazon for example, were in excess of sustainable trade levels.

Some closed-ringed pet birds were allowed to enter the USA from approved CITES-member countries' breeding facilities. Appendix 1 species could be imported only under a special permit. Before 1993 the USA was one of the largest importers of wild birds, bringing in more than 450,000 annually. In 1974, 28,000 birds were imported in commercial shipments; in 1984 the number had increased to 742,000. In the year 2000, when the importation of wild-caught parrots was not permitted under normal circumstances, 140,000 birds were imported.

I strongly endorse the importance of the Wild Bird Conservation Act (WBCA) and the need for similar legislation to be passed in Europe and elsewhere. The World Parrot Trust has campaigned for a ban on the importation of wild-caught birds into the European Union since 2001. A petition to stop the trade received 32,984 electronic signatures from individuals in 140 countries and was presented to the Prime Minister on World Parrot Day in May 2004. (Thousands more signed on paper.)

The WBCA had the effect of lowering the number of young parrots removed from nests. In the ten species for which direct comparison was possible, the rate was 48% before the Act was passed in 1992 and about 20% afterwards. Over all study sites it was lower after 1992 (26%) than before (36%). It was higher in unprotected sites than in protected sites for the four species for which direct comparisons could be made: Red-lored, Double Yellow-head, Green-cheeked and Yellow-naped Amazons.

The European Economic Union (EEU) accounted for more than 75% of all parrots legally imported in the three years after 1992. If importation restrictions similar to those of this Act were brought into the EEU, poaching rates would probably decline even further.

In 2003 there were worrying developments in the USA. It seemed that country was about to renege on its obligations. There was extensive discussion, with contributions from many conservationists, regarding re-opening trade with Argentina to allow in hundreds of wild-caught Blue-fronted Amazons. By then this parrot was known to have suffered severe declines due to over-trapping. How could the USA possibly justify this action? The proposal to import these Amazons had been through a number of processes and the U. S. Fish and Wildlife Service had published a "Proposed Rule" for approving and implementing importation. By 2006 the proposal officially remained "under review". No Amazons had been imported.

The suffering of wild parrots

Various reasons are given in favour of continuation of trade in wild-caught parrots – *but surely ethics should overwhelm every other consideration?* Do those in favour never give a thought to what a parrot suffers in the process? Or do they simply not care? The trauma inflicted on parrots caught after fledging and as adults is quite horrifying (see colour page 8).

Diana May watched the trapping of Grey Parrots in the Congo (*PsittaScene*, May 2001). Two methods were described, using glue on a tree branch, or baiting to lure parrots into ground nets. She observed that when trappers closed the net "the parrots are tightly sandwiched together; when the parrots struggle to bite and claw their way free, they maim each other and themselves. If they do not die immediately, some will die days or weeks later, from stress, infection (from wounds or respiratory infection due to poor living conditions), and pre-existing parasites. The main problem with the glue method is that a number of parrots that get glue on their wings will escape and die because they cannot fly and are likely to be killed by predators".

Both methods removed 10% to 50% more parrots from the population than are eventually

▌ *No – not a picturesque shot of Grey Parrots in the Cameroon sunset. These Greys are tethered to the branch. They are call birds, used to trap others.*

Photograph: Iolo Williams

exported (according to her interviews with trappers). Another cruel method is used to catch Senegal Parrots. A single bird is caught, its flight feathers are hacked off using a machete, the parrot is chained to the ground and nets are set up around it. Its screams of panic cause large numbers of Senegals to approach, then the nets snap shut.

These methods do not describe exceptional cruelty: they are the norm. In Guyana, another country from which Britain receives wild-caught parrots, the large macaws are treated in a brutal manner. Their flight feathers are also hacked off with machetes. As a result, many will never fly again. Figures can only tell the part of the story that is documented. The number of deaths from trapping activities can never be quantified. From the perspective of a large adult parrot, it probably would be preferable to die very soon after capture than to suffer the physical and psychological torture and imprisonment that follow.

How could anyone who cared about parrots condone the trade, especially as captive breeding supplied the demand? During the 1980s and 1990s the magazine *Cage & Aviary Birds* invariably published more letters from readers who were adamant that trade should continue than those in favour of ending it. In February 1988 a European Community meeting was held at which the decision was made to prohibit the importation of *Poicephalus* parrots (such as Senegals) from all parts of their range. (They occur only in Africa.) One reporter commented: "It is believed that the decision was taken because of concerns about the number of birds being taken for the bird trade. It is another blow to aviculturists in EU countries..."

The attitude that this would be a "blow to aviculturists" assumed that most of them would want the trade, with its horrific mortality rate, to continue. Even if they did, the decision to end trade would actually have been in their favour. Senegal, Meyer's and Red-bellied Parrots, the species most commonly trapped, were bred in large enough numbers in Europe to make importation unnecessary. Cessation of imports would have effectively increased the market value of breeders' offspring. How could this be a blow? According to official figures, in 1998 EC countries imported 34,302 Senegal Parrots. Most imported birds were adults that could

∎ *Young Senegal Parrots – captive-bred.*

never be tamed and these birds diminished the species' reputation as a pet bird.

Those who see nothing wrong in taking wild parrots should observe these birds experiencing all the joys – and the hazards – of a natural existence. They might then begin to question what right we have to deprive them of this when *the only possible motive is commercial gain* – and sometimes such an insignificant amount that no one benefits. In 2004 wild-caught Senegal Parrots could be bought for £38 each.

Invalid arguments for continuation of trade

In a so-called civilised society, the trade in parrots and other creatures taken from the wild should be illegal. This trade is cruel, wasteful and unnecessary. The arguments in favour of its continuation, often heard in Europe, were all invalid and based on misconceptions. Many breeders stated that "new blood" was necessary to maintain the rarer species in aviculture. Despite the fact that enormous numbers of certain species had been imported, these species were not been established in aviculture. One example was the Orange-flanked or Grey-chinned Parakeet (*Brotogeris pyrrhopterus*) from western Ecuador and extreme northern Peru. This pretty little parakeet was heavily exploited during the 1980s before which it was abundant in the wild in its limited area of distribution. From 1983 to 1988 at least 60,000 birds were exported. Taken from nests and hand-reared, they were very popular as pets in the USA. Despite the tens of thousands exported, it was a rare bird in aviculture by the end of the century, with perhaps fewer than ten breeders

Lilac-crowned or Finsch's Amazon.

are contributing towards the financial support of local communities. In most cases, except perhaps in India, this is not so.

In Mexico, Katherine Renton studied the Lilac-crowned Amazon (*Amazona finschi*), another species that has declined drastically due to trade. She told me: "It is often falsely assumed that those involved in parrot trapping are poor and hungry. This frequently is not the case because it requires a certain economic level to maintain and transport the birds, as well as a level of business acumen to trade in them. Having become familiar with the individuals in the community who are involved in parrot trapping, it is surprising to find that they are not the poorest members, but tend to have means of employment, large houses and good vehicles."

In Argentina impoverished people, tree fellers and charcoal-makers collected nestling Blue-fronted Amazons. In 1991, they were paid about US$4 for each one. The limited economic benefits of this trade were short-lived and had a high cost in terms of environmental degradation and loss of resources. According to Professor Enrique Bucher, these earnings did not lead to an improved standard of living or to ensuring the continuation of the trade. The people involved needed education, sustained income, land ownership and the knowledge of how to manage the land sustainably.

It was often claimed that breeding rare parrots was contributing towards their conservation. Chapter 10 explains that this was not the case. Another false suggestion was that "the expected lifespan of a captive parrot is greater than a wild one". Today we have some

in the USA and a similar number in Europe. The total population of the Grey-cheeked Parakeet, classified as Endangered, was estimated to be only about 15,000 birds – just one quarter of the number exported in that five year period. In this case trade had a lasting impact on its numbers and, due to deforestation, there was no possibility for recovery.

Income generated in exporting countries by the trade in wild caught birds has been estimated as follows: trappers, 6.3%; middlemen, 22.3%; exporters, 67.3%. The biggest profits go to those who are already affluent. Some purchasers of wild-caught parrots purport to believe that they appreciation of quality of life being greater than the length of imprisonment. However, millions of parrots taken from the wild survived only a matter of days or weeks, so even the supposed longevity was untrue. As an example, a man bought two Orange-winged Amazons in 2001, recently imported from Guyana. One died and was replaced. All three birds were dead within two weeks. Sadly, there is nothing unusual about this: death is due to disease and stress. The man had telephoned expecting me to commiserate. My sympathy was entirely with the birds.

Species with high mortality

Some parrot species were trapped despite the fact that their survival rate was almost nil. The Long-tailed Parakeet (*Psittacula longicauda*) seldom lives more than a few months in captivity. Breeding successes were few and never sustained over the long term. The worst scenario, which I personally witnessed, was a box of birds just arrived from the airport with not one alive. Another species from Malaysia with a low survival rate was the little Blue-rumped Parrot (*Psittinus cyanurus*) (see colour page 15). Clearly, the export trade was solely aimed at making money with absolutely no consideration for the birds involved. While this should not surprise anyone, trade in species with an exceedingly high mortality should be outlawed. Unfortunately, it is likely to be many years (if ever) before ethics play any part in the export trade.

■ *The mangled remains of Long-tailed Parakeets imported into Europe. There were no survivors.*

Exporting countries: Indonesia

The most scandalous aspect of trade in Indonesian parrots was that it wiped out populations and nearly caused extinctions of white cockatoos. Despite the fact that Indonesia had been a party to CITES since 1978, laws were unenforced, the trade was uncontrolled and, given the number of possible ports of export, uncontrollable. Too much money was involved, all along the line. A rare cockatoo sold in Indonesia for 3 million rupiah (US$260) could change hands for US$2,000 overseas. One dealer admitted that there was no difficulty in passing customs and other airport officials with these forbidden cargoes. "We just give them money and they take care of it", he said. The international value of animals smuggled out of Indonesia has been estimated at US$1 million per day (Yamin, 2003). Indonesia was believed to be the world's fourth largest bird-exporting country after Senegal, Tanzania and Argentina. Compared with smuggling, the legal trade is small.

The magnificent Moluccan (or Seram) Cockatoo (see colour page 7) occurs only on the island of Seram. It covers about 7,200sq miles (18,650 sq km or one seventh the size of England). Between 1981 and 1987 approximately 54,000 Moluccan Cockatoos were legally exported. In 1989 the species was placed on Appendix I of CITES. In the preceding few months the trappers, knowing what was coming, caught every cockatoo they could lay their hands on. Between 1983 and 1990, CITES figures showed that 66,654 Moluccan Cockatoos were exported to countries that were signatories of CITES. That was a shocking statistic, to which one must add exports to non-CITES countries, domestic trade within Indonesia and the birds that died before export. It is not only shocking but intolerably sad. Perhaps no species of parrot suffers more in captivity than this stunningly beautiful but emotionally intensely sensitive bird.

I received a photograph for this chapter that I considered too shocking and heart-breaking to publish. It showed a Moluccan Cockatoo that had been beaten about the head by smugglers. The vireous fluid had drained from its eyes and it died soon after.

The cockatoos continued to be illegally trapped and exported and were regularly offered for sale in Jakarta, Ambon and Singapore. Researcher John Taylor was told in 1990 by the local people that they had ceased to trade in the Moluccan Cockatoo on the instructions of PHPA officials. This was untrue: sales went underground. While overall trade numbers probably declined, the effect of the cockatoo ban was that trappers turned their attention to lories and *Tanygnathus* parrots (such as the Great-billed). The Purple-naped Lory (*Lorius domicellus*) is a beautiful red, green and black nectar-feeding parrot, endemic to Seram, and prized among the local people for its talking ability. As a result lories and *Tanygnathus* species declined to dangerously low levels.

John Taylor commented: "It is very easy for us in Western countries to sit back and demand that birds and animals be left alone, but alternatives must be offered. Many people in Seram and on other Indonesian islands depend on the trade as a source of income, it is part of their economy and they cannot be blamed for the decline of any species" (Taylor, 1991). Individuals might not

be to blame but governments are. In the case of Indonesia, no attempt was made to enforce the legislation that could have protected parrots from excessive trade. The European Union banned the importation of most species of Indonesian parrots in 1987.

In July 2002 the Indonesian organisation KSBK (Animal Conservation for Life) issued a report on parrot trade. In the province of North Maluku, for example, 15,000 parrots were trapped annually. No limit was set on the numbers of some species (such as the Umbrella Cockatoo) that could be caught. The birds were sent to Jakarta and Bali to be sold in markets. The psychological torture suffered by such intelligent birds as cockatoos when they are removed from their natural environment into harsh and unstimulating conditions results in feather plucking, mutilating their own flesh and in death. Such highly social birds cannot tolerate solitary confinement and must have the company of their own species or a sympathetic human companion if they are to thrive. Sadly,

▌*Above:* *Lesser Sulphur-crested Cockatoo – critically endangered by over-trapping.*
Above right: *the female Eclectus, confiscated in poor condition, who survived to moult into a beautiful bird.*

■ *Citron-crested, Goffin's and Triton Cockatoos awaiting purchase in a market in Denpasar, Bali.*

Photograph by Werner Dobnig

the ethics of the trade in wild-caught cockatoos and other highly intelligent parrots is seldom considered because comparatively few people have any understanding of the capacity for suffering of these magnificent parrots.

The National Army of Indonesia (TNI) was involved in this trade. Soldiers returning from duty in other parts of Indonesia brought hundreds of parrots back in warships, including Umbrella Cockatoos and Chattering Lories. With the smaller parrots, such as Violet-necked Lories, dozens of birds were packed so tightly into wooden boxes that they could hardly move. Heat and lack of food caused high mortality at this stage especially when birds were left uncovered in open boats and when waiting to be loaded onto aircraft. People involved in the trade were apparently unable to comprehend that survival and therefore profits would be higher if the birds were more humanely packed.

Of the Indonesian species trapped, 47% were "protected" by law. Trade had resulted in the local extinction of Moluccan Cockatoos, Red and Blue Lories, Purple-naped Lories and Chattering Lories. In the early 1990s one UK importer would have as many as 200 Red Lories and Chattering Lories in stock. Both these species were decimated by over-trapping and their numbers never recovered. The same was true of the Lesser Sulphur-crested Cockatoo,

a familiar companion bird. By the end of the century it was a Critically Endangered species due to the extinction of entire populations by trappers.

From January to March 2002 KSBK, supported by the RSPCA, investigated five markets in Java. The most common species on sale was the Black-capped Lory. Also heavily traded were other *Lorius* and *Eos* lories, Eclectus Parrots, Green-winged King Parakeets and *Tanygnathus* parrots. Some illegally held parrots were confiscated, such as the female Eclectus Parrot depicted on colour page 7. She was one of the lucky ones who, despite her bad condition, survived. The aim was to release her in due course.

Trade quotas had been broken many times, yet the local forestry department (KSDA) continued to issue trapping and transport permits. Dealers in Jakarta and Bali shipped birds to Pakistan, Qatar, Taiwan, Italy and Spain, most of which were dishonestly reported as captive-bred.

Large numbers of wild-caught parrots, including Appendix I species, were imported into the Arab States. For example, during 2002 many Indonesian cockatoos were imported into Bahrain and Saudi Arabia, including Moluccans, Tritons, Lesser Sulphur-crests and Citron-crests. One prospective buyer took the precaution of carrying out blood tests on 40 of these cockatoos. About 90% of them proved positive for psittacine beak and feather disease, a highly contagious and usually fatal viral disease. The infected birds included two Palm Cockatoos; they died a few days after being imported.

India

In India there was a total ban on the bird trade. This ban could not be enforced and every year approximately 50,000 parakeet chicks (representing between 20% and 30% of the parrot trade there) were collected. Most of these chicks were Ringnecks (*Psittacula krameri manillensis*), aged between two and four weeks. Also collected were Alexandrine, Moustache, Slaty-headed, Blue-winged and Blossom-headed (*Psittacula eupatria, alexandri, himalayana, columboides* and *roseata*). Chicks were removed from their nests from February to April using lengths of curved wire tied to a rope inserted into nesting cavities. These little birds, most of them without feathers, were collected by local or visiting trappers and sold to dealers. They were then sold in open markets. Some were smuggled to western Asia through Nepal and Pakistan.

Until 1991 India was a major exporter of parakeets. Between 1981 and 1990, 300,000 parakeets of five species were exported. The main importing countries were the Netherlands, Germany, Belgium and France. Thousands of parakeet chicks were seized from markets but in the absence of rescue centres most of them died because there was no one to feed them. A government release stated: "More wildlife volunteers need to come forward to help check the widespread trade of these hapless creatures."

In India Calcutta was the centre of trade, with a huge market and animal exporters all around the town. Another trade grew out of the parrot trapping and dealing. Men who were called "parrot pluckers" would visit the dealers, buying all the dead parrots they could lay their hands on. The bodies were thrown on refuge heaps and the pluckers would scavenge for them. They then plucked all the dead parrots and sold the feathers to novelty stationery emporiums. These places employed people to glue the feathers onto cards and sheets of writing paper (Nichol, 1987).

South America

The situation in South America was different with a much wider understanding that parrots and other birds bring eco-tourists and dollars. Many trappers realised that their knowledge could be used to greater financial advantage as a bird guide, and that this occupation has long-term economic gain for the region (see Chapter 17). Despite this, trapping continued unabated in many regions.

Legal export of wild-caught neotropical parrots changed with the decades. Brazil banned the export of its fauna in 1967, Costa Rica and Venezuela did likewise in 1970 and Colombia in 1973. In the early 1970s the major exporters were Mexico, Colombia, Peru and Paraguay. By the early 1980s, Belize, Ecuador and Mexico had ceased to export birds. The major exporters were Argentina, Bolivia, Guyana, Honduras and Peru. In 1984 Bolivia banned the export of wildlife and Argentina was the single largest exporter of new world parrots. Guatemala banned export in 1986 and Honduras in 1990. By then most parrots exported to Europe came from Guyana, Nicaragua and Argentina. However, some of these countries retained a large internal trade in wild-caught parrots and the illegal export and smuggling of many species continued as before. Many parrots crossed borders illegally.

International trade figures for the year 2000 show exports in order of volume of trade for selected species (page 111).

Note that two Mexican species (one endemic, the Finsch's Amazon) appear on this list. After nearly 20 years of prohibiting export of its fauna, Mexico again permitted export of some parrot species.

Excessive trade in neotropical parrots

One of the reasons why Amazons featured so prominently in trade was their popularity as pets. Across their range, hundreds of thousands of chicks were taken from the nest every year, and large numbers of some species were trapped as adults or young birds. The most destructive practice was that of destroying nests to obtain chicks. Approximately 100,000 nests of Blue-fronted Amazons in the Argentine Chaco were destroyed or damaged between 1981 and 1989 by poachers (Bucher *et al*, 1992). The combined effects of habitat loss, nest destruction and poaching of chicks from nests was catastrophic. Amazon populations crashed.

One British visitor to a bird exporter in Asuncion, Paraguay, in 1978, found 8,000 parrots in stock. Most of them were native species, such as Blue-fronted Amazons, Nanday Conures, Quaker and Canary-winged Parakeets and Green-winged Macaws. There were also Brazilian species, such as Golden-capped Conures and Purple-bellied Parrots which had been illegally imported. Smuggling across borders was common.

PARROT EXPORTS

	Year:	2000	2001
AFRICA			
Senegal Parrot: from five states		39,541	14,421
Grey Parrot: from nine states		34,282	23,109
Timneh Grey Parrot: from three states		6,332	3,675
Ringneck Parakeet: Africa and Pakistan		27,675	51,073
SOUTH AMERICA			
Monk Parrot (Quaker Parakeet):			
Argentina, Paraguay and Uruguay		12,923	3,381
Lesser Patagonian Conure: Argentina		10,275	4,120
Orange-winged Amazon: Guyana and			
Suriname		10,255	9,193
Red-lored Amazon	Nicaragua	2,262	1,984
Yellow-fronted Amazon:	Guyana, Suriname	1,375	1,176
White-fronted Amazon	Nicaragua	1,297	8
Yellow-naped Amazon	Nicaragua	673	587
Finsch's Amazon	Mexico	73	355
Yellow-lored Amazon	Mexico	42	48
Mealy Amazon	Guyana	753	752
	Nicaragua	553	945
	Suriname	352	256
Mealy Amazon total:		1,658	1,953

A study in the late 1990s of the international trade in parrots listed by CITES found that 1.2 million parrots were exported legally between 1991 and 1996, with the majority coming from the neotropics (South and Central America). These figures are thought to be a gross underestimate of the actual numbers of birds taken from the wild. They exclude pre-export mortality, which has been estimated to reach 60% of all birds trapped or taken from nests. International trade figures did not include the substantial illegal international trade and the equally serious domestic trade. When these factors were taken into consideration, the number of chicks taken from the wild in the neotropics was estimated at 400,000 to 800,000 *per year* from 1982 to 1986.

Data was collected between 1979 and 1999 from field studies of neotropical parrots in 23 studies in 14 countries. (Wright *et al*, 2001). There was probably a bias towards threatened species because research funding was often directed towards them. Between 1979 and 1999, 4,204 nesting attempts were recorded and the average poaching rate was 30%. Four studies reported more than 70% of nests poached. Only six species escaped having their young stolen. If a nest failed, nesting by pairs (various species) in the same year was extremely rare: only 1% of pairs nested again. (This is an important statistic that might surprise aviculturists. However, even in captivity many Amazons, unlike other parrots, will not nest again.)

The estimates of poaching levels were considered to be conservative. In most cases researchers probably provided some protection to nests under study by inhibiting poaching; inadvertently alerting poachers is unlikely

∎ *Purple-bellied Parrot.*

Prior to the 1980s, the trade was primarily national. Trapping was concentrated in the citrus-growing areas such as Salta and Tucumán. Removal of nestlings occurred mainly from the Chaco forests. Throughout the Chaco, local people systematically removed whole broods, precluding recruitment of young birds into the wild population. If they left any young, other people might steal them later, thus families guarded nests night and day as the time approached for the young to be removed. Fear of "robbery" often led to premature removal, thus decreasing the nestlings' chances of survival.

Interviews conducted with traders in Joaquin Gonzalez, Salta Province, indicated that about 3,000 young were taken annually from a forested area of 90,000 hectares of public land (Salta Forestal) in 1986. Fewer than 500 were taken from the same area during the 1990–1991 breeding season. This was due to forest cutting.

∎ *A Blue-fronted Amazon is tied to a stick. The stick will be fixed high in a fruiting tree containing nooses to catch more Blue-fronts. Once trapped by the noose, and before being released by the trapper, a parrot might be attacked and killed by a bird of prey.*
2005 WorldParrotTrust.org

because of the conspicuous behaviour of many parrots around nests, and because of the tendency to use nest sites over many years. Most of the populations studied were protected in some form, either legally (usually ineffective), or by patrolling of nesting areas by armed guards.

Argentina

In the early 1980s the demand for Blue-fronted Amazons for the international pet trade increased dramatically. CITES reports indicated that the minimum trade (international) in this Amazon increased steadily from 10,644 in 1981 to 58,464 in 1988. In 1989 there was a steep decline to 21,753 birds. According to official figures, approximately 310,000 were exported during the period 1981 to 1989. CITES member nations took 280,000, including the USA (46%) and Germany (FDR) (21%). About 97% of the birds originated in Argentina. In 1990 and 1991 Argentina had an annual export quota of 23,000 Blue-fronts. By then, export from all other range countries was prohibited. The large export trade was based on the bird's supposed status as a pest (Bucher *et al*, 1991). This was unjustified.

The collectors stated that even 20 years previously Blue-fronted Amazons were easy to find near towns; by 1991 they had to travel 50 miles (80km) north of the town to buy parrots from campesinos (country people).

Employees of local timber companies discovered nests, monitored them and removed the chicks when they were old enough. One dealer stated that the average number of young Blue-fronts that passed through his hands in one year was 7,000 and that in 1973 he fed 13,500 chicks. Young were fed twice daily, at about 7am and 4pm, on a thick mixture of boiled rice, high-protein baby cereal and cooked corn meal. As many as 300 chicks could be fed in an hour. An infamous piece of film, shown on television many times, shows chicks of this species being fed. Those that were over-fed died, probably almost instantly, and were thrown aside. Many must have died of stress and overcrowding and many more would have died from disease at holding stations. Surely no bird lover could continue to condone the trade in wild-caught parrots after seeing this film...

Argentina actually banned the export trade in 1993 but faced pressure from several sectors, notably from Europe, to re-open it. Domestic trade continued. Each province had autonomy in terms of management of its natural resources, thus the scale of capture was difficult to assess. A large proportion of the pet trade in Argentina went through the underground economy and did not appear in official statistics. According to Professor Enrique Bucher, of the National University of Córdoba, in 1996 the domestic trade probably totalled 3,000 to 4,000 Blue-fronted Amazons annually, a figure that was about 10% of the international export levels of the previous decade (Bucher, pers. comm., 1996).

Stopping the export trade

As already mentioned, after the U. S. regulated the importation of wild-caught parrots in 1993, export of some parrot species from the neotropics did decline. It would decline further if the European Union were to follow

Income from the sale of these toys can replace the need to trap parrots in Guyana.
Photograph: James Gilardi, World Parrot Trust

suit. However, there are still many countries, especially in the Far East, that import large numbers of wild-caught parrots and it is likely to be many years before they ban the trade. It seems probable that in due course most countries will not allow the importation of wild-caught parrots. However, by the time that occurs many parrot species will have declined so much in the wild that the export trade will not be viable. It has already done irreversible damage to many parrot populations.

There is hope, though, that some species can be saved before they are trapped to extinction. Hope lies in replacing the income from trapping parrots with income from another source. Realistically, this is the only way to end the trade in live birds. In the Rupunini region of Guyana a few men have become balata artists. Balata is the rubber tree and the men carve parrots, toucans and other birds from this material. They are sent to Europe and the USA where parrot lovers realise that their purchase can stop trappers trapping. With help from overseas, the same story – to produce parrot related craft items – could be repeated in every country where parrots occur.

Man's conscience and awareness relating to humane treatment of animals increased immeasurably during the last two decades of the century – but too late to save some of the world's most valuable habitats and such charismatic creatures as parrots. We must continue to fight for the rights of these birds to be left where they belong – in the wild.

Species endangered as the result of trade

Many parrots were endangered due to the combined pressures of habitat loss and trapping. The species listed below are those for which trade was the primary cause of endangerment. Trade had a serious negative impact on many other species for which habitat loss has been even more harmful.

Species		Threat status
INDONESIA		
Lesser Sulphur-crested Cockatoo	(Cacatua s. sulphurea)	Critical
Moluccan Cockatoo	(Cacatua moluccensis)	Vulnerable
Umbrella Cockatoo	(Cacatua alba)	Vulnerable
Purple-naped Lory	(Lorius domicella)	Vulnerable
Red and Blue Lory	(Eos histrio)	Endangered
Chattering Lory	(Lorius garrulus)	Vulnerable
Pesquet's Parrot [1*]	(Psittrichas fulgidus)	Vulnerable
AFRICA		
Fischer's Lovebird	(Agapornis fischeri)	Near-threatened
SOUTH AND CENTRAL AMERICA		
Hyacinthine Macaw	(Anodorhynchus hyacinthinus)	Endangered
Lear's Macaw	(Anodorhynchus leari)	Critical
Blue-throated Macaw	(Ara glaucogularis)	Critical
Military Macaw	(Ara militaris)	Vulnerable
Red-masked Conure	(Aratinga erythrogenys)	Near-threatened
Yellow-faced Parrotlet	(Forpus xanthops)	Vulnerable
Grey-cheeked Parakeet	(Brotogeris pyrrhopterus)	Endangered [2]
Red-tailed Amazon	(Amazona brasiliensis)	Endangered

THREAT STATUS – DEFINITIONS

Critically Endangered
The species has an extremely high risk of becoming extinct in the wild in the near future.

Endangered
High risk of extinction in the wild in the near future (next 20 years).

Vulnerable
High risk of extinction in the wild in the medium-term future.

Near Threatened
Close to qualifying as Vulnerable.

[1*] Trade in feathers and skins, as well as in live birds.

[2] Listed as Endangered in *Threatened Birds of the World*, and as Near-threatened *Handbook of the Birds of the World, vol4.*

NO DUST - BRILLIANT PLUMAGE

CAPERN'S
PERFECTLY CLEAN
BUDGERIGAR SEED

FOR BUDGERIGARS & ALL FOREIGN FINCHES
F·CAPERN | IN PACKETS | POSTAGE PAID
BIRD FOOD | | ON
MANUFACTURE | 3ᵈ 6ᵈ 1⁄- ᴀɴᴅ 5'- | 5'- PACKETS
BRISTOL

8. FROM PEANUTS TO PELLETS

Throughout the 20th century the subject of dietary needs of captive parrots was one that evoked much debate and controversy. In the early 1900s feeding newly imported parrots was problematical, since the buyer did not know on what they had been fed or what was suitable. Boiled rice, bananas and cooked maize were usually offered to recently trapped birds but some parrots were on the point of starvation before the owner found something they would eat. This might have been rusk or bread dipped in milk, peanuts or cooked potatoes, and nuts for the larger parrots. Hemp, rapeseed and buckwheat were commonly fed to finches, so they were also offered to parrots. In 1951 one owner wrote about his Blue-fronted Amazon, purchased in Las Palmas in 1921: "I had difficulty in weaning him off boiled maize on to the usual seed diet, and nearly lost him whilst the acclimatizing process was going on."

Parrots in Captivity, written by W. T. Greene during the 1880s (in three volumes) provides information about parrot diets of the times, which were probably unaltered at the start of the 20th century. Greene described how he fed his Goffin's Cockatoo on oats, maize, canary seed and hemp, with boiled potatoes, a crust of bread or a plain biscuit and a slice of carrot (raw or cooked), as an occasional treat. Greenfoods included groundsel in flower, dandelion and chicory. In the event that a pair hatched chicks, he suggested that ants' eggs (pupae), crickets, black beetles or mealworms, cockroaches or daddy long-legs should be offered. If eaten, this would have been a more varied and nutritious diet than was usual a century later. Many parrots take insects when breeding but this fact was ignored by most breeders.

Greene recommended that Barraband's Parakeet from Australia (the male has striking yellow forehead and cheeks and a red crescent on the upper breast) should be offered canary seed, millet and hemp, plus fresh ants' eggs, mealworms and, as an occasional treat, a piece of sponge cake, and boiled rice sweetened with sugar, figs or soaked currants, flowers such as cabbage blooms, mignonette pea and bean blossoms, plus greenfoods.

Owners needed to give careful thought to diet, because all their parrots were wild-caught. By the end of the century the majority of parrots had been captive-bred for some or countless generations and the species that could survive on uncomplicated diets were the most popular.

Packet parrot foods contained a large amount of hemp. By 1930 there was not much improvement; sunflower, safflower and hemp were the main seeds with, stated Lord Tavistock (who later became the 12th Duke of Bedford): "A proportion of useless extras such as dry maize, wheat, dari, and pumpkin seeds, which no normal parrot ever touches. Plain, wholesome seed like canary is conspicuous by its entire absence" (*Avicultural Magazine*, October 1929). The result, he said, was that many parrots were victims of liver trouble and feather plucking. There was much debate regarding the suitability of sunflower seed. Seventy years later, not much had changed (including the useless hard maize) – except that an alternative to seeds was available.

In the USA Max Geisler Bird Co was established in 1888. In 1930 it offered an extensive range of products. Max Geisler's Health Food for Parrots cost 25 cents a packet. Prepared Food for Baby Parrots (too young to eat seed) cost 20 cents and probably included corn meal and/or egg. Parrot Spray, which was claimed to "cure parrots of the habit of destroying their plumage", cost 50 cents a bottle. Parrots were sold with detailed instructions for feeding that included at least six of Max Geisler's products. There was a warning against "the old style of feeding Parrots, namely, bread or crackers soaked in coffee".

The products available and the advice given in their catalogue certainly encouraged parrot owners to offer a varied diet. Max Geisler's Parrot Biscuit was surely the forerunner of today's pellets! A carton of 48 biscuits cost 25 cents. For 30 cents one could obtain a vial of Max Geisler's Vegetable Extract, to add to the drinking water every spring and during the

moult. It claimed to be "the best blood tonic and blood producer in existence".

The principal diet, Geisler stated, should be seed: best Russian hemp, Russian sunflower, Sicilian canary seed, unhulled rice, Mexican black corn and quality nuts, as contained in his Mixed Parrot Seed. In addition the parrot should be offered one quarter of a parrot biscuit, two teaspoonfuls of Health Food, slightly moistened and water with Vegetable Extract added. It was suggested that every other day sweet ripe fruit should be offered and, twice a week, a tablespoonful of Parrot Corn.

The proportions of the different items in the Parrot Seed are unknown but overall the diet suggested appeared to be quite well balanced (perhaps a little high in fat for Amazons) and certainly better than that received by many parrots at the end of the century. Reading the advice that "Young Parrots must have soft food" made me think that parrot care has not progressed; indeed, it has gone backwards. When hand-rearing of parrots became big business in the 1980s young parrots were sold with seed or pellets with no mention of the vital importance of soft foods during and after the transition period. As a result many died or proved very difficult to wean.

In 1933 an American company called Justrite, from Milwaukee, Wisconsin, issued its catalogue of pet foods. This contained advice on parrot care, plus a few claims that could be taken with a pinch of salt! The first sentence was undoubtedly true and, unfortunately, applies today to many parrots:

"Most parrots kept in captivity die young on account of being improperly fed and cared for. It takes years in some cases before the parrot breaks down with deranged bowels, weak stomach, etc. Follow the directions given herein and a healthy bird with a long life should result, parrots living to be 100 years old." The exaggeration regarding longevity persisted to the end of the century and beyond.

The advice on feeding newly imported young parrots (in the USA these would have been mainly Amazons from Mexico) was fairly good except (this time literally) for the pinch of salt: "Give corn meal mush cooked not too well, about as for a person, with a little salt. Give it at first with a spoon and force them to taste it if they do not at first eat it."

But not a drop to drink

The next sentence was based on the old myth that parrots should not be given water: "This food contains plenty of water and no water should be given until they are acclimated or one year old. Then begin by giving a little from a spoon in which oatmeal has been boiled, but allow it to cool. After a week you can begin giving ordinary drinking water boiled but cooled off."

■ *In 1931 Capern's claimed that their Budgerigar seed resulted in "brilliant plumage".*

Today we cannot imagine withholding water from our parrots, especially species that evolved in rainforest. Those from desert areas (Cockatiels, Budgerigars, etc) could survive without it. This poor advice to withhold water, surely with fatal consequences for many parrots, probably arose from the days when wild-caught parrots were transported on steam ships, with a number of birds in one cage. The water would quickly become fouled and a source of disease, thus it was considered safer to withhold water altogether.

Today we take for granted a readily available supply of water that is free from pollution. However, in Britain it was not until the 1930s that all towns received a mains water supply and improved drainage systems that drastically reduced the incidence of water-borne diseases. It is likely that parrots, especially newly imported birds, were previously susceptible to diseases contracted from the drinking water.

Contents of parrot mixtures

Justrite recommended their Parrot Food, said to be an "ideal mixture containing sunflower seed, hemp, cracked corn padda, polly crackers, peanuts, beech nuts, pepper pods, etc." Presumably corn padda was cracked hard yellow maize such as might be fed to chickens – a worthless food for parrots that is still added to cheap mixtures today. Most of the other items, except chilli peppers, amounted to a mixture that was much too high in fat for Amazons but would have been acceptable for macaws. Peanuts are not good for most parrots, not only due to their very high fat content but also because many are contaminated with aflatoxins. This is a compound produced by a mould fungus that can damage the liver. My own view is that the risk is too great to feed peanuts to parrots, yet they are still included in nearly all parrot mixtures. I ceased to feed them in the 1970s when a beloved bird died of liver disease, almost certainly the result of eating peanuts. Only human-grade peanuts should be fed to parrots (not those sold for wild birds) and some from each batch should be opened to check their condition. Aflatoxin contamination is common in cereal grains and nuts and is often the result of careless storage.

The long tradition of feeding sunflower seed might have originated from observations of wild parrots feeding on sunflower crops. The same might be true of peanuts, another item that wild parrots (Red-tailed Black Cockatoos in Australia and Red-fronted Macaws in Bolivia, for example) will eat given the opportunity. However, traditionally many parrots, such as Amazons and Greys, were fed on maize (often in the form of meal) and on bananas.

The widespread ignorance about feeding parrots was reflected in Max Geisler's statement: "Of all Parrots kept in captivity, there will be, we claim, at least ninety out of every hundred which, regarding food, are treated entirely wrong. Not on account of carelessness of the owner, but simply because he does not know any better." (Unfortunately, at the end of the century avian vets knew that this statement was still true.)

The owner of a Grey Parrot that plucked itself suggested that this was not due to "improper food" as it was allowed only eight or nine sunflower seeds daily. Even a century ago too much sunflower was believed to be harmful. Mr Bamford wrote (*Bird Notes*, January 1910) that he had kept his Grey, an "excellent linguist", for seven years, but 18 months previously it had started to pluck its breast and shoulders. The diet consisted mainly of canary seed and fruit. Cherries were its favourite, followed by grapes, redcurrants and walnuts. Some months later Mr Bamford reported that feather plucking stopped when half the canary seed was replaced with white millet! Then its plumage was "practically perfect". This was surely a coincidence as clean canary seed is an excellent food.

Remedies

Mrs G. Simmons of Oklahoma was convinced that Geisler's bird tonic had saved her parrot's life: "My Poll parrot was so sick, refused to eat or move and after giving your tonic she is cured and talking well again." The tonic was probably based on herbal recipes or other natural products and certainly had its devotees. Ray Meusenkamp wrote: "I received the medicine I ordered for my parrot. I must say it sure is wonderful and it didn't take long to bring him back in shape."

In 1900 one bird keeper used spices and plant extracts to cure digestive disorders in newly imported birds. Gentian, cinnamon, aniseed and ginger in powder form, mixed in equal parts, were lightly dusted on the seed of the sick bird.

An anonymous contributor to *Bird Notes* (August 1916) described how he saved the life of a young Grey Parrot "not yet feathered out fully" (wild-caught). He vomited, had attacks of palpitations and "drowsily settled himself upon his perch to die... swaying from side to side preliminary to the final fall to the cage bottom. All this within six hours".

An electric flat-iron was put under the cage-covering and the current turned on (presumably as a source of heat!). A few drops of castor oil on a dilution of blackberry brandy and a pinch of sodium bicarbonate were urged down the young parrot's throat. In a few minutes he was trying to move about but fell from the perch because he had cramps in his feet. He was rolled in a blanket and the clenched feet were held in hot water, then massaged. At half hour intervals throughout the night brandy and alkali were administered. Next day the little parrot was almost fully recovered. The writer reminded the reader: "A young Parrot's digestive apparatus is more sensitive than a baby's; the least carelessness or uncleanness in feeding is likely to cause swift and fatal mischief."

Brandy featured high on the list of emergency cures. Maud Knobel recounted how she saved the life of a parrot belonging to a little girl. It was lying on its side on the cage floor "looking for all the world as though it was about to give up this life". Given a teaspoonful of brandy and warm milk, with a second ten minutes later, it was up on its perch within a short time (Knobel, 1948).

In the UK before the 1980s it was unusual to consult a vet because vets had no training to treat exotic birds. Clients who did so received an antibiotic powder, either Aureomycin or later, Sulphamezathine, whatever the ailment. It was more usual to visit the chemist and ask for a bottle of Parrish's Chemical Food. A few drops in the drinking water were believed to cure the problem, if such was possible. During the 1970s antibiotics started to be widely used for sick parrots. They often had harmful side effects and, by the end of the century, many parrot owners were rejecting them in favour of herbal remedies.

Breeding diets

Few large parrots were bred in the early years probably due to an inadequate rearing diet. In the UK Miss M. Drummond, who achieved the first breeding of the Red-sided Eclectus Parrot in 1912, offered a nutritious fare when chicks hatched. Boiled corn and seed was the staple diet, with the addition of Osborne biscuits in boiled milk and sugar, a little Mellin's (an invalid or baby food), a boiled potato or some baked rice pudding, apple, nuts and chickweed.

It was several decades before parrot-rearing foods, containing egg, were manufactured. The larger parrots need soft, nutritious items when rearing young and these were usually given in

If he must eat cake, let it be carrot cake!

the form of hard-boiled egg and bread and milk. In the 1970s there was a lot of controversy about parrots being unable to digest dairy products such as milk, although many breeders had been rearing excellent young for years using brown or wholemeal bread and milk as a rearing food.

Today, fruit is so easy to acquire that we never stop to think that this was not always the case. Edward Boosey, proprietor of Keston Foreign Bird Farm in Kent, wrote in 1950 that ripe sweet fruit was difficult to come by in the spring and early summer. In that era there were no tropical fruits available, except bananas and oranges. Home-grown soft fruits such as raspberries and gooseberries were exchanged among friends and neighbours. Boosey was convinced that fruit, unless sweet and ripe, could do more harm than good to the "delicate stomachs of nestlings". In the wild, of course, many parrots take fruit that is neither sweet nor ripe.

Scientific advances: pellets

Research into avian nutrition had centred almost exclusively on poultry until the 1980s. When parrots became big business in the USA some of the large pet food companies started to research parrot nutrition. They concluded that the only way to ensure that parrots received the necessary nutrients was to provide them in the form of pellets or extruded foods. Their manufacture was developed from broiler chicken food. Was this appropriate when chickens live for only a

few weeks and parrots can live for decades? Pellets are cold-pressed and usually brown. Extruded foods are made from ingredients that are heated to a high temperature. The extrusion process kills important vitamins, enzymes and probiotics, and produces a light food containing many air pockets. Extruded foods are sprayed with vitamins, oils, fats, scents and colours. Many parrot owners quickly accepted this new form of feeding because it was quick and there was no mess.

What did these formulated foods contain? One very well known company whose pellets and extruded foods are widely used, listed the ingredients of their food for parrots and large conures as ground corn, ground wheat, ground oat groats, wheat middlings*, corn gluten meal, dried whole egg, dried beet pulp, corn oil, soybean meal, corn sugar and various supplements plus artificial colours. "Animal by-products" (offal) were contained in some pellets.

Most extruded foods are made from by-products and not from whole grains. The corn could have originated from the left-overs from the production of corn chips or corn oil, for example. Only a well-known and widely-used organic nugget (the term pellet is more correctly applied to pressed foods) stated that whole ground corn was used.

The companies manufacturing pellets claimed that these were complete diets and no other food needed to be offered. But parrots are not chickens. The many taste buds in their tongues mean that they are avian food connoisseurs. They can distinguish subtle differences in flavour. They love their food. For many parrots feeding time is the high spot of their day. (This applies especially to breeding birds that often have little else to look forward to.) The different colours, tastes, textures and varying methods of consuming food items add to the enjoyment of

---

* The dictionary defines middlings as poor-quality flour made from coarsely ground wheat or bran.

their meal times. To be presented with a bowl that contained the same item day after day, possibly of a taste that was not agreeable, was to deprive them of one of their few enjoyments in life.

No one knows how many parrots refused to convert to pellets and starved to death or how many were finally given their old diet when they became lethargic through hunger. It saddened me to read in avicultural publications that pelleted foods were even recommended for little seed-eating birds like Budgerigars that had survived decades in captivity on seed and iodine nibbles. They probably could not even recognise the pellets as food. They ground them up but did not swallow the powder. Some died as a result in the hands of people who were convinced that all parrots should be converted to pelleted diets.

Large parrots such as macaws and cockatoos needed the activity provided by cracking nuts and other seeds. They needed to hold a piece of orange in the beak, to tip up the head and let the juice run down their throat. They needed the pleasure of taking out the seeds from a pomegranate or the pips from apples. They craved variety. They needed stimulation. Instead they got monotony and boredom, and even inappropriate and perhaps dangerous foods like offal. Unlike chickens, cats and dogs, domesticated for centuries and bred to adapt to a certain lifestyle, parrots needed fresh foods that were recently growing.

It became obvious that as *part* of the diet pellets were valuable for certain species and useful for many pet owners not prepared to take the

■ *An extruded food in a variety of shapes and colours.*

time to offer variety. However, a diet consisting totally of processed foods was not healthy. Fruits, vegetables, seeding weeds, berries and nuts were also needed. Some manufacturers of pellets gradually came to realise this and to recommend it. Others claimed that pellets or extruded foods were a complete diet. Could this be true when there are more than 300 species of parrots, almost no two of which have the same dietary needs? It was perhaps appropriate to manufacture dry foods for domesticated animals such as dogs, all of which have roughly the same dietary requirements, but in the wild the various parrot species take an enormous range of food items.

Many potential purchasers of pelleted foods objected to the artificial colouring, flavours and scents they contained. Their fears were justified. Pellets proved harmful to Eclectus and, strangely, to mutation parrotlets. Kidney and/or liver problems occurred. Some species, small African parrots, for example, liked pellets and could readily be persuaded to eat them, while others rejected them. In some large collections where individual parrots were not closely monitored, some died. Many breeders experienced good results when feeding pellets. Others found their birds stopped breeding. Outside the USA pelleted foods did not achieve great popularity.

Anyone could manufacture parrot pellets. The problem for purchasers was how to distinguish those that were nutritionally valuable, or those that suited the species they kept. Many vets in the USA and Europe recommended and sold pellets. In their practices they saw many parrots die of diseases caused by nutritional deficiencies. Pellets offered a better standard of nutrition for the multitude that had been kept primarily on sunflower seed. The problem was that such birds could prove difficult or impossible to convert to the new foods.

Professor Robert Pavlis of Pittsburg State University had deep concerns about pellets, primarily because of the dangers of aflatoxin contamination and about the safety of dyes used in some of them. He thought that seeds and nuts, and greens, fruits and vegetables plus some animal protein such as boiled eggs and well cooked chicken, was the best diet for parrots (and for humans!). He noted the harmful effects of aflatoxins with the words:

"Feeding badly aflatoxin contaminated food to fish on fish farms or to poultry for just a few days will result in a large fraction of the stock developing malignant tumors... It seems likely that worldwide hundreds of thousands of people and countless other creatures die from it each year" (Pavlis, undated – written in 1997).

During the last two decades of the century avicultural conventions in North America usually included a speaker who represented one of the pet food companies and explained why those present should use pellets. They described the research behind the production. I listened carefully to these talks. The people presenting them had no experience outside the laboratory. Without the necessary empirical knowledge they sometimes formulated foods that were useless and, furthermore, caused the deaths of some birds.

Feeding lories

During the 1980s the production of powdered lory foods commenced. A poultry nutritionist with an interest in aviculture visited me to find out how I fed my lories. At that time it was usual to make up liquid foods consisting of such items as baby cereal, malt extract, honey or glucose and condensed milk. The nutritionist analysed my food and told me that it had some shortcomings. I did not modify it. In due course he manufactured and marketed his own lory food. It was widely used in Europe. When I returned to the UK to live in 1995 I decided to try it out. The first chick hatched by a *Chalcopsitta* species in my collection, a Yellow-streaked, failed to thrive and died at three weeks. I was puzzled but did not associate its death with the food. Then I lost two adult birds of a rare and irreplaceable *Chalcopsitta*. Not long after, in discussion with a lory keeper in Europe, I found out that this food (widely used in Europe) was known to kill many individuals of this genus. This is one reason why they have become rare in captivity. In contrast, my own food has kept individuals alive for 30 years.

There are at least two good brands of lory food made in Europe. However, certain brands were a serious problem for some of the more than 40 species of lories and lorikeets. After breeding these birds for more than 30 years, I was very aware of the widely varying dietary requirements of the different species. Dry foods were manufactured for lories as a complete diet. Some lorikeets, such as the Green-naped, are virtually omnivorous, widespread and found in large flocks. They can exist on most lory mixtures, and even the formulated dry foods, with fruit. Other lory species, such as some of the *Chalcopsittas* (Black, Duivenbode's, etc) are highly nectivorous. In the wild they have small areas of distribution and are not found in large flocks, indicating that their dietary requirements are more specialised. Offered no liquid foods (that replicated the nectar on which they subsist in nature) many starved to death in the USA. Yet still the manufacturers promoted them as complete foods. Perhaps nutritionally they were but if pollen- and nectar-feeding birds cannot recognise them as food they are useless.

Lory diets evolved slowly over the decades. E. J. Brook, a successful breeder during the early years of the century, fed his lories on bread and milk containing barley water, also fruit syrups and unlimited ripe fruit. Dealers instructed purchasers of the Australian lorikeets – Swainson's and Red-collared – to feed them on nothing but canary seed. Their lives were short. A more enlightened aviculturist, Mrs Burgess, fed her Red-collared Lorikeets on milksop, a little seed, and lots of fruit and seeding grasses, especially the tall varieties.

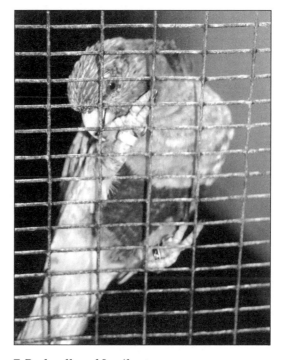

▮ *Red-collared Lorikeet.*

Supplements

Parrot owners should not let convenience parrot foods cloud their commonsense. Perhaps the biggest step forward in feeding parrots during the 20th century came in the form of additives, such as vitamins, minerals and probiotics. A dietary intake that basically was not good could be corrected with their use and the health of the bird enormously improved. Many parrots, especially those that ate primarily seed, were deficient in Vitamin A, and died as a result of diseases caused by its deficiency. This deficiency was easily corrected with the multi-vitamin supplements that were made especially for birds from the 1980s onwards.

The same was true of calcium supplements. When my first parrot, a Grey, died after suffering from fits, I had no idea that this could have been prevented with calcium supplementation. No one had heard of hypocalcaemia in the 1970s. By the end of the century many informed owners ensured that their Grey Parrots received, on a regular basis, a calcium supplement made for parrots, but probably more were unaware of its importance. There were still too many owners who never read anything about parrots and relied on unreliable sources of information.

■ *The author as a teenager with her first parrot. It died of hypocalcaemia before the disease was recognised in Grey Parrots.*

During the last decade of the century probiotics for parrots became available. These powdered supplements improved the state of the gut by introducing beneficial flora. This supported the health of parrots that were sick, under stress, old or young or had recently been on medication. Digestion occurs naturally in a healthy gut, partly by beneficial bacteria that live in the digestive tract. Antibiotics kill all bacteria, including the beneficial ones, thus probiotics are invaluable.

Educating owners

Scant research was carried out regarding the content or suitability of seed mixtures until the 1980s. In 1985 in Canada the Hagen Avicultural Research Institute (HARI) was founded as a world-class captive breeding and research facility. Hundreds of breeding pairs of parrots were maintained. HARI formulated a mixture containing seven different grains and nuts. It recognised that the quality of protein (its amino acid balance) was as vital as the total level in the diet. The different amino acid profiles of the various protein sources complemented each other, resulting in a protein content of high biological value. The researchers bore in mind that the high calorie nature of oil seeds, such as sunflower, limits their consumption, thus lowering the amount of amino acids available for the growth of new feathers and for muscle maintenance. Although oilseed kernels have a higher percentage of protein than other seeds, excessive consumption could result in poor feather growth, malnutrition and obesity. Parrots fed on large amounts of sunflower and other oil seeds might still not receive enough protein or they might be offered a balanced mixture but select only the oil seeds. Representatives of companies such as HARI were regular speakers at conventions in North America during the 1990s, thus gradually parrot owners were educated regarding nutrition of their pets. Articles in various avicultural magazines also highlighted the dangers of unbalanced diets.

For the first time owners of Grey Parrots were made aware of the disadvantages of the oilseeds that these birds were addicted to. Although it appeared that phosphorous levels in most oilseeds and grains were sufficient, some of the phosphorous was unavailable to the parrot because it was bound up with phytic acid. After a few years on an oilseed diet, many Greys developed muscle tetany (prolonged muscle contractions) and needed emergency calcium injections to save their lives.

In the early 1990s one enterprising UK company started to make 12 different seed mixtures for specific groups of parrots and parakeets (e. g., conures, African parrots). They used 37 items in their range of mixtures and employed an aviculturist to test them. Like other bird food specialists they offered separately items that were previously unobtainable commercially such as dried elderberries and berries of juniper and mountain ash. (One of the best possible foods for most parrots, hawthorn berries, free for the picking, were neglected by most parrot owners.) A wider range of nuts became available, including macadamias, beloved by large macaws, and oil palm nuts (colour page 9), specially imported from Africa. This progress was counteracted by the deteriorating quality and availability of certain seeds and by soaring prices.

Other aspects of feeding parrots changed over the years. Fruits are an important part of the diet of many species. The variety of tropical fruits available since the 1980s was an asset for parrot keepers, with pomegranates in particular proving extremely popular with their parrots and highly beneficial to their health. Cactus fruits and guavas, mangos and papaya, previously unheard of in cooler climes, were also available and relished. However, the quality of most fruit had deteriorated, especially its flavour and freshness. The greatly increased use of pesticides, whose residues might remain on the skin with harmful effects, was another risk.

In days gone by most households had an apple tree or two. By the end of the century the trend towards small gardens usually precluded growing one's own fruit and vegetables. The majority of city-dwelling parrots suffered from the lack of fresh branches for gnawing or for perches. This requirement was greatly underestimated by most parrot owners.

By the end of the century awareness of the dietary needs of parrots had improved dramatically – but not enough. Too many parrots died due to ignorance and laziness, not to lack of information. At the other extreme, especially in the USA, countless companion parrot owners dreamed up nutritious recipes with which to pamper their cherished pets and even published

Palm nuts – especial favourites with Grey Parrots.

Photograph: Sonny Stollenmaier

parrot cookery books! Parrots could be tempted with sweet potato and pellet muffins, French toast made with whole-wheat bread, egg, milk, crushed pellets and a pinch of cinnamon, and pasta salad made with dandelion leaves, hard-boiled egg, thawed frozen sweetcorn and broccoli.

Many of these recipes reflected the improvement in the variety of items available in the human diet. Formerly many parrots received nutritious items from the table and it was often these foods that enabled them to live long lives on a mainly seed diet. During the war years when birdseed was unobtainable small birds such as Canaries could not survive; most parrots readily adapted to a diet of human foods. It had become apparent that many parrot species, especially popular birds such as Amazons and macaws, could be described as omnivorous. They thrived with owners who were prepared to experiment to find out about the wide range of healthy items they might take.

Bird food manufacturers had also become creative. In the USA one could purchase "birdcakes" containing various fruits, beans, eggs and vitamins (baked fresh every week), Crazy Corn (with 50 thrilling natural ingredients like colourful pasta, fennel seeds and ginger), and Nuts'N'Nuggets (chunky nuts and sweet tempting nuggets in a crispy, crunchy crackly little ball). These items were imported into the UK. The catalogue of one company that specialised in parrot products featured seven pages of food treats. If you wanted to indulge your parrot, the choice was yours!

9. PETS AND PARROT PARAPHERNALIA

In the earlier years of the 20th century, a crotchety old spinster who lived alone might have typified the kind of person who kept a parrot. By the end of the century it would have been difficult to type-cast the companion parrot keeper. One of these birds might be found in any home – one of 50 or more species. Long gone were the days when the chances were that it was an African Grey or an "Amazon Green". The word African was used to distinguish it from the Australian grey parrot (cockatoo) – the Galah – and the "African Green" (the Jardine's). Even today most people use the popular term African Grey rather than Grey Parrot.

The history of companion parrots during the first half of the 20th century is mainly anecdotal but we do know that Grey and Amazon parrots were the favoured species and, to a lesser degree, cockatoos such as the Greater Sulphur-crested. Between the 1880s and the start of the new century it is unlikely that the cost of purchasing a newly imported parrot would have risen very much. When W. T. Greene wrote the first volume of *Parrots in Captivity* in 1884 the wage of a miner (a typical working man) at Whitfield Colliery was 5s (25p) per day, or about £1.50 per week. The prices given by Greene in volume I and (written in 1887) volume II, for newly imported parrots in England were as follows:

Species	Prices in 1887	Status
Grey Parrot	10shillings to 15shillings (50p to 75p) each	commonly imported
Senegal Parrot	5s to 6s (25p to 30p)	very common
Jardine's Parrot	25s to 30s (£1.25 to £1.50)	uncommon
Blue and Yellow Macaw	£5	uncommon
Blue-fronted Amazon	25s (£1.25)	common
Mealy Amazon	30s to 50s (£1.50 to £2.50)	common
Cuban Amazon	20s to 30s (£1 to £1.50)	common
Yellow-naped Amazon	£2 to £3	rare
Sun Conure	£2 to £3	uncommon
White-eared Conure	£2	common
Umbrella Cockatoo	£3 to £4	regularly available
Goffin's Cockatoo	£3	uncommon
Purple-capped Lory	50s (£2.50)	uncommon
Ringneck Parakeet	24s to 30s (£1.20 to £1.50) per pair	common

Talking ability of the species and of the individual was reflected in the price. As much as £20 could be paid for a "highly educated" Purple-capped Lory that is, one that mimicked well. A talking Ringneck could cost as much as 90s (£4.50). At the start of the 20th century the attributes of the different species available were well documented, usually accurately but in a few cases according to current fashion. Galahs were not popular. Greene quoted the German writer Weiner that the species was "stupid and uninteresting". Greene added that they had "not proved themselves teachable or endearing in any way". They usually learned only one or two words. The Rev. Dutton's view was different. "So charming a bird would always attain a good price," he wrote, "were it not that one Rose-breasted Cockatoo is enough to supply not only a street but a district. Its screams have been described as like 'a little pig being killed'."

Greene warned of the quicksilver changes in the behaviour of the Great Salmon-crested Cockatoo, the Moluccan. He wrote: "... to listen to it as it whispers, with depressed head and uplifted crest, in the softest and sweetest of feminine tones, 'Oh! you pretty, pretty Cockey, how I love you,'" or some such phrase, is to adore it ... as it presents its head to be rubbed with the most bewitching confidence.

■ *Rose-breasted Cockatoo (Galah)*

"... the sudden discovery that the beautiful possessor of that entrancing voice can transform itself at will into a shrieking fiend, is almost too distressing to be borne with equanimity; and the latter phrase of its character comes like a pleasant surprise upon the owner, who had only known his acquisition by its demonical yells, and had already meditated the wringing of its neck, notwithstanding the beauty of its coat, in the fear that he himself might be rendered stone deaf, or at least be summoned by one of his neighbours as a public nuisance."

Mr Greene's warning is as appropriate today as it was in 1887! Then the Moluccan Cockatoo was seldom imported and cost about £6 each – an expensive purchase.

I suspect that many pet cockatoos of the early years had much better lives than the hand-reared ones at the end of the century. It was usual to give them their liberty in the large gardens possessed by the owners. Mr S. Williams' Ducorp's Cockatoo (*Cacatua ducorpsi*) was acquired with one wing clipped wing. When the feathers grew he seldom attempted to fly. "Cocky" was spotted in a bird shop in the East End of London, "a dirty white bird, looking like a chief mourner at a funeral". Mr Williams opened the cage door and Cocky scrambled on to his shoulder. Three months later his snowy-white plumage was unrecognisable as that of the same bird. Cocky enjoyed much freedom. He would walk across the lawn, climb on to Mr Williams' shoulder, kiss him, bark like a dog and imitate a hen calling her chicks. His favourite food was porridge from the breakfast table. Most parrot cages of that era had bell tops. This one was interesting for a perch was sensibly incorporated into the design.

Throughout the century small parrots also enjoyed popularity as pets. In 1940 Mrs Elton Cotton lamented the death of "Billy", described as remarkable, loving and faithful. He was a Tovi or Orange-chinned Parakeet (*Brotogeris jugularis*), a little 7in (18cm) bird with a big personality. His owner wrote: "His besotting sin was jealousy; he would not allow anyone to touch me, and if anyone did was always told to 'Go away, that is my Mammy'... If I happened to come down in the middle of the night he would know and whistle his special call, with 'Pretty dear Mammy'; but if any other member of the house came down there was dead silence, although his cage was covered with green baize,

■ *Mr Williams' Ducorp's Cockatoo.*
Photographs reproduced from *Bird Notes*, March 1914

two thicknesses, and he could not see... He used to sing, 'Ven I glow too old to gleam' just that first line, and no matter what temper he was in, this song always seemed to calm him. My Amazon loved him dearly, and strange though it may seem they were great friends" (Cotton, 1940).

Maud Knobel was renowned in London for her passion for parrots. In her five-storey house in Regent's Park (close to the Zoo), she lived with up to 50 parrots and, at one time, as many as 22 Pekinese dogs! She could not resist talking Grey Parrots. One day in 1917 she was walking her dog when she encountered a Belgian man who had come from the Congo to join up for the war. He had two Grey Parrots on his walking stick. She gave the man £2 10s for one of them and walked back home with the parrot on her hand. For three days "Cuckoo" refused to feed and Miss Knobel was at her wit's end. Then she suddenly had a brainwave. She removed the white porcelain pots with tin ones and instantly he started to eat. He never would feed from a white dish. Very fond of the cook, he roamed around the kitchen, in and out of boxes and coal scuttles. "A most cheery bird, never dull," Miss Knobel wrote to the *Avicultural Magazine* in 1944 to lament his death – after 27 years.

She also bought Amazons, macaws and cockatoos. Seduced by a description of the Senegal Parrot as "easily tamed, quiet and intelligent", she decided she must have one. She went to Gamages Department Store in London, which had a famous pet department. From a consignment of newly imported Senegals she chose one and "carried him home in triumph". Alas, her disappointment in "Jobo" was great! Every time she entered the room the Senegal remained still and terrified with his head down. If she tried to touch him, he went for her with "his sharp little beak".

One day, as she passed one of her Amazons, he put his head down to be scratched. To her great surprise, she saw that Jobo had done the same thing, going to the side of the cage to be close to her. She gently rubbed the top of his head – and from that moment he was a changed bird and the ideal pet she had hoped for. When she spent many hours in bed after two operations, Jobo was the constant companion who helped her through "many a weary hour". He would climb across her bed and snuggle down into her neck (*Bird Notes*, May 1917).

Maud Knobel was a remarkable woman, who held office in the Avicultural Society from 1922 (26 years as secretary) until 1967, when she was president. Her death occurred in that year at the age of 97.

In those days only wild-caught parrots were available. Buyers knew that it often took much patience to tame them, so they persevered. How different today! People have no patience for taming: they demand hand-reared birds. They are unaware that a parent-reared parrot that becomes tame usually makes a far better pet than a hand-reared one. It is not as demanding, it can amuse itself and is not confused about its identity.

❚ *Maud Knobel, a remarkable woman, in 1961. Note the parrot cages in the background. It was difficult to obtain any other type at that time. The bases were metal and rusted through after a few years.*

Photograph: Fox Photos. Courtesy of Roy Chester

Feather plucking

The year might have been 1901 or 1999 but the problem was the same: feather plucking. During a century its possible causes were debated endlessly, often with no recognition of the fact that the major causes can be classified under about ten headings (Low, 2000). In 1911 a bird described as a "green West Indian Parrot" was probably an Amazon. He had plucked himself almost naked for the previous ten years of the 30 years he had been with Dr Charles Blair. (In any era, 30 years with one owner, is notable.) To cure the feather plucking the parrot had been sprayed with Fir Tree Oil twice a week. This had apparently been effective and the feathers grew back in two or three months! Then application of the oil was neglected and the first signs of feather plucking were again evident. Dr Blair had the interesting theory that the plucking was the result of a skin irritation due to parasites – which were then destroyed by the oil (*Bird Notes*, January 1911).

Most of the theories relating to feather plucking concerned diet. Lord Tavistock was one of the first to recognise that there might be other causes, although he did not state what these might be. However, a sweep in Cheltenham claimed to cure feather-plucking parrots. He covered them in soot!

First recorded case of PBFD?

In the second half of the century a disease known as psittacine beak and feather disease (PBFD) first became apparent in white cockatoos. It was many years before its cause was recognised as the circovirus, by which time it had spread to other species with devastating effect. In the first half of the century this disease was not recognised. However, an interesting (and sad) photo appeared in the September 1916 issue of *Bird Notes*. It depicted a Sulphur-crested Cockatoo in Australia that was reputed to be 119 years old when it died, although the bird had been with its current owner for only 12 months. Apparently in an advanced stage of PBFD, with about five straggly white feathers on the underparts, its appearance added to the illusion of great age. Its grossly overgrown upper mandible reached as far as its crop when its neck was stretched upwards. The beak overgrowth was quite thin – yet apparently no one had thought about trimming it.

Reproduced from *Bird Notes* 1916

The story, reprinted from an unknown Australian journal, stated that the bird, which had previously belonged to the last owner's aunt, Sarah Bennett, had been featherless for 20 years. It had lived at the Sea Breeze Hotel, Canterbury (near either Sydney or Melbourne). "Cocky Bennett" was said to have journeyed seven times around the world with its owner!

Longevity exaggerated

The belief that cockatoos could live to more than 100 years was widespread. G. F. Quartermain of Eastcote, Middlesex, reported that his Greater Sulphur-crested Cockatoo had just died. He believed that it had been in the family for 120 years. It had laid an egg every spring, including the year before it died, he reported (*The Foreigner*, April 1936). The idea of a cockatoo living to 120 years (the oldest authenticated age is 66 years) is incredible enough but that it could continue to lay until it was 119 is preposterous!

Amazons in the USA

During the 1920s Amazons were the most readily available parrots in the USA. Max

Photo: Sonny Stollenmaier

21 Jean Pattison, a lover of parrots and fashion in the USA, combined the two – right down to her hair colour! (CHAPTER 9) **22** Palm fruits entered the parrot scene during the 1990s, much to the enjoyment of this Grey (CHAPTER 8). **23** The Blue-cheeked Amazon *(Amazona dufresniana)* was smuggled out of Guyana when it was very rare in aviculture (CHAPTER 6).

23

Photo: Michael Schooley

PARROTS ARE OUR PRIDE

SYMBOLIC OF OUR UNIQUENESS, BEAUTY, FREEDOM AND INDEPENDENCE. THE SAINT VINCENT PARROT IS THE PROUD NATIONAL BIRD OF **SAINT VINCENT & THE GRENADINES**

PROTECT OUR PRIDE
* Stop the illegal capture and sale of parrots; it's our heritage that is being traded.
* Protect our forests, home of the Saint Vincent Parrot.
* Plant more trees.

VINCIE IS OURS TO PROTECT!

SAINT VINCENT PARROT
Amazona guildingii

ONE LOVE • ONE BIRD • ONE **Hairoun**

24 Conservation education often focussed on a sense of pride at the existence of an endemic parrot (CHAPTER 12). **25** An attempt was made to smuggle this Major Mitchell's Cockatoo *(Cacatua leadbeateri)* out of Australia in this cylinder. It was one of the lucky ones that was discovered in time (CHAPTER 6).

Private aviculturists were involved in breeding **26** the Orange-fronted *(Cyanoramphus malherbi)* and **27** the endangered Orange-bellied *(Neophema chrysogaster)* parakeets – part of the Australian Government programme to breed for release. (CHAPTER 10).

28 Echo Parakeets *(Psittacula eques)* from Mauritius have been saved from extinction by captive breeding and habitat protection (CHAPTER 10). **29** Thick-billed Parrots *(Rhynchopsitta pachyrhyncha)* bred in the UK by Ken Dolton (CHAPTER 4).

Photo: Thomas Brosset

30 Richard Friseus in Costa Rica is almost unique among private aviculturists in being permitted to release his young birds (Scarlet Macaws) into the wild (CHAPTER 12).
31 Puerto Rican Parrot (*Amazona vittata*) in the Luquillo Forest (CHAPTER 11).

Photo: Parrots International

Geisler Bird Co had been trading in parrots in Omaha since about 1890. Their 1929 catalogue listed their speciality as "The Human Talker". These were Amazons selected for their talking ability; they cost $5 more than the $18 charged for apparently less exceptional Double Yellowheads and the $20 for the less talented Panama Amazons. Also available at $8 each were Greencheeked Amazons and Cuban Amazons from the Isle of Pines, from where the export trade was thriving. In contrast, African Grey Parrots, described as "very rare" (in the USA) cost $75 each and were reputed to talk as well as the most favoured Amazons. These parrots were offered with a written guarantee that they would "learn to talk within six months"! They were all wild birds that had been removed from nests at a few weeks old and hand-reared.

The popularity of parrots came to a sudden end in January 1930. A newly discovered disease called "parrot fever" (psittacosis) struck fear into parrot owners because it could be transferred from parrots to humans. Outbreaks were reported in New York, Ohio, Switzerland and Germany. In the USA the surgeon general urged that all contact with parrots and their cages should be avoided. People ran past pet shops with handkerchiefs pressed against their faces and released parrots were seen flying in Central Park. However, one community ridiculed the suggestion that parrots were causing disease. The inmates of Sing Sing jail, who already had ten parrots, suggested that unwanted birds should be sent to them! (Stern and Stern, 1990). During the parrot fever panic 169 cases were confirmed and 33 people died of psittacosis. Since then antibiotics have reduced human deaths from this disease to almost zero.

Lack of understanding

The unfortunate habit had evolved of chaining large parrots such as macaws and cockatoos to a stand or perch, using some kind of ring on the leg – shackled like a prisoner. This inhumane method of constraint must have resulted in countless parrots with broken legs. I can recall parrots kept like this in mainstream European zoos into the 1970s. In total contrast there were other private owners who did not want to confine large parrots and kept them at total liberty.

Parrot keeping had seemed innocent enough but during the ensuing decades the popularity of parrots caused them great suffering. Their psychological needs were seldom understood and their cognitive abilities were grossly under-estimated. Too often they were treated like throw-away possessions, neglected or even ignored. Parrots have a charisma that is irresistible to many humans. The appeal of colour, personality, amusing habits and the ability to mimic human speech is a combination found in no other bird or animal. Added to that is the extraordinary capacity for affection of many species. No wonder people wanted parrots as companions! But could these people give the commitment, attention and stimulation that these wonderful birds so desperately need?

The answer was usually "no" because parrot behaviour was (and is) greatly misunderstood; parrots do not respond to attempted behaviour modification by means of punishment. Most people who cared for pet parrots knew little about their psychology and natural behaviours. This led to many parrots being abused and yelled at to try to stop them biting or vocalising. Although behaviour modification methods that did not involve punishment were being researched decades earlier, it was not until the end of the century that the message slowly began to reach parrot owners. In the 1940s B. F. Skinner, an American behaviour scientist advocated the use of positive reinforcement instead of conventional forms of punishment, as do most contemporary behaviourists.

TALKING PARROTS

Panama Parrot   Mexican Double Yellow Head

OUR SPECIALTY
"THE HUMAN TALKER"

■ *A Scarlet Macaw chained to a perch – shackled like a prisoner.*

Scientific research proved that behaviour that is rewarded will either be increased or maintained. Unwanted behaviour, however, will not necessarily decrease or even be eliminated if punishment, particularly physical forms, is used.

Trainers and scientists throughout the 20th century continued to learn, and to experiment with and study the successful effects of positive reinforcement methods, yet even at the end of the century punishment and food deprivation were commonly used in the attempt to teach or undo behaviours. This prompted professional trainers and behaviour scientists to offer courses and workshops to educate pet parrot owners. Few such courses were advertised in the UK but in the USA there were many. Most were presented in the form of short workshops and some were run via the Internet. Parrot training videos were another medium on offer by the mid-1990s. One set of four training videos made by a fashionable "behaviourist" commanded a staggering £250!

Budgerigars and parrot mania

Although native people have kept parrots for centuries and early travellers brought them back from the tropics as items of curiosity, parrot mania is relatively recent. It surfaced briefly in 1840 when John Gould brought the first Budgerigars to England from Australia. They caused a sensation! Pretty, dainty parakeets, Budgerigars reproduced readily *and* their young were talented mimics. The Budgerigar was the first of more than 100 species of parrots that came to be bred regularly in captivity. As a companion it ranks very high among small parrots. It lost its popularity when a much wider choice of species became available in the 1970s when parrot mania surfaced again. Budgerigars were considered too "ordinary" by many people; they overlooked the qualities of these extraordinarily good and appealing companions. If acquired when young they are suitable for any bird-loving household, being adaptable, easy to care for, relatively quiet and adored by many. Males can be exceptional mimics, often with vocabularies that exceed those of parrots. In 1993, "Puck", owned by Camille Jordan in California, was said to have a vocabulary of 1,728 words.

The diminutiveness of Budgerigars gave them great charm in an age when big, showy birds like macaws were trendy – but totally impracticable.

There was a general misconception that small parrots were not intelligent. Other small species, such as parrotlets (*Forpus*) and lovebirds could also make endearing pets for people with time to handle them daily, who had no other pets.

From the early years of the century until the late 1960s, when the Parrot Society was formed in the UK, there was little contact between parrot owners: no specialist magazines or clubs – only word of mouth. There were no toys, except mirrors, bells and ladders for Budgerigars. Over two or three decades had come the realisation that parrots need to be busy – not bored. Sensitive keepers knew this 70 years previously. In 1906 one lady regretted that she had never seen any mention of providing toys: "... many keepers of a wretched and solitary Parrot or Cockatoo never think of providing their prisoner with toys. A splendid Lemon-crested Cockatoo, a member of a family I know well (I cannot speak of her in any other terms!) is given all sorts of toys, and my Yellow-nape also, empty cotton reels especially if presented in a blown-out paper bag, cinders, a lump of rotten wood with the bark on, a bit of tape tied to the wire to pull at, post cards, and so on" (Williams, 1906).

Cages, stands and toys

Parrot cages were bare. There were no modern books on companion parrot care and even avicultural magazines seldom mentioned the subject, except from the aspect of talking ability. In short, there was no parrot industry. Until the 1980s cages were of the most basic and often unsuitable design, and had hardly altered since the beginning of the century. Usually they had a domed top, and were tall, not wide.

At the end of the century countless companies were involved in the manufacture or sales of parrot products, especially in the USA where the roots of the industry had been put down. Soon parrot toys, cages and accessories outsold items for the dog and cat industry. A huge range of imaginative products was developed, many of which eventually reached Europe. European manufacturers who could find a niche did well.

Cages were no longer simply a place in which to keep a parrot locked up – they became furniture. A multitude of cage types and styles were produced and, in the 1990s, prices fell. If space was of the essence one could choose a corner-shaped cage, if cool styling was the ultimate criteria there was an array of shiny stainless steel cages that sold at a staggering £3000. If a parrot

156 Blechrohr-Käfig
speciell für Sittiche.

▌*Above: Parrot cage in a catalogue for German bird fanciers printed in 1910.*
Right: Parrot cage circa 1920, with decorated base.

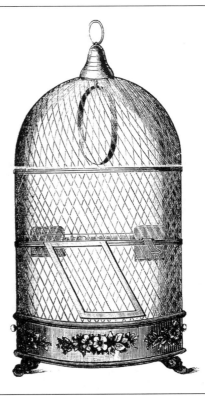

owner could not afford a separate playstand he could buy a cage that had a play area complete with perches, ladders and feeders attached to the roof. Powder-coated cages became available in a selection of colours. The buyer could choose the size that was appropriate for his or her bird, then select the shape – flat, domed or even scalloped roof.

Throughout the century it was not unusual for parrots to be purchased to adorn the owners' living rooms or hallways; these parrots spent their entire lives confined to a cage. As the pet parrot industry began to grow so did the realisation that parrots were more than ornamental items: a permanently caged parrot was an unhappy one. This opened yet another niche in the market and it did not take long for cage manufacturers to design innovative playstands. Until the nineties all that was available was a simple and unattractive T-stand to which the poor parrot might have been chained. Now there were play areas incorporating swings, ladders, ropes and toys.

Increasing demand for attractive playgyms resulted in the manufacture of a large variety, including tabletop models. Some stands were made of bendable latex, allowing the parrot

keeper to rearrange the shape; others were constructed from steel or hard plastic. Among the most attractive were dried java trees, stripped of their bark and dried and buffed – but they commanded prices up to £300! Their success was surprising considering that any parrot owner could cut a large fruit tree branch and simply fix it into a small coffee table or an ornamental plant pot with some cement at a cost of £10 or so.

By the end of the century the UK had the largest pet parrot industry in Europe; France and Scandinavia were other thriving areas. Worldwide, of course, the United States had the largest markets, with those in Australia and South Africa increasing, but far behind Europe. In the UK a number of stores sold only parrot-related items.

A multitude of toys

The companion bird keepers were the most important clients; many were frequent buyers of expensive toys. Their treasured parrots might have been equally happy with easily destroyed items such as apple branches and small blocks of wood – but these were not always easy to acquire.

■ *Left: Scarlet Macaw entertains visitors to Jurong BirdPark, Singapore. **Above:** Scooters and skates, made in acrylic, keep cockatoos and macaws amused.*
Photograph (left): Jurong BirdPark, Singapore

By the end of the century parrot toy manufacturers were producing species-specific items. For larger birds with powerful beaks, toys were constructed from hard woods such as manzanita, dragon wood or grapewood. Metal toys held together with wing nuts and bolts were made for cockatoos to unscrew and manipulate – ideal for their elevated intellect and genius for taking things apart. Balsa wood was used to make appealing toys for Budgerigars and Cockatiels.

As people became more aware of their parrot's need for mental stimulation and interaction with the person they had bonded to, manufacturers invented toys and games that would involve parrot and owner. Little roller skates, scooters, miniature basketball courts and shape puzzles all required the owner to teach their bird how to use them. The sizes of parrot toys ranged from inch long "foot toys" to 3ft (1m) long mobiles with countless pieces of coloured wood, acrylic and leather tied together with multicoloured sisal and cotton ropes. Prices for a toy could range from a pound or two to a staggering £50.

Recording devices

Parrots' talking abilities and parrot owners' desires to have talking parrots, ideally with large vocabularies, did not go unnoticed by the industry. In the 1980s cassettes, and later CDs, became available; they contained several words, phrases or songs that a parrot could learn. These CDs were played repeatedly while the parrot's owners were away in order to teach the chosen words and phrases with little effort on the owner's behalf. By the end of the century recording devices in the shape of a parrot toy, made of hard plastic, were available. The parrot owner could digitally record his words onto the microchip inside the device. When the parrot pressed the recorder's very large button with its beak, its owner's voice was played back.

Hand-rearing commenced

The need for such toys was partly due to the increased interaction between humans and hand-reared parrots. In the UK of the 1970s I was one of the pioneers of hand-rearing. The purpose was NOT to provide tame birds for companions; it was to increase the numbers of certain species that had only recently become known in aviculture and which, for all we knew, might never be available again. Breeding of the larger parrots was spasmodic – a hit or miss affair, since the gender of most parrots was unknown and rearing diets were experimental. The general view was that one should not look in nest-boxes for fear of disturbing breeding pairs.

At that time all parrots were bred in outdoor aviaries. In Europe many parrots nested during winter and chicks would succumb to the cold. Hand-rearing was a means of saving these chicks of rarer species. It took off quite slowly and was not adopted by breeders of established groups such as Australian parakeets, Cockatiels and lovebirds. If you wanted a pet parrot you searched the premises of importers (or pet shops) for a young one. In those days before the instant tameness of hand-reared young, people knew they would probably have to work hard to tame their parrot. There was no alternative: it was wild-caught or parent-reared. In my opinion most of these parrots, when tamed, made better pets than their hand-reared equivalents. They were more independent and were much less likely (with the exception of cockatoos) to suffer behavioural problems. Of course there were also adult wild-caught birds that never lost their fear of people after capture and never became tame.

■ *Feeding a lorikeet chick.*

During the 1980s

Hand-rearing of larger parrots, cockatoos and macaws for the pet trade became common among small breeders. The demand for hand-reared parrots had become insatiable. The buyers were seduced by the appealing, cuddly babies. A young Grey Parrot, for example, is irresistible with its doe-like eyes; it does not have the piercing, hard yellow iris of an adult. It looks trusting and trustworthy. Young cockatoos, so soft and vulnerable and clinging, encouraged impulse buying.

Thus it came about that parrot mania reached very large numbers of households that wild-caught parrots had never entered. In the USA in the 1970s, parrots were the "in" pets and prices were soaring. In 1978 one pet shop owner in Milwaukee said that a tame macaw would sell for $1,600 to $4,000 depending on "how well trained" it was. Five years previously a tame macaw sold for about $800. Due to increasing production, prices for some species of hand-reared parrots remained roughly the same from the beginning of the boom right through to the end of the century except for Grey Parrots, for which the demand never ceased.

Incubators and brooders

With the growing market in hand-reared parrots new ways of increasing production had to be found. As many small breeders relied more and more on the income their hand-reared birds generated, it become important to increase egg production and the hatch rate. The only way was to remove eggs from the nest in order to incubate them artificially. Breeding pairs then usually produced an extra clutch or two per season.

Incubators produced for the poultry industry usually proved too inaccurate for successful incubation of exotic birds' eggs. They were usually too large – and very expensive. Several companies recognised the need for a reliable, small and reasonably priced machine. In the UK Brinsea's Octagon 20 incubator, first marketed in 1989, was small, portable and comparatively inexpensive; it was also aimed at the poultry keeper. By the mid-1990s the Mark III version was produced to cope with the sensitivity of parrot eggs, making incubation easy and affordable for the small breeder. Sales were around 4000 units per annum. In the UK only 20% of these incubators were sold for parrot incubation; in the USA the figure was 80%. Brooders to care for the resulting sensitive, altricial chicks became available in the late 1990s and sales more than doubled after five years.

There was room for improvement in incubation methods, in order to increase hatchability. In 1980 Frank Pearce tried to develop an incubator that warmed the egg by direct contact from above, much as a parrot does in the nest. He used a bed sheet that inflated, positioned across the eggs. His attempts failed as the contact between the inflated sheet and the eggs did not conduct sufficient heat. The breakthrough came in the late 1990s when he realised that a thin plastic skin, permanently inflated and pressurised by a fan, would inflict roughly the same amount of pressure on the eggs as the parrot's breast. By the year 2000 an incubator had been developed that could be programmed to treat the eggs in the same way as the incubating parrot, including turning the eggs at specific angles, and controlling the humidity.

Millions of parrots

Various estimates have been published regarding the number of parrots in the USA. In 1988 a survey was carried out on behalf of the American Pet Products Manufacturers' Association (APPMA). The survey indicated that 6% of all residences (5.2 million homes) kept a total of 13.9 million exotic birds, of which 1,946,000 were parrots. Kaytee carried out a survey at the same time and concluded that at least 10% of households owned at least one exotic bird. It suggested that the total in the USA was 31 million pet birds of which 3,100,000 were parrots. In the two surveys, the percentages of the species kept were as follows:

	Parakeets (Budgies)	Cockatiels	other Parrots	Canaries
APPMA	43%	18%	14%	7%
Kaytee	35%	16%	10%	6%

The results of the two surveys show a discrepancy of more than 33% in the numbers of parrots maintained as pets. Nevertheless, if a figure mid-way between that suggested by the two surveys is fairly accurate, then approximately 2.5 million pet parrots were maintained in the USA in 1988.

Unfortunately, knowledge regarding the level of commitment required to keep them happy had not increased at the same rate as their popularity. At first there was no awareness that hand-reared parrots were so much more demanding emotionally and of your time than those that had been wild-caught and parent-reared. Soon there were so many cries for help from people experiencing problems with these complex and misunderstood creatures, that a new profession was born: parrot psychologist. They surfaced in the USA under the name of "parrot behaviorists". Usually it was the owner whose behaviour needed to be modified. Nevertheless, parrot magazines carried numerous articles from American "gurus". Outside of the USA, a parrot behaviourist would soon be out of work.

No formal qualifications were acquired by most of these advisers. The best qualifications would probably have been a degree in psychology (especially child psychology), experience of the behaviour of many parrot species, an extremely sympathetic attitude towards parrots, and patience with their human carers. A few good behaviourists emerged but some others gave such damaging advice that it seemed unlikely that they had any of the suggested qualifications. By the end of the century a change had taken place in America. "Behaviour analyst" was an officially recognised title granted only to professionals holding the relevant licence. Unqualified parrot advisors could refer to themselves only as consultants. In the USA and Britain, unqualified consultants offered their services via telephone consultations and/or house visits, often charging high fees.

Often the advice of "parrot behaviourists" was challenged because it was invariably based on the premise that the parrot is wing-clipped. In the UK this practice was rare until American parrot books became available. In the USA the assumption was that a parrot would be wing-clipped; this was carried out at a very early age, often with disastrous physical and emotional results. My books offered the reverse advice: that parrots should be wing-clipped only in exceptional circumstances or for a limited period to facilitate training, and never when very young. By the end of the century more American parrot owners were inclined towards that view. One American reader of my book *The Loving Care of Pet Parrots* wrote to me:

"... I really didn't know any other option but to clip their wings. I am re-thinking the entire concept after reading your book. Here in the U.S., as you noted, we are scolded if the wings are not clipped."

Parrot books

There is no better indication of how parrot keeping changed during the century than that reflected in the books devoted to the subject. Greene's two volumes, already mentioned, were the standard works at the beginning of the century. In the years prior to the First World War, C. P. Arthur's *Parrots for Pleasure and Profit* was readily available, priced 6d (5p). Its 36 pages included advice on the treatment of newly imported specimens. During the 1920s there were two avicultural landmarks. In 1926 *Parrakeets* by David Seth-Smith was published. It was illustrated by a well-known bird artist, H. Gronvold. *Parrots and Parrot-like Birds in Aviculture* by the Marquis of Tavistock (later the 12th Duke of Bedford) was published in 1928 and illustrated with eight coloured plates by Edward Boosey. (It cost 15 shillings, or 15s 9d post-paid.) Both books were based on extensive personal experience and both were soon out of print. The Depression of the 1930s and the war and its aftermath in the 1940s stopped the publication of specialist titles. However, throughout this period the British *Avicultural Magazine* (journal of the Avicultural Society) maintained its high standard and was the most important reference for aviculturists. The articles it contained then were perhaps the most readable and interesting of any era.

During the late 1950s two more classic books were published. *Parrots, Cockatoos and Macaws* was an anecdotal work by Edward Boosey, a leading aviculturist who opened the first bird farm in the UK. The authors of *Parrots and Parrot-like Birds* were Henry Bates and Robert Busenbark in California, who ran a bird farm there. This was the first treatise since the Duke of Bedford's book although many of the species were covered by description only. Nevertheless, this was a landmark publication since it was the only one available that listed all the species available in aviculture and, for the first time ever, many were illustrated by colour photographs. Most parrot owners were unaware of the existence of these books, or could not afford to buy them. *Parrots, Cockatoos, Parrakeets,* one of more than 30 pet titles in Ditchfield's Little Wonder Book series, was their sole source of reference. It cost a few pence and its 32 pages, measuring 4in (10cm) x 5 ½ in (13cm), contained much good advice.

Over the next two decades in the USA, Bates and Busenbark's book was followed by a stream of much smaller, poorly produced titles on parrots. They sold in huge numbers in pet stores, especially initially when few other parrot books were available. In the UK more substantial works were being produced. These included, in 1980, my book *Parrots, their Care and Breeding*, the biggest volume on parrot aviculture. It went to three editions, the last in 1992, and was published in three languages. When aviculture started to decline in the mid-1990s, and more people turned to the Internet for information,

the publishing company saw the writing on the wall. Falling sales ended its publication of books on aviculture. The same trend was observed in Germany while, in Australia, *Australian Birdkeeper* magazine was publishing the most successful, colourful and extensive series of avicultural books ever seen.

An innovation was the publication of books for children reinforcing conservation values with parrots as the central characters. Dale Smith's enchanting *What the Parrot told Alice* was the first, in 1996. It has been enjoyed by many an adult! In German, Lars Lepperhoff's *Arinos Grosse Reise* (1999) tells the story of a Blue and Yellow Macaw reared by Indians in the South American jungle and sold to a dealer. Such books gave children an insight into the trade in wild-caught parrots.

The growth of magazines for bird breeders and pet bird keepers in the USA was enormous during the 1980s. These magazines, such as *Bird Talk, American Cage Bird Magazine, AFA Watchbird* and *Bird World*, had a combined circulation of 200,000 in 1990 (Clubb, 1992). Articles on parrots took up most of the editorial pages.

The 1980s saw the publication of books exclusively on parrots as pets. Some were species specific and nearly all had American authors. There was even a gourmet pet parrot cookbook! By the end of the century most commonly kept pet species had their "own" book; there were at least ten exclusively about the popular Grey Parrot. Countless publications explained how to handle, train and discipline,

usually written by people who loved pet parrots but were not trained in animal behaviour. Much of the advice was wrong and, in some cases, dangerous. In Europe books on parrots were best represented in the German language. Wolfgang de Grahl, an aviculturist who died in 1992, was the most prolific

■ *Above:* Plate painted by Edward Boosey **(right)** *for* Parrots and Parrot-like Birds in Aviculture, *depicting a Many-coloured Parakeet and a Dusky Pionus Parrot.*

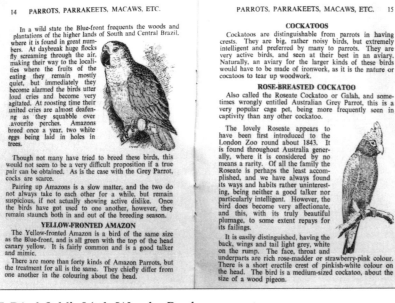

Ditchfield's Little Wonder Book *on parrots.*

author. Thomas Arndt set up his own publishing company, exclusively for two magazines and various books on parrots.

Parrot art

It was during the 1980s that some artists started to specialise in parrot art. One of the first was Elizabeth Butterworth. In 1996, after 20 years of painting parrots, she completed the most monumental work of parrot art ever accomplished. It consisted of 12 life-size (elephant folio) plates of macaws. Work started in 1990 in a London studio specially set up for the

Elizabeth Butterworth with the life-sized Green-winged Macaw plate from Macaws.

purpose and financed by a banker, the late Rodolphe d'Erlanger. Four hand-colourists worked full-time on the plates. The modest title, Macaws, gave no hint of the extraordinary complexity of the work. It was completed using a technique known as *a la poupée* – seldom used due to the enormous expense involved. The resulting 50 sets sold at £25,000 each. This was a historic work, to rival that of anything produced by John Gould. Elizabeth Butterworth is the only artist ever to have had work showing parrots hung in the prestigious New York Metropolitan Museum of Art and in the Graham Gallery.

More modest oil paintings and watercolours of parrot species by various artists, especially in Australia, became so poplar that jigsaw puzzles and prints of the originals were produced.

Parrot clubs

When cage bird societies were at the peak of their popularity in the UK in the 1950s and 1960s it was unusual to see a woman at a club meeting, except performing the wifely duty of making the tea! (As a teenager I was a female Budgerigar breeder in a man's world.) Cage bird societies were for breeders and exhibitors – all men. Over several decades the numbers of pet parrot owners gradually exceeded those of breeders, and the avicultural societies and cage bird clubs that had existed for decades started to decline. They did not cater for pet owners. In the USA pet parrot lovers banded together in the 1980s to form their own clubs. Then the gender majority was reversed and most of the members were women.

Indeed, there were so many female parrot owners that a new consumer market opened up. Parrots were depicted on jewellery, T-shirts, jackets, shopping bags and stationery. Even the fashion-conscious could be appropriately attired! At an avicultural convention in Miami, Jean Pattison, a leading breeder of African parrots known as the "African Queen", wore a stunning dress of imaginative Grey Parrot design (see colour page 9), with scarlet boots (representing its tail). Her hair was tinted in layers: blonde and black and tipped with scarlet. This was a smart and sophisticated outfit!

In the UK the parrot club situation was quite different. Formed within the Parrot Society were up to 20 area groups since its formation in 1966. In its heyday, the 1980s, the monthly meetings attracted good attendances. These started to decline until by the end of the century the attendances were so small, between ten and 20 members, that the survival of most of these groups was in doubt. They had not moved with the times to embrace the keepers of pet parrots.

When I started a club in Nottinghamshire in 2000 it was soon apparent among those who attended that keepers of pet parrots outnumbered those with aviaries by about three to one. By ensuring that the programme of monthly meetings reflected this, and that advice for all parrot owners was freely available, the level of attendance at meetings was maintained at between 30 and 40. However, I found I was single-handedly responsible for devising the programme and realised that throughout the country there were few people with the contacts and enthusiasm to do this, especially in view of the few speakers available. For this reason it seems unlikely that the small number of parrot clubs will greatly increase in the UK. This is regrettable because the friendships formed, the monthly gatherings of people with like interests and the knowledge gained make membership very worthwhile. Parrots also attended the meetings on occasions and this broadened the knowledge of members and parrots of other parrot species! It could be a disadvantage, though, when a macaw tried to compete with the speaker! (A cautionary word: only *healthy* parrots in the owner's care for some years

should be admitted to meetings due to the risk of disease transference.)

The Internet

The dawn of the Internet brought with it new parrot clubs: those that existed in cyberspace. Many of these *groups* were very specific: for owners of pet macaws, Amazons, Grey Parrots and many others. Some groups discussed training or behaviour, diet, how to make toys or even how to train a parrot for outdoor free-flight. These groups were mainly hosted by large Internet companies and were open to everyone. Furthermore, anybody could found and run such a group. Communication was conducted via e-mails or "posts" which could be read on a virtual message board or in one's own e-mail inbox. This global system allowed people from different countries to participate simultaneously. Some groups had several hundred members, resulting in pet-parrot-chat taking place practically every hour of every day.

The Internet was used by parrot fanatics to search for merchandise. Products ranged from the really useful, such as computer software programmes for breeders' records, to the ridiculous in the form of parrot diapers. In the early part of the century parrot paraphernalia did not exist. The occasional print from an old book, or an oil painting or watercolour depicting parrots was prized by parrot owners. Prints at popular prices were not available. By the 1980s jewellery such as little cockatoo or macaw earrings and pendants became available along with shirts, sweatshirts, caps and tote bags depicting favourite parrots.

Computer owners could download little parrot-shaped cursors, parrot desktop wallpapers and animated parrot cartoon gifs (computer-generated images). The faces of Grey Parrots, Amazons and cockatoos adorned anything from coffee mugs, jewellery boxes, notebooks, writing paper and wall clocks to aprons, mouse pads and wall tiles. Parrot paraphernalia became big business. If you wanted to show that you loved parrots there were a million ways of doing so.

■ *Orange-fronted Kakariki.*

10. DID AVICULTURE CONTRIBUTE TO CONSERVATION?

Parrot breeding by private aviculturists cannot normally be classified as conservation. In other circumstances captive breeding sometimes has a useful role. The Parrot Action Plan (*Status Survey and Conservation Action Plan 2000– 2004*) states:

"Captive breeding has served a crucial function in the recovery of a number of species of critically endangered wildlife, and has a role to play in the recovery of certain parrots. However, there are significant limitations to this technique when it is used to breed birds for ultimate release to the wild. In general, the technique is advisable only as a short-term measure when other preferable conservation options are not immediately available."

Private aviculturists have very rarely had an opportunity to breed endangered parrots for release. Even in the unlikely scenario of an aviculturist residing in the locality of an endangered parrot, the government might not give permission for the release of captive-bred parrots.

Breeding for release

I know of only two examples of government-sponsored programmes that sought aviculturists to breed endangered birds in their own aviaries, one in New Zealand and the other in Australia. In Australia, one individual (who asked not to be named) was invited to take part in a government conservation project. In order to do so he needed Federal Government and State Government approval. He described himself as "a conservationist who became an aviculturist", and he kept no other species. He was provided with pairs of Orange-bellied Parrots (*Neophema chrysogaster*), Australia's most endangered psittacine species (see colour page 10). He achieved excellent breeding results and the young reared were successfully released. A typical grass parakeet, not unlike a dull-coloured Turquoisine, the Orange-bellied Parrot (colour page 10) breeds in Tasmania and migrates every winter across Bass Strait to Victoria and South Australia.

To boost its numbers (fewer than 200 since the 1970s), a government-run captive-breeding programme was set up in 1986. Between that year and 1999, 280 Orange-bellied Parrots were bred at the Hobart facility and 79 at Healesville Sanctuary in Victoria (Smales *et al* 2000). In 1999 the captive population consisted of 81 birds and another 68 had been released into the wild. These figures suggest that mortality among captive birds was high. However, in the 2000/2001 breeding season 71 young fledged in aviaries, giving the best results for one season. Furthermore, the captive-bred birds were able to migrate to their breeding grounds in Tasmania (more than 200km away), the ultimate proof of the success of this venture.

The second case involved private aviculturists who had the expertise to save a parakeet from extinction but who were ultimately thwarted by officialdom. The Orange-fronted Kakariki (colour page 10), sometimes known as Malherbe's Parakeet (*Cyanoramphus malherbi*), is very close in appearance to the Yellow-fronted Kakariki (*C. auriceps*). For many years it was the subject of debate by systematists: was it just a colour morph? When scientists studied this problem using the latest DNA techniques it indicated that the Orange-fronted Parakeet was a distinct species, most closely related to the Red-fronted Kakariki (*C. novaezelandiae*).

Described as Endangered (due to its small range and population) as soon as it was given species status, the Orange-fronted was known from only two valleys in the South Island. During the 1990s its total population was estimated at between 200 and 500 birds. By 2003 it was found only in one patch of beech forest with an 18-mile (30km) radius, in Arthur's Pass National Park and in the Lake Sumner Forest Park.

In 1980 about 8% of the Kakariki population in the North Canterbury region consisted of Orange-fronted Parakeets. The Wildlife Service (which became New Zealand's Department of Conservation, known as DOC) trapped four and reared others from eggs removed from a nest there. Placed with two experienced aviculturists, Edwin and Eileen Heatherbell in South Island, they proved to be prolific, early and consistent breeders. When the Heatherbells were instructed by DOC to break up the pairs and give them new partners, not one youngster was produced for several years. Forced-pairing was a failure. Finally, in 1992, a male in his twelfth year bred with a new female and five young were reared.

The prolificacy of the Orange-fronted Parakeets was a problem. The Heatherbells were not allowed to part with them and their aviaries became overcrowded. Eventually DOC reclaimed these birds. What happened to them is unknown. Under normal circumstances DOC would not release captive-bred birds into the wild.

In September 2003 reports appeared in the *Christchurch Press* headlined: "Native parrot at risk of extinction" (September 10) and (ironically) "DOC embarks on bird-saving mission" (September 20). Kamala Hayman, the

▌ *Red-fronted Kakariki.*

writer in both cases, reported that three-quarters of the Orange-fronted Parakeet's population had been wiped out in the past two summers by exploding populations of introduced rats and stoats. Environment Minister Chris Carter stated that the Orange-fronted Parakeet was the most endangered forest bird in the country. (Most native forest birds are already endangered or critically endangered.) He said: "We did not recognise them as a distinct species until 1999 when there were 700. Now there could be as few as 150. It's the worst crisis I have had to deal with as minister."

For anyone who knows about the captive history the next statement, made in September 2003, is loaded with sad irony: "Early hopes of breeding the bird in captivity were dashed when a February hunt turned up just one nest of five eggs. These were taken to the Department of Conservation (DOC) aviary in Te Anau and four hatched. Two weeks ago the only female died and with it DOC's immediate insurance policy." Later three of the chicks also died.

One could say that DOC had burned its insurance policy a decade previously when it so carelessly squandered the valuable population of captive birds, carefully reared by the Heatherbells. If more aviculturists had been permitted to take these birds, there could have been hundreds, perhaps thousands, by now. There are thousands of the closely-related Red-fronted Kakarikis in aviculture (mostly mutations, unfortunately) but in 1958 there were none outside New Zealand. The captive population there was low, only 103 individuals, because the government had only recently permitted the keeping of native birds. However, only six years after the 1958 captive census, the numbers in private hands had risen to 2,500.

"Captive breeding is conservation" became the slogan of the American Federation of Aviculture during the 1990s. Alas, this has been the case only in exceptional circumstances. Private aviculturists participated in the cases related above, also in Costa Rica when, at the century's end, Richard and Margo Friseus (colour page 12) had government permission to release captive-bred Scarlet Macaws to augment the dwindling population there.

In the 1980s there was much talk of release of captive-bred birds to bolster wild populations or to re-establish a species where it had been extirpated. An early attempt, in 1986, was made with the Thick-billed Parrot in Arizona. The supply of confiscated wild birds soon ceased and the project then used captive-bred birds. Nearly all were hand-reared and none survived when released. The project was a failure.

Many parrots of certain endangered species are bred in captivity, but hand-rearing has unfortunately become the norm among private breeders. This is to maximise production (and income). It is not impossible for hand-reared parrots to survive in the wild, but the chances are poor. Most are disadvantaged, often lacking the opportunity to learn the normal behaviour of their species and even confused about their identity. To survive in the wild any bird needs to be very quick-witted and to have knowledge, much of it inherited or learned from adults, about food and predators. Lacking this vital knowledge most released hand-reared parrots die or are killed or need to be recaptured soon after release.

Three or four parrots were saved from extinction during the 20th century with the use of avicultural techniques. Breeding and release programmes of endangered species are normally *in situ*. Only four parrot conservation projects used captive-bred birds on a regular basis and in significant numbers, those for the Puerto Rican Parrot, the Echo Parakeet, the Kakapo and, as already described, the Orange-bellied Parrot.

Puerto Rico's parrot

The Puerto Rican Parrot (*Amazona vittata*) is one of the least distinctive members of the genus (colour page 12). Once it inhabited almost the entire island of Puerto Rico and was found in great flocks but by 1835 one third of the forest was gone. By 1900 the human population had doubled in 50 years to reach one million. Three-quarters of the island had been cleared for agriculture and by 1912 less than 1% of virgin forest survived. By 1940 the parrot had been pushed up into the wet and inhospitable Luquillo Mountains.

The first population estimate, made in 1954, suggested that 200 individuals had survived. This Amazon had never appeared in the international pet trade but young were taken for sale locally, trees were cut down to rob nests and its nest tree (*Palo colorado*) was felled for charcoal. In 1967 only 24 birds were known and the species was belatedly listed as endangered. Its catastrophic decline was hastened by military exercises in connection with the Vietnam war, testing of herbicides, road construction and increased shooting. In 1975 the Puerto Rican Parrot population had reached an all-time low of 13 birds. An intensive programme of protecting and repairing nests commenced, followed by captive breeding.

The first breeding attempts were carried out by U. S. Fish and Wildlife Service scientists. They had no experience of rearing parrots: they lacked basic skills and the feeling for what these parrots needed. In 1988 I visited the place where the breeding pairs were kept in small wire cages on the second floor of a building in the Luquillo forest of Puerto Rico. Breeding results were poor. I was saddened by the living conditions of these unfortunate birds whose entire population numbered about 50 at that time. It was some years before notice was taken of aviculturists

■ *Puerto Rican Parrots inside a building in the Luquillo forest in 1988.*

who were anxious to help. Then the parrots were moved to outdoor flights and other improvements were made. In 1993 a second breeding programme was established, this time with the Puerto Rico government in the Rio Abajo forest. Aviculturists were employed and established avicultural techniques were used. At the close of 2001 there were 140 captive birds at the two locations, including 29 reared that year. Between 2000 and 2002 there was a significant increase in the number of captive breeding pairs, from 27 to 37.

The first release of captive-bred birds, ten individuals (aged one to four years) occurred in June 2000. They were fitted with small radio transmitters with a battery that lasted about one year, so that their movements could be followed. One parrot lived only four days. By May of the following year four more were known to have died, two had survived and the fate of three was unknown. Released birds were very vulnerable to hawk attacks. In June 2001 a second group, consisting of 16 birds, was released. By 2002 the total number released was 35, with a survival rate of about 50%.

In 2004 the wild population was estimated at 23 to 36 birds, thus mortality was higher than the number of birds released. The population had never exceeded 50 individuals since conservation efforts commenced, indicating that factors such as predation and hurricanes render survival in the forest impossible for more than a short period. Unless suitable habitat survives, which clearly it does not in the Luquillo forest, there is no point in releasing captive-bred parrots. In the late 1980s discussion commenced regarding releases into the Rio Abajo forest in the north-west of the island, projected to commence in 2005. If this proves impossible, a small Caribbean island where no parrots exist should surely be sought. Luquillo is a death sentence.

There were no Puerto Rican Parrots in captivity outside the island except, possibly, those that were stolen in 2001. (Their whereabouts were unknown.)

The case of the Puerto Rican Parrot demonstrates something that aviculturists who laud the release of captive-bred birds as a means of saving a species should consider: their release does not result in a population increase unless conditions are advantageous for their survival.

Echo Parakeet

Without question, *in situ* captive breeding played a significant role in saving the Echo Parakeet (*Psittacula eques*). It looks much like a Ringneck but has a heavier build and a shorter tail. Reduced to only double figures in the 1970s, by the end of the century it had increased to about 135 birds. This wonderful success story was achieved against all odds using intensive management of wild nests, rearing and release of under-fed chicks in the conservation centre on Mauritius, supplementary feeding and improvement of the surviving habitat. On occasions Ringneck Parakeets acted as foster parents; established captive-breeding techniques proved useful.

The Kakapo

One cannot help resorting to superlatives when mentioning the Kakapo (*Strigops habroptilus*). It is the most endearing, the most extraordinary and, of course, the heaviest of all parrots (colour page 13). It is unique. Large, over 2ft (60cm) in length, it is by far the heaviest parrot, males weighing up to 7 ½ lbs (females less). Its unusually soft plumage is barred and streaked with brown and yellow, being mainly green above and greenish-yellow below. It is the only nocturnal parrot, hiding away in a secluded and well-shaded corner or tree during the day, the only flightless parrot and the only flightless lek[1] bird in the entire world. It is also the only parrot in which the male has an inflatable thoracic air sac with which to make a booming call to attract a mate. And to think we nearly lost this unique and remarkable creature!

Found only in New Zealand, it belongs in the far-off days when there were no introduced predators to kill vulnerable females (ground-nesters) and their chicks and to eat their food. Captive breeding in the usual sense, that is, confined to cages, could never have been successful due to the species' complicated

behaviour. In the 1970s transfers to predator-free islands around the coast of New Zealand commenced. Kakapo were not captive in the normal sense: they ranged free on offshore islands. Predatory mammals took eggs and chicks and food sources for rearing females were limited. Population growth was insignificant because DOC policy had been one of little intervention.

Something had to be done! That something was the use of avicultural techniques. From the mid-1990s eggs were removed to be hatched, or chicks to be reared in captivity. Then the young were released. From only about 50 in the mid-1980s, and with little increase in the next decade, the population increased to 86 in 2003. At long, long last there was hope for a parrot so extraordinary that if you were privileged to see one, you wanted to cry at the thought of what the human race had done to its species.

These trusting birds had been abused by man for centuries. Maoris hunted them for feathers to make cloaks, also for their flesh, which was considered a delicacy. Early settlers hunted them for food – and even fed them to their dogs. They killed them for their skins to sell to museums around the world for a few shillings each. Later settlers introduced deer and possums that gradually destroyed the Kakapo's food sources. Rats and stoats killed the females and their young and feral cats decimated whole populations. It is little short of a miracle that

▌*Kakapo chick.*

---

[1] A lek is a mating system in which males gather together and perfom courtship displays to attract a female.

the Kakapo has survived to this day. If there is one parrot species that epitomises the changing attitude towards birds, contrasting the year 1901 to the year 2000, this is it. At the start of the century these truly unique and remarkable creatures were killed with no more thought than one would kill a rat. By the end of the century the New Zealand government had spent millions of dollars in its attempt to prevent their extinction.

The role of private aviculturists

The question "Did private aviculture contribute to conservation?" must be answered honestly. It did not. Certain parrots became more numerous in captivity than in the wild only because wild populations had been brought close to extinction by over-trapping. Aviculturists were major consumers of wild-caught parrots. Unfortunately, rather few bred a species over a long period or co-operated with the stud-book, if one existed. This was partly because most breeders do not specialise. One exception is a breeder of the Philippine Cockatoo in England (who preferred to remain anonymous). He probably bred more young than in any other collection (with the exception of Birds International in the Philippines.)

Some aviculturists suggested that this Critically Endangered cockatoo could be saved by captive breeding. In fact there have only ever been a handful of consistently successful breeders. The studbook for this species usually

shows more deaths annually than hatchings. The dream of the most dedicated breeder to return his or her young to the wild could never be fulfilled because psittacine beak and feather disease (PBFD) was not uncommon among captive birds.

If aviculturists were to maintain some of the rarer and less popular species over the long-term they needed to organise consortiums to ensure their continuity. This did not happen. Instead, there are such small captive stocks of some formerly common species, such as the Orange-flanked Parakeet (see Chapter 5), that they are likely to be lost in aviculture.

Many scientists believe that the value of captive breeding for parrot conservation has been exaggerated, sometimes to the detriment of other potentially promising techniques. According to Derricksen and Snyder (1992), "Captive breeding is a preferred conservation method only under very specific conditions, and only in the short-term sense. When reliance is placed on this technique in a recovery program, we believe that it should always be coupled with efforts to either supplement or re-establish wild populations as soon as possible".

When attending conventions in the USA during the late 1980s and 1990s I usually spoke on conservation issues and tried to explain how membership of the World Parrot Trust (see Chapter 11) benefited conservation. Unfortunately, this had little impact. At the American Federation of Aviculture convention in San Francisco in 1996, 235 people registered, nearly all of whom were parrot keepers; only a handful were already members of the Trust. During the meeting only ten people joined. Many participants could see no further than the parrots in their own cages. I found this very disappointing. A few would thank me for opening their eyes to a very different world and ask if there was anything they could do to help. They were usually pet bird owners – not breeders.

▌*A highly successful British breeder of Philippine Cockatoos.*

■ *Orange-winged Amazon chicks, captive-bred and closed ringed.*

American aviculturist Layne Dicker wrote that some breeders think of conservation as important only when it is "aligned with their continued right to breed and keep birds. In instances where the two goals are at odds, aviculture fails conservation" (Dicker, 2000). Another American aviculturist, Eb Cravens, pointed out: "... when some breeders say they 'love parrots', they really mean they 'love their parrots'."

Dr Stewart Metz, an active conservationist and parrot keeper, wrote: "Conservation reflects a desire to preserve the *intrinsic* value of animals, rather than their *extrinsic* value because they belong to us or can be used for personal gain" (Metz, 2001).

Some breeders claimed that captive breeding was saving parrots from extinction because they supply the demand and this prevents parrots being trapped. This argument is totally flawed. (See Chapters 5 and 7.) Captive breeding and trapping wild parrots are two unrelated issues except that in Europe some imported species such as Orange-winged Amazons are so cheap that breeders cannot sell the young they breed.

This often results in them selling the breeding pair.

Endangered species in private hands

Discussion on the ethics of keeping threatened parrot species started in the 1980s. Never before had known endangered species been available to anyone who could hand over the asking price. Their availability was partly due to the fact that logging had opened up certain areas (Indonesian islands, for example), resulting in parrots being trapped and exported on a scale so large that it threatened their existence. It was during this decade that field studies of parrots were initiated. Before then, aviculturists were keeping most parrot species with no knowledge of their status in the wild.

By the last 15 to 20 years of the century there were many examples in captivity of endangered or critically endangered parrots originating from illegal sources. The question of ownership loomed large. Brazil claimed that as no Spix's Macaw (extinct in the wild by 2000) had ever been legally exported, those overseas were the property of the Brazilian government and should be returned, or they might remain in the same location but their ownership would remain with the Brazilian government. The whole issue was highly complex. It received international press coverage and became the subject of a book (*Spix's Macaw* by Tony Juniper, ISBN 1-84115-650-7).

Illegal ownership applied equally to another species, the Critically Endangered Lear's Macaw, in which the entire captive population, bar two, consisted of illegally exported birds or their offspring. Wealthy individuals acquired wild-caught Lear's, regardless of whether or not they had any experience in parrot breeding. Apart from the breeding of three young Lear's Macaws in Florida in 1982 and 1984, there was no reported breeding in captivity. From the population believed to number about 200 birds at the end of the century, probably an equal number had been removed from the wild population since the species' discovery in the wild in 1978. At least 20 were caught and sold between 1992 and 1995 and at least 19 in 1996, for example.

Some aviculturists claimed that by breeding rare parrots still being imported from the wild, often illegally, they were contributing to their conservation. They failed to see the connection between illegal trafficking and rapidly declining populations. Harry Sissen, a breeder who brought into Britain wild-caught Lear's Macaws, was imprisoned as a result (see Chapter 7). He claimed that his sole aim was conservation.

Other recipients kept very quiet about their illegal Lear's Macaws, thus no breeding successes were known. But if breeding had occurred, what could the breeder do except pair brother to sister, or father to daughter? Because acquisition depended on wealth, not experience, the prospects for the smuggled birds were not good. The Singaporean man caught at Paris airport (see Chapter 7) with two Lear's Macaws in a bag was a collector of birds with no experience in breeding macaws.

Sam Williams, who visited the breeding locality of this macaw in 2002, wrote: "It is the demand for these rare birds that is the problem. It can no longer be socially acceptable among parrot keepers to keep such endangered species."

Twenty years earlier many aviculturists held very naïve views. In the November 27 1982 issue of *Cage and Aviary Birds* a Mr Hamilton, a newcomer to aviculture, suggested that scattered endangered parrots kept as pets should be located, a committee should be formed to administer a fund, and the proceedings should be used to breed from them. (That assumed that

■ *St Vincent Parrots being hand-reared by Ramon Noegel and Greg Moss in Florida.*
Photograph: Greg Moss

the owners would give them up, which seemed unlikely.) The committee would seek out persons of experience, dedication and time to devote to a serious breeding programme. In fact at that time few individuals of parrots of known endangered species were in private hands and, by the end of the century, those known to be threatened, such as the Moluccan Cockatoo, were so numerous in captivity that such an exercise would have been pointless.

Even if the funds had been available, how could the plan have operated? Who would have been the recipients of the birds bred in this way? Perhaps the committee members and their friends would have benefited. The private ownership of endangered and threatened parrots was a thorny subject as motives for ownership were not always genuine. In some people pride of ownership was stronger than the desire to conserve a species through captive breeding. Some collectors became interested in a species only when it was declared endangered, echoing the myth that they were going to conserve it by breeding. Instead they brought species such as Lear's Macaw to the brink of extinction by creating a demand for wild-caught birds.

By the end of the century the argument that captive breeding could save species like the St Vincent Parrot (*Amazona guildingii*) and the Hyacinthine Macaw had worn thin. No one believed it any more. In the case of the big macaw, 99% of the young were hand-reared and lacking in the qualities needed for survival in the wild. The argument is rendered more complex in the case of island species, such as the imposing and beautiful St Vincent Parrot. Every year its habitat dwindled due to deforestation. Well before the end of the century the wild population had almost certainly reached saturation point, given the limited area of habitat. St Vincent Parrots or their eggs continued to be smuggled out of the island. Morally this was wrong. It was theft and the people involved were wildlife criminals, whether or not they were caught. But it was probable that, due to the diminishing habitat, the impact on the wild population was nil.

Most breeding attempts of the St Vincent Parrot had proved to be dismal failures, with the notable exception of those by Ramon Noegel and Greg Moss that had spanned more than two decades in Florida. Their birds were legally exported from Barbados where a former marine biologist by the name of Bill Miller had taken a liking to this parrot. The reason why he succeeded in breeding them, during the 1980s, when others failed was probably because of their sparse diet! (This parrot easily becomes overweight.) By 2004 Ramon Noegel had 39 St Vincent Parrots, including two of the original birds acquired 23 years previously. But one cannot, in all honesty, say that their breeding success had helped the wild population. However, he had made contributions to the welfare of the parrot on its native island in other ways.

Disadvantages of captive-bred parrots

The disease risk to wild populations is a major reason why private breeders cannot participate in breeding programmes for endangered species. Government-controlled programmes consist of only the endangered species (perhaps also a closely related species to act as foster parents) and disease is tested for. In the last two decades of the century viral diseases had a very serious impact on parrot collections worldwide. These diseases resulted from mass export of wild-caught parrots, where birds were held in insanitary and overcrowded conditions. Wild

■ *The author with one of Bill Miller's St Vincent Parrots on Barbados.*

parrots have lived with these viruses for eons but in times of stress, and when birds from different continents are kept in the same premises, captive parrots encounter viruses to which they have no resistance, with fatal consequences. Outbreaks of psittacine beak and feather disease (PBFD), proventricular dilatation disease (PDD), Pacheco's disease and others surface in breeders' aviaries, no matter how good the conditions are, because breeders have brought in parrots that were harbouring a virus. There are tests for some of these diseases (but not for PDD) but tests are not 100% reliable and the risk of contamination of samples can be high.

In discussing the limits of captive breeding two biologists stated: "In large part, the failure of many institutions and private aviculturists to implement and maintain rigorous preventive measures for disease stems from the trouble and considerable expense that such efforts demand. However, without preventive measures, experience shows that the proper question is not whether disease problems will eventually develop, but rather how soon. In recent years, captive breeding programs for a number of endangered birds have suffered losses and sometimes severe setbacks due to disease" (Derrickson and Snyder, 1992).

This was the case with two endangered parrots. The Orange-bellied Parrot breeding programme in Australia was heavily hit by PBFD in the early years. Because captive-bred parrots were released into the wild, this disease had the potential for a terrible disaster. In private aviculture, PBFD contributed to the poor breeding results with the Red-vented Cockatoo.

Breeding for release is expensive

Cost is a major obstacle in the release of captive-bred birds. In the 1990s the cost of the U. S. Government Puerto Rican Amazon programme was in the region of $250,000 per annum. In just one decade the $2.5 million spent could have purchased huge tracts of land in the tropics that would have preserved countless species of flora and fauna. Is it worth spending so much money on one species, especially when most of its habitat has gone? This is a question that is likely to receive a negative answer in future.

Costs are a major headache in privately-financed programmes, such as one in Costa Rica, called Amigos de las Aves, for the release of Scarlet Macaws. Expenses are usually under-estimated, especially when the government takes many months (or longer) to give permission for release. There are three release sites. At Tiskita, for example, there were 28 introduced captive-bred Scarlet Macaws by 2004, most aged between two and five years. Four of the original released birds had been recaptured because they were too tame. These macaws were fed once daily with sunflower seed for several weeks after release, but soon learned to eat wild foods, such as beech nuts and guavas.

In at least two unconnected parrot release projects several birds died in aviaries due to lack of proper care while waiting to be set free and, at another location, macaws were stolen before they could be released. Success depends on the right staff – committed, dedicated, and expensive because usually they must be brought from another country.

Empty habitat and hundreds in captivity

Cost was less of an issue in the case of another endangered macaw because it bred so freely in the USA that its value there was not high. The beautiful Blue-throated Macaw (*Ara glaucogularis*) from Bolivia was almost trapped to extinction in the decade ending in the early 1990s. Its export was legal until it was placed on Appendix I of CITES in 1983. By the end of the century many palm-islands amid savannah, the species' natural habitat, were empty of these lovely macaws. Possibly as many as 1,200 Blue-throated Macaws were trapped for international

■ *Blue-throated Macaw, bred by Gill du Venage.*

trade during the 1980s, although the area in which they occurred was not known to scientists until 1992. By 1998 eight locations were known and the total population was estimated at no more than 100 to 150 individuals. Since then numbers might have fallen at several sites. Fieldwork carried out in 2002 suggested that only 50 to 100 birds had survived, making this the rarest macaw in the wild and one of the rarest of all parrots.

This is the scenario that aviculturists have boasted about: empty habitat and large numbers of the species in captivity. Why have they not been put back into the wild? The short answer is that officials in Bolivia either are not interested or will not give permission. At the time of writing, some birds acquired with the hope that they might be permitted to re-stock palm islands in Bolivia, are still in the USA. But even if permission is given, will these hand-reared birds be suitable for release and is the risk from PDD and other diseases too great? The idea is to release them in areas where they would not come into contact with the existing wild population. However, they might move to another location.

EUROPEAN STUDBOOK FOR PALM COCKATOO
Probosciger aterrimus
No 7 (1998)

EEP Co-ordinator
Roger Wilkinson
North of England Zoological Society
Chester Zoo

Breeding endangered species

Aviculturists who were genuinely interested in breeding endangered species to "save them from extinction" might have acquired, for example, Cuban Conures (*Aratinga euops*) (see colour page 13). These little parakeets were endangered by loss of habitat. They were kept in Europeans collections but interest was minimal. They almost died out. Why? Because they are green except for a few flecks of red in the plumage and hidden red under the wings. In contrast, the closely related and common Sun Conure (*Aratinga solstitialis*) was bred in large numbers because of its glorious plumage: fiery orange and yellow.

A parallel situation occurs with the popular Cuban Amazon and the Hispaniolan Amazon (*Amazona ventralis*). Almost identical, the Cuban (well established in captivity) was highly valued for its beautiful pink facial markings. These are missing in the Hispaniolan Amazon which was in danger of being lost from aviculture and, in the wild, was sliding towards extinction due to deforestation. Given the choice aviculturists always favoured colourful birds

rather than endangered species that were less gaudily attired.

A thorny issue during the last two decades of the century was co-operation between the private sector and zoos. Consortiums and studbooks that involved both sectors failed to unite them. This was not surprising. Endangered species in zoos had no monetary value. In the private sector they were worth a fortune. In 1992 the price of a pair of Spix's Macaws was, reputedly, $60,000 (about £40,000 at the rate of exchange that applied then). The private holder who could afford such birds was not going to forego that kind of income for the "good of the species".

Anything to increase productivity

The lack of ethics displayed by some breeders seemed to indicate that the lofty aspirations of conservation had not been acceded to. Breeders would apparently stop at nothing to increase productivity. White cockatoos are among the most difficult parrots to breed if the conditions are wrong. In the USA most parrots were bred in small wire cages – a recipe for disaster for these sensitive birds. Sooner or later the male would kill the female in a frenzy of frustration at being closely confined. Then a well-known vet came up with a solution. It was to remove the tip of the male's upper mandible so that he could not maim the female. Simultaneously elsewhere in the USA, at ABRC (see Chapter 4) a similar idea was being explored. The end of the male's upper mandible was removed (on a level with the lower mandible). Then a stainless steel pin was inserted through the beak and trimmed so that approximately 2–3mm extended outwards. Light-sensitive acrylic was then applied to make a hard ball tip to the beak that was incapable of injury. In initial trials the beak balls stayed in place for 24 to 51 days.

A parrot's beak is highly sensitive to injury because a nerve runs almost to the tip of the upper mandible. Parrots that suffer injuries to the tip experience much pain and might not eat for several days. To purposely remove part of the beak is the height of cruelty. A sensitive creature like a Moluccan or an Umbrella Cockatoo, the species to which this cruel method was most likely applied, would suffer severe psychological problems – depression at the very least. Any interest in breeding would probably be lost for a month or two by which time the beak ball would have fallen off. Then it would take some months (possibly even years) for the beak to grow back to its normal length.

The insensitivity of vets and others who recommended this kind of treatment was frightening. One well-known avian vet who probably pioneered the idea published an article about it. He later wrote: "I had no idea of the firestorm of controversy it would create in the bird community" (*Pet Bird Report*, January 2001). "I will discontinue performing this procedure in the future and will discourage others from doing so as well. I want to personally apologise for the anguish that I have created among my fellow veterinarians and pet bird owners in regard to this issue."

But it was not the vets and owners who suffered the most anguish... It was not they who had been mutilated. Breeders who would submit their cockatoos to this kind of maiming clearly had no regard for them, only for the profits

to be made. Yet breeders of Moluccan Cockatoos (endangered by trade) were among those most likely to claim that captive breeding was conservation.

Hybridising is another irresponsible action that contradicts the statement that captive breeding is conservation. This commonly occurs with macaws, especially in the USA. Threatened species such as Scarlet, Military, Great Green, and even the Hyacinthine, are involved. Hybrids are given names such as Harlequin, Ruby and Camelot Macaws, as though they are genuine species. Hybridising seriously undermines the credibility of aviculturists.

Transmitters tested on captive macaws

During the 1990s radio telemetry was increasingly used in researching the biology of endangered parrot species. Macaws are difficult to study, because they range over such big distances and spend much time high in the forest canopy. Telemetry was used to track the ranges of some parrots but a transmitter had never been successfully fitted to a large macaw. Radio-transmitters had been fitted on Military Macaws in a reintroduction attempt in Guatemala, but the macaws destroyed them very quickly. With the help of an American macaw breeder, Joanne Abramson, a device was tested on her birds. Similar transmitters were then fitted to wild Great Green Macaws in Costa Rica to obtain information that was essential for their conservation.

■ *Great Green Macaw.*

A brass cylinder measuring 17mm x 40mm (3/4in x 1 3/4in) contained the transmitter, battery and a brass collar (1cm wide) that functioned as the antenna. The collar was permanently attached to one end of the cylinder; it fitted around the back of the macaw's neck and fastened on to the other end of the cylinder with a corrodible locking nut. The unit weighed about 3% of the macaw's body weight. For the first two years radio-tagging was limited to nestlings in order to avoid capturing adults. During the third year adults were trapped at the nest using a special kind of safe trap. (After several years no more macaws were fitted with transmitters.) The radio-tagged macaws were tracked in off-road vehicles. This method collected invaluable information and would not have been possible without the help of an aviculturist.

Endangered species in captivity

Most parrot breeders know something of the plight of some threatened and endangered parrots, such as the Moluccan Cockatoo and Spix's Macaw, but they have not heard of many of the parrot species that are globally threatened with extinction. Globally means threatened throughout their range, not just in part of the range, such as the Scarlet Macaw in Central America.

Some of these threatened species have never been kept in captivity and others are represented by only a handful of specimens. Many aviculturists might be surprised to know that of the 89 species listed as endangered or threatened* only 54 are known in aviculture or in captivity plus another ten species represented by 20 birds or fewer. (The numbers are so small as to be unsustainable in aviculture.)

The Maroon-fronted Parrot (*Rhynchopsitta terrisi*) (see colour page 13) is the sister species to the Thick-bill. It was kept in one collection in its native Mexico (with government approval) during the 1990s. Otherwise almost unknown in captivity, Fundación Ara had acquired confiscated birds or those that had been picked up injured from the forest floor. This private collection was disbanded in the late 1990s. The fate of those birds is unknown. It illustrates how

rare and important birds in private hands are dependent on the whim of the individual.

In the list on pages 153–154 the double asterisk denotes species that were represented only in government hands: three species in New Zealand, two in Australia, one in Mauritius and one for the United States. Echo Parakeets do not exist in private aviculture; all belong to a breeding programme that is an integrated part of the species recovery programme, as is also the case with the Puerto Rican Amazon. The government programmes are in the more affluent countries because most countries in the tropics cannot afford to invest large sums in bird conservation.

During the 1980s the Cuban government considered the idea of captive breeding of its two endemic parrots (the third, the macaw, is extinct). It consulted with a leading aviculturist in the USA. Regrettably for the Cuban Conure, nothing came of this. Its situation has worsened since then. Conures breed readily in captivity and captive breeding might have ensured that it remained extant – in cages. Although it survived in some reserves, loss of nesting sites was a major problem, partly due to hurricane damage to trees. The Cuban government could have spent large sums on a captive breeding programme for the Amazon – but would there have been any point when so many exist in aviculture in the USA and in Eastern Europe? In this case aviculturists have perhaps saved a government time and money.

The species for which captive breeding programmes might be most useful are those which

- are members of a genus which is known to breed readily in captivity;
- are seriously threatened by loss of habitat;
- have a small range in the wild.

For example, the *Pyrrhura* conures (small neotropical parakeets) are all prolific breeders in captivity. The four Endangered or Vulnerable members of the genus listed on page 154 that were not represented in aviculture, fill all the above criteria. However, they come from Colombia and Ecuador where aviculture is not well established, thus *in situ* breeding programmes might not be successful. But even

---

* Source: *Threatened Birds of the World*, BirdLife International, 2000.

if they were, how could captive-bred conures be released when the reason the species were endangered was deforestation?

Assessment of endangered parrots in aviculture

There are 54 threatened or endangered species in private aviculture. I assess that a maximum of only 34 species would be sustainable for more than 20 years without relying on wild-caught birds to bolster declining captive populations. These species are indicated #. This is an optimistic assessment, especially in the case of the *Cacatua* cockatoos. Most hand-reared males are not suitable for breeding purposes so short-term continuity depends on the longevity of wild-caught males in breeding situations, because more than 90% (probably nearer 95%) of young produced by the end of the century were hand-reared.

The most important factor overall that has resulted in parrots becoming endangered is loss of habitat. There might be some rare cases in which habitat loss is reversed or where a population could be established on an island – not necessarily currently inhabited by that species but not inhabited by a competing species. However, this should not be too far in the future because multi-generations of captive breeding can produce birds that are no longer fit for survival in their natural habitat. For example, thousands of captive-bred Hawaiian Geese (*Branta sandvicensis*) have been returned to Hawaii. Few survived, partly due to the fact that inbreeding (pairing closely related birds) caused an alteration in the structure of the down in goslings, which rendered them unfit for survival. In-breeding leads to loss of genetic variability, resulting in poor fertility and hatchability and possibly alterations to their genes that would threaten their survival in the wild. Some private breeders pair brother to sister or sell siblings without informing the buyer of their relationship. Such irresponsible actions can ultimately adversely affect the long-term survival of a species in aviculture.

I believe that captive breeding of endangered species that have had small or fragmented populations over a long period of time has a high chance of failure. This is due to loss of genetic variation. Examples are the *Vini* lories endemic to small Pacific islands. For example, breeding the Tahiti Blue Lory (*Vini peruviana*) has been beset with problems.

There is one way in which aviculturists could have a very positive impact on conservation. They could donate 1% of the annual income from the sale of their young parrots to a conservation organisation or project. If every breeder had done so, millions of dollars or pounds would have been raised by the end of the century. In fact enormous sums from captive breeding have been raised only by one organisation: Loro Parque Foundation (see Chapter 13).

Captive breeding of privately owned parrots is not conservation: we know this now. But the existence of large captive stocks of some species *might* one day somehow be of benefit for their future survival.

■ *Tahiti Blue Lory, captive-bred.*

GLOBALLY THREATENED PARROTS

+   Classified as Vulnerable (other species listed are Endangered or Critically Endangered).

\#   Likely to survive in aviculture for more than 20 years without importation (author's assessment).

**   Species that exist only in government-sponsored aviaries, not in private aviculture.

In aviculture	Not represented in aviculture
Red and Blue Lory *(Eos histrio)*+	Kuhl's or Rimatara Lory *(Vini kuhlii)*
Black-winged Lory *(Eos cyanogenia)*+	Stephen's Lory *(Vini stepheni)*+
Chattering Lory *(Lorius garrulus)* #	Ultramarine Lory *(Vini ultramarina)*
Purple-naped Lory *(Lorius domicella)*+	Palm Lorikeet *(Charmosyna palmarum)*+
	Blue-fronted Lorikeet *(Charmosyna toxopei)*
	New Caledonian Lorikeet *(Charmosyna diadema)*
	Red-throated Lorikeet *(Charmosyna amabilis)*

Carnaby's Black Cockatoo *(Calyptorhynchus latirostris)*
Lesser Sulphur-crested Cockatoo *(Cacatua sulphurea sulphurea)* #
Citron-crested Cockatoo *(Cacatua sulphurea citrinocristata)* #
Moluccan or Salmon-crested Cockatoo *(Cacatua moluccensis)*+ #
Umbrella or White Cockatoo *(Cacatua alba)*+ #
Philippine or Red-vented Cockatoo *(Cacatua haematuropygia)* #
Kea *(Nestor notabilis)*+ #
Kaka *(Nestor meridionalis)*+**
Salvadori's Fig Parrot *(Psittaculirostris salvadorii)*+

Blue-headed Racket-tail *(Prioniturus platenae)*+
Blue-winged Racket-tail *(Prioniturus verticalis)*
Black-lored Parrot *(Tanygnathus gramineus)*+

Pesquet's Parrot *(Psittrichas fulgidus)*+
Red Shining Parrot *(Prosopeia splendens)*+
Barraband's Parakeet or Superb Parrot *(Polytelis swainsonii)*+ #
Antipodes Island Parakeet *(Cyanoramphus unicolor)*+ **
Golden-shouldered Parakeet *(Psephotus c.chrysopterygius)* #
Norfolk Island Parakeet *(Cyanoramphus cookii)***
Horned Parakeet *(Eunymphicus cornutus)* #
Orange-bellied Parakeet *(Neophema chrysogaster)* ** #
Swift Parakeet *(Lathamus discolor)* #

Night Parrot or Parakeet *(Geopsittacus occidentalis)*

Kakapo *(Strigops habroptilus)* **
Black-cheeked Lovebird *(Agapornis nigrigenis)*+ #

Sangihe Hanging Parrot *(Loriculus catamene)*
Wallace's Hanging Parrot *(Loriculus flosculus)*

Echo Parakeet *(Psittacula eques)* **
Hyacinthine Macaw *(Anodorhynchus hyacinthinus)* #
Lear's Macaw *(Anodorhynchus leari)*
Spix's Macaw *(Cyanospitta spixii)* #
Blue-throated Macaw *(Ara glaucogularis)* #
Military Macaw *(Ara militaris)*+ #
Great Green or Buffon's Macaw *(Ara ambigua)* #
Red-fronted Macaw *(Ara rubrogenys)* #

In aviculture

Illiger's or Blue-winged Macaw *(Propyrrhura maracana)*+ #
Golden or Queen of Bavaria's Conure *(Guaruba guarouba)* #

Cuban Conure *(Aratinga euops)*

Hispaniolan Conure *(Aratinga chloroptera)*+
Golden-capped Conure *(Aratinga auricapilla)*+ #

Thick-billed Parrot *(Rhynchopsitta pachyrhyncha)* #?
Blue-throated Conure *(Pyrrhura cruentata)*+ #

Yellow-faced Parrotlet *(Forpus xanthops)*
Grey-cheeked Parakeet *(Brotogeris pyrrhopterus)*

Yellow-billed Amazon *(Amazona collaria)*+ #
Hispaniolan Amazon *(Amazona ventralis)*+ #
Puerto Rican Parrot *(Amazona vittata)* ** #
Red Spectacled Amazon *(Amazona pretrei)* #
Green-cheeked or Red-crowned Amazon *(Amazona viridigenalis)* #
Red-browed Amazon *(Amazona rhodocorytha)* #
Red-tailed Amazon *(Amazona brasiliensis)* #
Yellow-faced Amazon *(Amazona xanthops)*+ #
Yellow-shouldered Amazon *(Amazona barbadensis)*+ #
Double Yellow-headed Amazon *(Amazona [ochrocephala] oratrix)* #
Vinaceous Amazon *(Amazona vinacea)*
St Lucia Parrot *(Amazona versicolor)*+
Red-necked Amazon *(Amazona arausiaca)*+
St Vincent Parrot *(Amazona guildingii)*+ #
Purple-bellied Parrot *(Triclaria malachitacea)*+#

Twenty legal specimens or fewer in captivity

Tahiti Blue Lory *(Vini peruviana)*
Green Racket-tail *(Prioniturus luconensis)*
Masked Shining Parrot *(Prosopeia personata)*
Forbes' Parakeet *(Cyanoramphus forbesi)* **
Orange-fronted Parakeet *(Cyanoramphus malherbi)* **
Ouvea Parakeet *(Eunymphicus uvaeensis)*
Maroon-fronted Parrot *(Rhynchopsitta terrisi)*+
Saffron-headed Parrot *(Pionopsitta pyrilia)*+
Black-billed Amazon *(Amazona agilis)*
Imperial Parrot *(Amazona imperialis)***

Not represented in aviculture

Socorro Conure *(Aratinga brevipes)*

Golden-plumed Parakeet *(Leptosittaca branickii)*+

Yellow-eared Parrot *(Ognorhynchus icterotis)*

Santa Marta Parakeet *(Pyrrhura viridicata)*
El Oro Parakeet *(Pyrrhura orcesi)*
White-necked Parakeet *(Pyrrhura albipectus)*+
Flame-winged parakeet *(Pyrrhura calliptera)*+
Rufous-fronted Parakeet *(Bolborhynchus ferrugineifrons)*

Red-fronted Parrotlet *(Touit costaricensis)*+
Brown-backed Parrotlet *(Touit melanonota)*
Golden-tailed Parrotlet *(Touit surda)*
Spot-winged Parrotlet *(Touit stictoptera)*+
Rusty-faced Parrot *(Hapalopsittaca amazonina)*
Fuertes' Parrot *(Hapalopsittaca fuertesi)*
Red-faced Parrot *(Hapalopsittaca pyrrhops)*+

■ *Vinaceous Amazon.*

PART II.

CONSERVATION

■ *Cuban Macaw.*
Illustration: Bernd Gerischer

11. DECLINE AND CONSERVATION

At the beginning of the 20th century a recent macaw extinction should have sounded warning bells. It might have done so in a few quarters but there was no international conservation movement. Indeed, the word conservation as applied to nature was unknown. In the magazine *Bird Notes* (June 1922) Dr Casey A. Wood lamented the extinction of the Cuban Macaw (*Ara tricolor*) in 1864. He wrote: "It seems outrageous that these lovely and sensitive animals should be treated by both natives and (some) whites as game birds, and that the edible quality of the parrot should be partly responsible for his extermination."

The Cuban Macaw was larger than a Severe Macaw but considerably smaller than a Red-fronted. Its plumage was unusual, with red forehead and underparts, yellow nape and hindneck. The feathers of the upper back were maroon, edged with greenish and the lesser wing coverts were brown with reddish margins. The upper surface of the tail was maroon, shading into bright blue and the under surface was golden orange-red. It is a tragedy when any bird becomes extinct – and one so beautiful!

Alas, Dr Wood's thinking was far ahead of his times. He quoted Austin H. Clark, writing in 1905 of the parrots in the Caribbean region, that "their conversational powers and their reputation as pets led to wholesale traffic in immature birds, and their nesting places were so constantly watched that scarcely any of the young were allowed to go free. Then, again, parrots are particular about their food, and

betray their presence by the litter of torn fruit on the ground about trees in which they habitually feed. Once such a tree is discovered all the (pot) hunter has to do is to sit nearby and shoot the birds as they fly in".

"Scarcely any of the young were allowed to go free" still applied at the end of the century to certain popular companion species, such as Yellow-naped and Double Yellow-headed Amazons which by then, were endangered by removal of chicks from the nest. As a group, parrots were, by the year 2000, the most endangered birds in the world, with 90 species, that is 26%, threatened with extinction. This compared with 11% for bird species as a whole. Another 40 parrot species (11%) were listed as "Near-threatened". IUCN (the International Union for the Conservation of Nature) defines Near-threatened as close to qualifying for the status of Vulnerable. Vulnerable is defined as a species facing a high risk of extinction in the wild in the medium-term future, e. g., the Black-cheeked Lovebird and the Yellow-shouldered Amazon.

The destruction of tropical rainforests during the last half of the 20th century was so serious that, worldwide, thousands of birds, animals, insects and plants came close to extinction. Despite this, many people denied that it was a period of ecological collapse. During the last two decades of the century many field studies were carried out (some on-going) to determine the conservation status of different species. The results were shocking. Unless attitudes change, especially those of politicians and heads of industries, many of the world's most extraordinary and loved birds, the parrots, are doomed to extinction.

> The decline of most species has been caused by one or more of the following factors:
> - Introduced predators (including man with gun)
> - Loss of habitat
> - Trapping for trade (see Chapter 7)

Introduced predators

New Zealand was one of the first countries where parrots lost most of their natural habitats *and* were fighting for survival against introduced mammals. In January 1916 a Sydney newspaper reported an extraordinary find:

"Mr R. Clouston, a mining engineer, recently made a remarkable discovery of bird life near Rockville, in the Nelson district, while exploring the ranges. Mr Clouston discovered an entire colony of birds of rare species, including thousands of kiwis and kakapos [both flightless nocturnal species]. The latter bird is so rare that recently an advertisement was published which offered £80 for one of its kind."

"Mr Clouston declares that he had not seen anything like the collection before. He secured a number of kiwis which he placed on the Little Barrier. 'Not only are there kiwis and kakapos,' he says, 'but dozens of mountain duck, saddle backs (worth £10

■ *Once the Kakapo needed nothing more than good camouflage to protect it.*

each), New Zealand robins, wrens, owls, coots, petrels (rain birds), keas, kakas, tui, makomakos, warblers, riflemen, creepers (rare), maori hens, fantails, tomtits, and pigeons. It was a harvest of rarities.'"

How sad that the monetary value of dead birds was mentioned! As a result of Mr Clouston's discovery, the New Zealand government paid him an annual warden's allowance until about 1932 on the Gouland Downs, north-west of Nelson. In the early 1920s he was instructed to catch some Kakapo and move them to small islands, but this did not occur. Don Merton (saviour of the Kakapo, see Chapter 17) told me that in 1958 an expedition (of which he was a member) visited the Gouland Downs to look for Kakapo. No recent sign of them was found. That they had once been common was evident by the presence of the unique "track and bowl" systems made by males as part of their courtship routine.

Parrot species that are confined to islands, even large ones such as New Zealand, are especially vulnerable. They cannot expand their range; if they occur in a small area that is deforested, or if they are persecuted, they are doomed. The Kakapo was exterminated from the two main islands by introduced predators, including stoats, and exists only on island reserves that have been cleared of introduced animals – at enormous expense. In Polynesia the exquisitely beautiful Ultramarine Lory (*Vini ultramarina*) (see colour page 14) was exterminated from all but one island by introduced rats.

The medium-sized green *Cyanoramphus* parakeets, including the Kakarikis known in aviculture, are found in New Zealand and the Pacific. The Norfolk Island Parakeet (*Cyanoramphus [novaezelandiae] cookii*) occurs only on the island of that name which covers just 14 square miles (36 sq km). It is located 465 miles (744km) west of the northernmost coast of New Zealand. Closely related to the Red-fronted Kakariki, it is sometimes considered as a sub-species. Its problems started in 1788 when a penal settlement was established on the island, which is Australian territory. This was abandoned in 1813 but in 1825 a second period of penal activities commenced and later descendants of the Bounty mutineers settled there. In times of food shortages birds were killed for food and predators, such as rats, were introduced. By 1908 the parakeets were rare and a special protection order was issued. The rich volcanic soil made the island ideal for cultivation, especially of bananas, and resulted in the destruction of the thick sub-tropical rainforest with which it was originally covered. Transect counts in 1978 suggested that 28 to 30 Norfolk Island Parakeets had survived. Their numbers were kept at a low level by competition from the abundant introduced Crimson Rosellas (Pennant's Parakeets).

▌ *Crimson Rosella.*

A recovery programme commenced in 1983 and included captive breeding, rat-poisoning, installing rat-proof nesting hollows and cat trapping within the national park. From 13 breeding pairs in 1996, the population increased dramatically. This parakeet is not found in captivity outside Norfolk Island.

Death by shooting

During the 20th century the availability of firearms made it easy to kill large parrots for food. In the previous century hundreds of thousands of Carolina Parakeet were shot in the United States, contributing to its extinction in the 20th century (see Chapter 17). For centuries parrots had been hunted – but not on a scale large enough to threaten their survival. As Gilbert White wrote in *The Natural History of Selbourne*, "... there is such an inherent spirit for hunting in human nature, as scarce any inhibitions can restrain."

In the United States the loud calls and noisy habits of America's only surviving native parrot drew the attention of gun-wielding frontiersmen. With the most northerly

distribution of any neotropical parrot, the Thick-billed (*Rhynchopsitta pachyrhyncha*) had occurred in Arizona and New Mexico. In the early years of the century soldiers, woodsmen and miners shot out of existence everything in the region that could be eaten: wild turkey, elk, pronghorn antelope and bighorn sheep. Along with them went the Thick-bill. It didn't stand a chance. In 1986 this parrot was the subject of a reintroduction attempt in Arizona. Sadly it was a total failure. But help for this species was to come a decade later (see page 171), when significant progress in parrot conservation had occurred.

Fund-raising

The World Parrot Trust's magazine, *PsittaScene*, was the first publication devoted to parrot conservation. Through its pages, appeals for funds or for equipment for conservation projects were successful. In the early days of The Trust, Paradise Park's free-flying eagles were used to raise funds. This UK bird park housed (and still houses) the Trust's headquarters. By the end of the century several organisations worldwide had invested significant sums of money in parrot conservation. Smaller groups raised funds and supported selected projects. Zoos were involved, either with a WPT collecting box or by fund-raising for specific projects. This alerted members of the public to the endangered status of many parrots.

Appropriately, parrots were used as fund-raisers. Some zoos made significant contributions to conservation through their bird shows. The presenters mentioned the plight of certain endangered species and invited contributions. At Paradise Park a Galah (Rose-breasted Cockatoo) called Billy started to collect £1 coins from visitors in the summer of 1999. They lined up for the privilege! He dropped the coins into a WPT collecting box – and raised £12,000 during the first two years! (By February 2006, when a Goffin's and a Lesser Sulphur-crested Cockatoo had joined Billy, more than £41,000 had been collected in this way.)

Combined threats

Destruction of habitat and trapping were the most common threats to parrots. Most species could cope with both on the scale that occurred

Paradise Park's curator David Woolcock trained the Galah to collect coins for the World Parrot Trust.

until the 20th century. When a species was suddenly confronted with both problems, its population declined rapidly. In Brazil the Red-tailed Amazon (*Amazona brasiliensis*) came under enormous pressure from trapping of adults, theft of chicks, and loss of habitat during the 1980s and 1990s. Paolo Martuscelli, who lived and worked with this Amazon, stated that land clearance was a major threat. From 1985 to 1990, 4.8 sq miles (12.5 sq km) of lowland and mangrove forests were destroyed in Sao Paulo – a 1.27% decrease in available habitat. During 1991–1994, all 49 nests studied by Martuscelli failed; 41 nests were robbed for the

pet trade. This was a recent problem, unknown in a commercial sense prior to 1980. It was made worse by poachers destroying some nest trees in order to reach the chicks. Such was the competition between nest thieves that chicks were taken at an increasingly early age, resulting in higher mortality. In some areas there was no recruitment at all of young birds into the population. In the 21st century conservation education could be a major force in saving this species (see Chapter 12).

Loss of habitat

At the beginning of the 20th century the human population was estimated at 1.5 billion; at the end there were 8 billion people on the planet. The advent of air transport and the increased human population put intense pressure on every kind of habitat in which parrots were found. During the last two decades, fieldwork became possible, also urgent, because formerly inaccessible areas were opened up by logging. In New Guinea, teams of researchers worked literally a few feet in front of bulldozers, recording for the first and last time in history the flora and fauna (about to be obliterated for ever). Forests and their inhabitants, which had evolved over millions of years, were wiped out in minutes to satisfy worldwide demand for hardwoods and to make a few men rich.

In northern Colombia, in the Magdalena region which had been so rich in bird life, nearly 4 million hectares of humid lowland forest were destroyed in little more than a decade from the 1960s in an internationally-financed colonisation programme. The most important areas of rainforest had existed in the Amazon region, in Indonesia and in central Africa. By the end of the century destruction of all rainforests was so serious that 45 parrot species had been assigned a threat status primarily due to loss of habitat. The species were as follows:

Rainforest in Papua New Guinea.

32 The Cuban Conure (*Aratinga euops*) does not interest aviculturists although it is an endangered species (CHAPTER 10). **33** The Kakapo (*Strigops habroptilus*) is the world's strangest parrot and one of the most endangered (CHAPTER 11). **34** Maroon-fronted Parrots from Mexico (*Rhynchopsitta terrisi*) are virtually unknown in aviculture (CHAPTER 10).

Painting: Bernd Gerischer

35 The survival of the rare Ultramarine Lories (*Vini ultramarina*) depends on the islands on which they live remaining rat-free (CHAPTER 11).

36 A huge decline in Red-tailed Amazons from Brazil was caused by illegal trapping and theft of chicks from nests (CHAPTER 11). **37** Blue-rumped Parrots (*Psittinus cyanurus*) are threatened by habitat loss (CHAPTER 11). **38** Black-cheeked Lovebirds (*Agapornis nigrigenis*) feeding on the cereal sorghum in Zambia (CHAPTER 14). **39** Within the space of a decade, the Red and Blue Lory (*Eos histrio*) was almost trapped to extinction (CHAPTER12).

Photo: Louise Warburton

🟤**40** St Vincent Parrots (*Amazona guilldingii*) in the aviary on their native island. 🟤**41** A bus decorated with an attractive motif, sponsored by the **World Parrot Trust**, was used to promote awareness of the parrot's plight (CHAPTER 12).

THREATENED BY HABITAT LOSS

Species		Threat status

AUSTRALASIA

Carnaby's (Short-billed) Black Cockatoo	*(Calyptorhynchus latirostris)*	Vulnerable
Major Mitchell's Cockatoo	*(Cacatua leadbeateri)*	Near-threatened
Mindanao (Mount Apo) Lorikeet	*(Trichoglossus johnstoniae)*	Vulnerable
Chatham Island Parakeet	*(Cyanoramphus forbesi)*	Endangered
Orange-fronted or Malherbe's Parakeet	*(Cyanoramphus malherbi)*	Critical
Hooded Parakeet (Parrot)	*(Psephotus dissimilis)*	Near-threatened
Golden-shouldered Parakeet (Parrot)	*(Psephotus chrysopterygius)*	Endangered
Turquoisine Parakeet (Parrot)	*(Neophema pulchella)*	Near-threatened
Swift Parakeet (Parrot)	*(Lathamus discolor)*	Vulnerable
Night Parrot	*(Geopsittacus occidentalis)*	Critical
Sulu Racket-tail	*(Prioniturus verticalis)*	Endangered
Superb Parrot (Barraband's Parakeet)	*(Polytelis swainsonii)*	Vulnerable
Echo (Mauritius) Parakeet	*(Psittacula eques)*	Critical
Sangihe Hanging Parrot	*(Loriculus catamene)*	Endangered
Wallace's Hanging Parrot	*(Loriculus flosculus)*	Endangered

SOUTH and CENTRAL AMERICA

Great Green Macaw	*(Ara ambigua)*	Vulnerable
Socorro Conure	*(Aratinga brevipes)*	Endangered
Hispaniolan Conure	*(Aratinga chloroptera)*	Vulnerable
Golden-capped Conure	*(Aratinga auricapilla)*	Vulnerable
Golden-plumed Parakeet	*(Leptosittaca branickii)*	Vulnerable
Yellow-eared Parrot	*(Ognorhynchus icterotis)*	Critical
Thick-billed Parrot	*(Rhynchopsitta pachyrhyncha)*	Endangered
Maroon-fronted Parrot	*(Rhynchopsitta terrisi)*	Endangered
Blue-throated Conure	*(Pyrrhura cruentata)*	Vulnerable
Santa Marta Conure	*(Pyrhura viridicata)*	Endangered
El Oro Conure	*(Pyrrhura orcesi)*	Endangered
White-necked Conure	*(Pyrrhura albipectus)*	Vulnerable
Flame-winged Conure	*(Pyrrhura calliptera)*	Vulnerable
Rufous-fronted Parakeet	*(Bolborhynchus ferrugineifrons)*	Endangered
Red-fronted Parrotlet	*(Touit costaricensis)*	Vulnerable
Brown-backed Parrotlet	*(Touit melanonotus)*	Endangered
Golden-tailed Parrotlet	*(Touit surda)*	Endangered
Spot-winged Parrotlet	*(Touit stictoptera)*	Vulnerable
Rusty-faced Parrot	*(Hapalopsittaca amazonina)*	Endangered
Fuertes' Parrot	*(Hapalopsittaca fuertesi)*	Critical
Red-faced Parrot	*(Hapalopsittaca pyrrhops)*	Vulnerable
Black-billed Amazon	*(Amazona agilis)*	Vulnerable
Puerto Rican Parrot	*(Amazona vittata)*	Critical
Red-browed Amazon	*(Amazona rhodocorytha)*	Endangered
St Lucia Parrot	*(Amazona versicolor)*	Vulnerable
Red-necked Parrot	*(Amazona arausiaca)*	Vulnerable
Imperial Parrot	*(Amazona imperialis)*	Endangered
Yellow-faced Amazon	*(Amazona xanthops)*	Vulnerable
Purple-bellied Parrot	*(Triclaria malachitacea)*	Vulnerable

The above might appear to indicate that habitat loss was most serious in the neotropics but this was the area where most studies occurred. Many more parrots in, for example, Indonesia might be added if and when fieldwork is carried out.

Parrot conservation starts

While many groups of birds had been studied intensively by scientists for decades, there had been long-standing neglect of parrots by the scientific community. Not until the 1980s did this begin to change. Many parrot conservation programmes were initiated to try to stop the decline of various species. Different aspects were addressed: protecting habitat, declaring reserves or national parks, attempting to stop the capture, erecting nest-boxes, and protecting birds at their nest sites and roosting areas. Unusual measures were taken, such as growing food trees (licurí palms) for Lear's Macaws and planting wax palms for Yellow-eared Parrots (*Ognorhynchus icterotis*).

By the early 1980s it was known that certain parrot species were endangered or declining but there was no clear picture regarding the worldwide situation. Parrots are among the most difficult birds to study because of their excellent

■ *Growing wax palms in Colombia for Yellow-eared Parrots.*

camouflage, their mobility and in many cases, wide movements throughout their range. Except perhaps in Australia, one needs more than ornithological skills to observe parrots at their nests, or when they are feeding. The stamina of the fabled explorers of the past, combined with the climbing skills of a Sherpa, are often called for. Most parrots breed at heights of 50ft (15m) or more, in locations where flooded forest, snakes, and trees protected by giant thorns, are likely to be encountered before nests can be located. In some areas such work is made almost impossible by the presence of drug barons.

Parrots were one of the least studied groups in the avian world. In 1992 scientists admitted: "There have been so few detailed studies of psittacines in the wild that parrot biology could be considered one of the present 'frontiers' of ornithology" (Beissinger and Snyder, 1992). BirdLife International (then ICBP) was funding and implementing countless field studies throughout the world, only one of which focused on a parrot species.

The shocking truth emerged: as a group, the parrots were the most endangered of all birds. Published information on the subject proliferated, in papers and in notable works of reference, especially in Volume 4 of that landmark series *Handbook of the Birds of the World*, and in the 852-page book *Threatened Birds of the World* published in 2000. The latter volume revealed that 15 parrots species were critically endangered, that is, they had an estimated 50% chance of surviving in the wild over the next three generations. Thirty-one species were assessed as endangered, with an estimated 20% chance of becoming extinct in the wild in the next 20 years. Forty-six were listed as Vulnerable, with an estimated 10% chance of becoming extinct in the wild during the next 100 years. Nearly as many were listed as Near-threatened (close to qualifying as Vulnerable).

The World Parrot Trust

By the 1980s an organisation solely concerned with parrot conservation was desperately needed. There would be so much to do. Where would one start and how could such an organisation gain credibility? If the established wildlife and bird conservation organisations had made no attempt, or attempted and failed, to conserve parrots, could a new organisation

▌*Mike Reynolds, founder of the World Parrot Trust.*

started by one man with his own funds, succeed? It could and it did.

Mike Reynolds, owner of Paradise Park in the UK, founded The World Parrot Trust in 1989. "Parrots are important because their beauty, character and adaptability have won them a special place in the hearts and minds of our species," wrote Mike Reynolds, director of the Trust until he retired in 2001. "Through this special relationship the parrots have the opportunity – not yet fully realised – to make people aware of the appalling speed at which so many wild and unspoiled places in the world are being ruined. We see the parrots as ecological 'pathfinders', leading the way to a wider understanding of what is at risk: nothing less than the survival of our planet." (*PsittaScene*, November 1992).

Mike Reynolds' statement focused on the fact that parrot conservation is, in the long term, also assisting the future of the human race. Ultimately the survival of man and that of most of the parrots depends on the same factor – the preservation of large tracts of rainforest (often described as the lungs of the world) and other habitats. Destruction of forests affects rainfall, causing drought and flooding, famine and disease. Many such catastrophes originate from deforestation.

Such events made headlines across the world because they touched or claimed the lives of so many humans. But few gave a thought to why they happened; many people believed that they were "acts of God". In fact most "natural" catastrophes resulted from man's abuse of the environment. Tropical forests were destroyed to grow sugar cane, bananas or plantations of oil palms, or to create grazing for cattle.

Loss of habitat

Destruction of forests and other habitats became the primary reason for declining populations. Deforestation resulted in easier access for trappers, or its scale was so serious that little habitat survived. Selective felling of trees usually targeted the larger specimens – those that were old enough to form holes in which parrots could nest. This had a serious impact on some species. In the earliest investigation of availability of nest sites, that of the Puerto Rican Parrot in 1978, only one suitable cavity every four hectares was found (Wiley, 1981 *in* Pasquier, ed, *Conservation of New World Parrots*). During field studies of Carnaby's Black Cockatoo, the annual rate of loss of nesting hollows at two sites in the wheat belt of Western Australia, was 4.8% and 2.2%, exceeding the rates of formation of hollows (Saunders, 1979).

Mauritius

In Mauritius, former home of the Dodo, the Echo Parakeet (*Psittacula eques*) was reduced to fewer than 20 individuals between the late 1970s

▌*Echo Parakeets, captive-bred in Mauritius.*

and the early 1990s. Most of its habitat had been replaced by sugar cane. Exotic plants invaded the small area of surviving forest; this was weeded by hand to save the critically endangered birds that survived there. The Echo Parakeet became the first species to be assisted by the World Parrot Trust and, eventually, Mauritius became the *cause célèbre* in bird conservation circles. The parakeet, plus the Mauritius Kestrel and the Pink Pigeon, were saved by restoration of habitat, management of wild pairs and captive breeding on the island. All were all thriving in the wild at the century's end.

South America

Loss of habitat was occurring wherever parrots existed. In 1990 seventeen parrot species in the neotropics were assessed as being endangered primarily due to habitat destruction[2] (Collar and Juniper, *in* Beissinger and Snyder, 1992). All were the subject of fieldwork and their status was watched with concern. There were more parrot conservation projects in South America than in any other continent – not because there are more parrot species but due to the proximity to North America where many students and scientists were involved in fieldwork.

Over-exploitation of forests occurred because people lacked land titles or legal land tenure, said Charles Munn. "Instead, the forest and its renewable resources belong to a nebulous, sometimes oppressive government or a wealthy, absentee landlord. There is no incentive for the poor forest dwellers to manage the forest for medium and long-term gain. Rather, their best strategy is usually 'grab it before my neighbour does'..." (Munn, 1992). The conservation crisis of parrots is likely to continue until means are found to counter this basic problem, he said. "It is time that conservation strategies be founded on the principles of selfishness and greed, human traits that are difficult to overestimate."

Munn proved that titling large areas of intact forest to local peoples and helping them to set up tourists' visits to clay licks protected macaws and the rainforest on which they depended (see Chapter 18).

Caribbean islands

The Caribbean islands form an area of particular interest; mention is made elsewhere of the Cuban, Hispaniolan and Puerto Rican parrots, that is, those of the Greater Antilles. The larger, handsome parrots of the Lesser Antilles, such as the St Vincent (see colour pages 10 and 16), attracted most attention. Each of the main Caribbean islands has or had one or, in two cases, two endemic Amazon parrots. Sadly, the species found on Martinique and Guadeloupe are long extinct.

The survival of the others caused concern early in the 20th century, partly because of the vulnerability of small populations to hurricanes and volcano eruptions, and because of the high incidence of shooting. During the century, threats to these parrots shifted until by the 1970s, illegal trapping and habitat destruction were the primary factors endangering their survival. Parrot conservation education was born here, on St Lucia, and successfully copied on other islands (see Chapter 12). It saved the parrots of St Vincent and St Lucia.

However, as the threat of illegal capture receded, habitat destruction increased. On St Vincent human dwellings were erected higher and higher into the mountains, where the parrot that had once inhabited the lowlands, had been pushed. Nevertheless, at the end of the century the population of the magnificent, colourful St Vincent Parrot (*Amazona guildingii*) was believed to be stable at about 530 birds. Then a new threat erupted. The mountainous spine of the island had provided protection for the parrots for millennia so a proposal to construct a road east to west across the mountains, was devastating news, fiercely opposed in some quarters. The idea was that it would be financed by a loan from the Republic of China. Road construction would cause disturbance and settlement, and illegal taking of parrot chicks from previously inaccessible areas.

In the early 1990s the future of the St Vincent Parrot had given some cause for hope. Now it was suddenly in doubt again. Following the increasing clearing of forest for the illegal

---

[2] Branicki's Conure, Yellow-eared Parrot, Maroon-fronted Parrot, four *Pyrrhura* conures (Crimson-bellied, El Oro, White-breasted and Brown-breasted), Rufous-fronted Parakeet, three species of *Touit* parrotlets (Brown-backed, Golden-tailed and Spot-winged), three species of *Hapalopsittaca* (Rusty-faced, Indigo-winged and Red-faced), Pretre's Amazon, Vinaceous Amazon and Purple-bellied Parrot.

Human habitation encroaches into parrot habitat in the mountains of St Vincent.

growing of marijuana, the threat of road construction was a most serious issue. The increasing rate of soil erosion and tree root instability caused by introduced armadillos was another concern. Here was a lesson in how quickly an apparent conservation success story can be reversed.

The national bird of Dominica in the Lesser Antilles (not to be confused with the Dominican Republic in the Greater Antilles) is the Imperial Amazon. Its large size, 18in (45cm), purple head and underparts with an unusual iridescent sheen, and imperious manner, set it apart from all other Amazons. It shuns humans, living in the most remote and inaccessible areas, unlike its congener, the Red-necked Amazon, who tolerates man.

Sparsely distributed across vast, mature mountain rainforest, the Imperial is shy, reclusive and difficult to study. Its stronghold, Morne Diablotin in the north, is rugged, steep and partly inaccessible. It was confined to this area after Hurricane David hit Dominica in 1979. The most devastating hurricane in the island's recorded history, it killed many parrots, leaving a remnant population of Imperials close to extinction. When I had the good fortune to see this magnificent parrot in 1980, my sighting was tinged with sadness. At the time it was believed to be the most endangered parrot of the neotropics. In December 2000 a small population of Imperials was seen on Morne Prosper, in the southern part of Morne Trois

Pitons National Park. Imperials were recolonising the southern part of the island! A population census was impossible (part of its habitat was impenetrable) but the Forestry, Wildlife and Parks Division personnel believed that by 2000 its population was stable or increasing.

In January 2000 a conservation milestone occurred, following a two-year, $1 million campaign spearheaded by the Rare Species Conservation Foundation in Florida and the Dominican government. Dominica formally declared the new Morne Diablotin National Park. It encompassed 8500 acres (3443 ha) of pristine rainforest and the principal nesting area of the Imperial Parrot.

Red-necked Amazon.

▌ *Tourism on Grand Cayman resulted in the destruction of mangroves and other coastal parrot habitats.*

How could its status be described as "vulnerable" (i. e., on a par with the Red-necked) in *Handbook of the Birds of the World*? The population was believed to number approximately 150 birds. When a species exists in such low numbers, a couple of devastating hurricanes could spell its extinction, thus the classification of Endangered would surely be more appropriate.

In contrast, the Red-necked Amazon rebounded more quickly after natural catastrophes. It lays three eggs (and usually fledges one or two young), and could exist in marginal and disturbed habitats. It often nested where there was easy access to cultivated fruits, thus even if the rainforest fruits fail, the young will be reared. A typical Amazon in appearance, with its mainly green plumage, some birds have pinkish-red on the throat (not the neck) and all have attractive blue head feathers. Widely distributed on Dominica, it was believed to number in the region of 800 birds at the end of the century, having made an excellent recovery after the hurricanes of the 1980s. Some of its habitat was lost to banana plantations but its future seems fairly secure.

The island of Grand Cayman lies between Cuba and Jamaica. Until the 1990s the beautiful Grand Cayman Amazon (*Amazona leucocephala*

caymanensis), which looks much like the Cuban Amazon, was classified as "game" to be shot. Hunters included G. Ray Arnett, the American Assistant Secretary of the Interior for Fish and Wildlife. At the time, he was responsible for protecting endangered species in the USA.

This Amazon's population increased during the 1990s, probably as the result of a new law that prohibited hunting. However, development of the island for tourism brought new hazards for the parrots. These included large quarry lorries that caused road kills, and the presence of hydro wires along roadsides. Loss of habitat forced parrots into prime fruit-growing areas and some farmers defied the law and shot parrots on their crops. On an island measuring only 23 miles (37km) in length, how long can parrots survive into the 21st century alongside tourists and farmers?

Indonesia

Indonesia's parrots received much less attention, partly because of the often difficult or dangerous political situation. The world's largest archipelago, Indonesia has a fascinating range of parrots within its 13,000 islands. They include cockatoos, lories, pygmy parrots, Eclectus, Great-billed and other *Tanygnathus*, tiny hanging parrots and racket-tailed parrots.

In the western extremity of Indonesia are found Asiatic *Psittacula* parakeets such as Moustache and Long-tailed. Indonesia can boast more parrot species than any other country – a total of 75, which is more even than Brazil and far more than Australia, with 52 species.

During the 1980s, huge areas of rainforest were destroyed by fire – 122,000 sq miles (195,000 sq km) in Kalimantan (formerly Borneo) and southern Sumatra alone. By 2000, Indonesia had more threatened bird species than any other country worldwide. If Kalimantan and Sumatra hardly receive a mention in these pages it is because they are poor in parrot species.

One parrot that was widespread, but listed as Near-threatened by the end of the century, was the Blue-rumped (*Psittinus cyanurus*). This little short-tailed parrot (see colour page 15) is probably destined to be driven high into the mountains, like the Amazons of the Caribbean. Forest destruction in the lowlands of the Sunda Islands (Sumatra, Java and Borneo, and the Lesser Sunda group that includes Java and Timor) was so extensive that it was predicted that all primary forest would be lost by 2010.

Timor in the Lesser Sunda Islands had dreadful political problems that prevented access by ornithologists for many years. In 1975 East Timor (the Portuguese part covering 7,300 sq miles) was invaded by troops from the western (Indonesian) part. Furious resistance from the Portuguese inhabitants resulted in 150,000 people (one quarter of the population) being slaughtered. Several parrot species are endemic to Timor (or its satellite islands). They include the Timor Crimson-winged Parakeet (*Aprosmictus jonquillensis*) and three *Trichoglossus* lorikeets: the Iris (*T. iris*), the Perfect (*T. euteles*) and Edwards' (*T. haematodus capistratus*).

Deforestation in the Lesser Sundas was severe. This fact and the extensive trapping and export of the *parvula* sub-species of the Lesser Sulphur-crested Cockatoo resulted in it and the other sub-species being classified as Critically Endangered.

For a decade or more it was perhaps the most commonly exported cockatoo. Most parrot keepers would have greeted with disbelief the suggestion that it was approaching extinction. In fact, *no other cockatoo* had its population reduced so catastrophically by trade.

To the east of Java are the islands of Bali and Lombok, the only places where Mitchell's Lorikeet (*Trichoglossus haematodus mitchellii*) was found. It might have become extinct on Bali, where hardly any forest survived, but apparently still existed high in the mountains of Lombok. One observer reported seeing 20 birds in a market there in 2003 (Tilford, pers. comm., 2004). Because it is a sub-species, it has received no attention from conservation organisations. A few birds survived in Europe where two or three keen breeders struggled to retain them in aviculture. Many problems were experienced, probably because of the small gene pool. During the 1960s and early 1970s this lorikeet was imported into Europe fairly frequently – but there were few lory breeders at that time and no hint of its endangered status.

Australia

In Australia vast tracts of land were irrigated to grow grain crops. In the wheat belt of Western Australia only small "islands" of forest survived within thousands of acres of cultivation, endangering the magnificent Carnaby's Black Cockatoo (*Calyptorhynchus latirostris*), one of the white-tailed forms. Between the 1970s and the 1990s, it disappeared from more than

▌*White-tailed Black Cockatoo.*

one third of its range. Breeding pairs had to fly so far to find food that chicks were left unattended in the nest for hours, incurring the risk of predation. Their growth rate was poor because they received less food. Fewer young fledged. The remaining fragments of habitat were threatened by increasing soil salinity and the invasion of weeds. A more sympathetic attitude towards the cockatoo was needed (see Chapter 12).

Parrots with specialised habitat requirements are extremely vulnerable. The Swift (*Lathamus discolor*) is a small parakeet with scarlet, yellow and blue head markings, scarlet under wing coverts and maroon tail feathers. It shared with the endangered Orange-bellied the habit of breeding only in Tasmania and migrating to south-eastern South Australia, Victoria and New South Wales. It also reached southern Queensland, including the Gold Coast – probably the longest migration undertaken by any parrot. By the end of the century its population was believed to be declining by more than 1% annually, and consisted of only about 1,300 pairs.

The reason for the decline was the rapidly disappearing habitat. In Tasmania the forests of blue gum (*Eucalyptus globulus*), on which Swift Parrots rely for food, occurred mostly on unprotected land. On the mainland the parrots were reliant on box-ironbark forest and most of that which remained was in highly fragmented blocks. Many of these trees were immature and provided less predictable nectar sources than

▌ *Double-eyed Fig Parrot from New Guinea.*

mature ones. At the beginning of the 21st century a Recovery Team for the Swift was working to identify areas of surviving habitat to try to alleviate the problems that this parakeet faces.

In Tasmania, Max and the late Bev Sharman, did more to conserve it than any government agency. In the mid-1980s they purchased 8,000 blue gum seedlings and distributed them to private landowners. By 1991, when Mrs Sharman died, she had distributed more than 30,000 blue gums. Visitors from all over the world congregated on their property, Forest Glen Bird Sanctuary, to watch these lovely parakeets arrive in their hundreds to be fed – six or seven times a day. They would stay for weeks!

Destruction of tropical rainforest is not exclusive to third world countries. In south-eastern Queensland it caused the decline to near extinction of Coxen's Fig Parrot (*Cyclopsitta diophthalma coxeni*). By the end of the century its population was estimated at 50 birds. The Queensland Department of Environment and Heritage formed a recovery plan in 1993. Its first objective was to locate living birds but a survey of its habitat carried out during 1993-95 failed to reveal any.

The nominate race, the 5in (13cm) long Double-eyed Fig Parrot occurs in New Guinea and has three sub-species in Australia; these are confined to three major tracts of tropical rainforest along the north-eastern coast (Forshaw, 2002). Two sub-species, Marshall's and the Red-browed, were quite common. Forshaw stated that further study might show that Coxen's should be considered as a separate species. Formerly it was found from near Bundaberg in Queensland to the Richmond River in New South Wales, from coastal and contiguous mountain forests. Coxen's Fig Parrot was common in the forests between Mary River, Bundaberg, and Port Macquarie then, in the 1920s, its habitat was virtually eliminated. As long ago as 1924 it was said to be in imminent danger of extinction. The remnant populations became more widely separated (disjunct) as lowland subtropical rainforest was cleared for agriculture.

At Currumbin Sanctuary in Queensland techniques for captive breeding of the Red-browed Fig Parrot were developed during the 1990s in case taking Coxen's into captivity is the last hope for its survival.

Threatened species not in decline

Species such as the Double-eyed Fig Parrot that has only one sub-species in a threat category were not included on the Threatened list which, at the end of the century, contained 125 of the 350 species of parrots. In some respects threat status does not tell the whole story. It needs to be considered along with the information given in *Threatened Birds of the World*; this indicates whether the overall population is declining, increasing or stable.

Status of parrots in 2000	
Endangered and Vulnerable	96 species
Declining	77
Increasing	9
Stable	6
Not specified	4

▌ *Golden-capped Conure.*

The species that were increasing were those that were the subject of captive breeding (Chapter 10) and those assisted by conservation education (Chapter 12).

From illegal trapping to successful release

In a number of countries, the confiscation of illegally trapped parrots posed a dilemma because there was nowhere for these birds to go. The parrots' wings had been clipped or their plumage was in poor condition, thus release was usually impossible. In Brazil, however, the wildlife protection division of an environmental agency took the responsibility for the care and reintroduction of confiscated birds. In 1997 it received ten green parakeets called Golden-capped Conures (*Aratinga auricapilla*) – eight adults and two young captive-bred birds. Following a period of quarantine the conures were released into a 700-hectare area. Platforms and feeders, containing local fruits and seeds, were available. Artificial nests made from PVC tube were erected and much information was gained on reproductive behaviour. The conures' numbers soon increased to 60 birds. Smaller parrots have a rapid rate of reproduction and the conures bred twice annually. This is one of the few release projects that has achieved outstanding success.

On the island of Margarita, off the coast of Venezuela, the Yellow-shouldered Amazon (*Amazona barbadensis*) was declining due to the illegal removal of chicks from nests. The community outreach programme resulted in the confiscation of a number of such chicks. Scientists who were studying the parrot had a very satisfactory way of solving the problem of what to do with them: they fostered them into wild nests.

This was not possible in the case of 14 chicks and they were hand-reared, then kept for one year in a large outdoor aviary. Before release the Amazons were screened to ensure they were in good health and four were fitted with radio transmitter collars. Ten of the 12 released survived at least one year, and one was seen 34 months later. Integration with wild groups varied in time from only five days to nine months. One of the parrots was seen attending a nest with eggs 28 months after release. This proves that hand-reared parrots can breed in the wild if the release is correctly carried out and – a very important point – if enough funds are available. The estimated cost per released bird was extremely high – about US$2,800 (£1,860).

▌*Hispaniolan Conure.*

Politics affect parrots

Not all endangered parrots will be saved. With the best will in the world it is difficult or impossible to protect parrots that occur on politically unstable islands. In 1991 an economic embargo was declared against the military government of Haiti, one of the poorest nations in the Caribbean and one of the most degraded states in the world. With the Dominican Republic, Haiti forms the island of Hispaniola. About 150,000 jobs were lost as the result of the economic embargo. The poverty of peasants was so acute that many had to sell their possession to buy food. Then there was only one way to survive: to cut down trees to make charcoal to sell in the markets. In some areas no trees had survived, so they used the roots. A 1998 satellite study showed that only 1.25% of forest cover remained. By 2002 the total had decreased to 1%.[1]

Two parrot species occur there: the Hispaniolan Amazon and the Hispaniolan Conure (*Aratinga chloroptera*). The Amazon is shot for food and nests are robbed to sell chicks at the roadside, perhaps to unsuspecting tourists who are ignorant of international and local laws. One cannot blame people who are starving: dictators and politicians are among the biggest enemies of wildlife.

Some ornithologists have stated that the Hispaniolan Conure might already be extinct on Haiti. This small green parakeet, with red at the bend of the wing, and yellow under wing coverts, is or was persecuted as a crop pest. In a country where crop failure can mean near-starvation, there must be sympathy for man and birds. But man destroyed the trees on which the conures depended. In the Dominican Republic, the conure is said to survive only in a few upland areas, such as the Cordillera Central.

Haiti and Timor are two examples of areas that were recently rich in parrots but have been torn by political strife. Wars, famine and poverty prevail in many parts of the world; conservation is an expensive luxury where people are starving or dying violent deaths.

The Parrot Action Plan

By the end of the century Action Plans had been drawn up to try to save a wide range of endangered species. The year 2000 saw the publication of *Status Survey and Conservation Action Plan 2000–2004 Parrots*, otherwise known as The Parrot Action Plan. It took five years to produce, after the failed first attempt, which commenced in 1993. The new plan was designed to aid managers and researchers entrusted with the conservation of parrots to evaluate the threats and to take appropriate action. It listed all threatened species and described the existing threats.

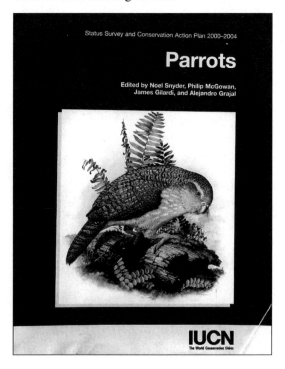

Status Survey and Conservation Action Plan 2000-2004

Parrots

Edited by Noel Snyder, Philip McGowan, James Gilardi, and Alejandro Grajal

IUCN
The World Conservation Union

---

[1] This lack of forest cover caused the mudslides of 2004 that killed hundreds of people in Haiti.

Positive moves

In the 1990s the population of the Endangered Thick-billed Parrot was variously estimated at about 3,000 individuals or between 500 and 2,000 pairs. A distinctive bird with its large black bill used for opening pine nuts and scarlet forehead and eye stripe, its breeding range is restricted to the pine forest of northern Mexico. (As described earlier, it was extirpated from the United States.) In the last years of the century it suffered a serious decline due to large-scale felling of the pine forests of the Sierra Madre Occidental. Its survival was solely dependent on protection of habitat. For nesting it needed holes in trees that must be about 2ft (61cm) in circumference at breast height – but the timber industry felled trees when they reached 50–60cm. The annual loss of Thick-bill nest sites in logged forest was 3.2% per annum; the rate in non-harvested forest was 0.85% p. a., thus logging has serious consequences.

The Parrot Action Plan's recommendations for this parrot, to be achieved within five years, were forest management modified to conserve its nesting habitat and wisely located and managed reserves to protect prime nesting areas. Also recommended were more research into its breeding biology and wintering ranges, better means of monitoring populations and recommencement of the programme to re-establish populations in Mexico and the USA.

A study of the ecology of this species started in 1995. It achieved the protection and the definition of forest reserve for the most important nesting area that covered 4,000 acres of relatively undisturbed forest known as Ejido Tutuaca. Here an estimated 10% of the total population was breeding. During the years 1995–2001 an annual average of 75 young birds fledged. This site was targeted for logging in 2002. After two years of negotiations a historic agreement was signed in 1999 calling for a 15-year moratorium on cutting timber there. To compensate for the loss of income, the community was to be paid "rent" that eventually will total 50% of the value of the timber that has not been harvested. Solutions can be found! Let us hope that in this case it will be a permanent one.

In 2000 an experimental translocation of two pairs of Thick-billed Parrots was carried out, from the southern-most nesting location to the

■ *Thick-billed Parrot.*

northern-most. Both pairs remained in their new nesting sites, selected a cavity and successfully reared young. However, radio-tracking revealed that they returned to their original breeding sites the following season.

Radio-tracking

Research, including radio-tracking and modest day-to-day living expenses for researchers, demands that inescapable element, money. As already mentioned, free flight shows are highly effective in raising funds and enthusiasm for conservation. At Adelaide Zoo in Australia, such a show featured two Blue and Yellow Macaws. Acquired at the age of six weeks and hand-reared by staff specifically for free-flying, at the age of 11 months they started their fund-raising activities. In the first seven months they raised $AU6,000 (more than £2,000). The money was used to help the survival of the imposing Great Green or Buffon's Macaw (*Ara ambigua*) in Costa Rica. It could be described as a larger, bigger-billed version of the Military Macaw.

The Great Green Macaw occurs in lowland humid forest in Central America, from eastern Honduras, Nicaragua and Costa Rica to Panama and north-western Colombia. It is almost extinct in Ecuador (the only other country in which it occurs). The countries of Central America are small. At less than 19,700 square miles (51,000 sq km), Costa Rica is two-thirds the size of Scotland. The macaw's breeding range there covered only about 50,000 hectares by the end of the century, and had been reduced by 95%,

principally due to uncontrolled logging and land clearing for cattle and bananas. Only about 35 pairs were breeding annually.

The project to save it in Costa Rica was started in 1993 by American conservationist George Powell, who contributed large sums of money. By 2000 the international conservation community could not comply with funding requests for which there was enormous competition. In that year, while in Costa Rica, I met Guisselle Monge Arias and Olivier Chassot who were managing the project. I was impressed by their dedication, and by their research documented in published papers. But without funding, time was running out.

I returned from my trip determined to raise the necessary funds. I wrote articles that appeared in avicultural magazines in several countries. The World Parrot Trust set up a special fund, and I made an appeal through *Parrots* magazine in the UK. The response from parrot keepers was overwhelming: more than £25,000 was raised in Europe and in the USA.

Radio-tracking devices (see Chapter 10) resulted in invaluable information on diet, nesting habits and range. Observation of nests indicated that 60% of clutches produced at least one young to the fledging stage. First year survival of 23 fledglings from 12 nests was monitored. Fifteen of them survived until the start of the next season, when juvenile birds separate from their parents.

Satellite images of the macaw's breeding area in Costa Rica revealed that about 35% of the forest was eliminated between 1986 and 1992. Sixteen per cent of all the 60 nest sites known since 1994 had been cut down. Half of these were felled since the 1996 law that prohibited the cutting of nest trees and hollow almendro (*Dipteryx panamensis*), the tree used by this macaw for food and nest sites, and favoured for the construction of truck bodies. Olivier and Guisselle later protected all known nest trees with metal plates warning that it was illegal to cut them.

When I returned to Costa Rica Guisselle and Olivier took me to a special place. The road

■ *Guisselle Monge Arias and Olivier Chassot.*

was muddy and slippery in the torrential rain and our four-wheel-drive vehicle slithered over bad sections of the track. We drove through secondary forest, inhabited by tapirs and peccaries, and past plantations of melina trees – grown for paper production. Soon we were on cattle pasture. After a few minutes Olivier pointed out an almendro tree; it contained a much-studied nest of a pair of Great Green Macaws. Formerly used by Barn Owls, the nest was so small it was impossible for the young ones to exercise their wings inside. It was unusual for macaws to choose such a small hole, and in an isolated tree in the middle of pasture, with the forest not far away. We parked under a nearby tree and were elated to see a young macaw looking out of the nest spout. After a while the parents entered to feed the two young, then they sat high in the huge tree, preening each other. After an hour the torrential rain drove us away. The first youngster fledged the next day and the second soon after.

For two years Guisselle and Olivier worked on a proposal for the establishment of a national park along the Nicaraguan border (the study area) between the San Carlos and the Sarapiqui rivers. The park was designed on the basis of the research findings, with a wildlife corridor that would connect it with other major parks in Costa Rica and Nicaragua. This would allow the birds to migrate between protected breeding and non-breeding areas. It would also preserve important species of fauna or flora, including the jaguar and the almendro tree. In July 2003 the Maquenque National Park was declared. This was a major triumph for all the friends of the Great Green Macaw.

Urgent plight

Parrot conservation was in its infancy. There was little time to experiment; the plight of many species was too urgent. Conservation biologists needed to learn fast. They tried to take, where appropriate, what has been learned from one species, and to apply it to another. Conservation is expensive and there will never be enough funds available to save all endangered parrots. Perhaps the answer is that the millions of parrot keepers worldwide should contribute to conservation in part-payment for the enormous pleasure they receive from their birds. Some are already doing so. For example, the Amazona Society in the USA and in the UK donate worthwhile sums to Amazon parrot conservation projects every year. Their members are parrot keepers with a conscience. We need more of them.

12. CONSERVATION EDUCATION

Gaining the support of local people is crucial to the success of any conservation programme. It can be difficult to change the attitudes and traditional thinking of adults. Children come to the subject with an open mind. When conservation is presented in an appealing way, through plays and song, children can develop an affection for a parrot equivalent to that of the cartoon characters beloved by the western world. This can be so strongly embedded through good teaching that it will not change in adult life, thus the attitude towards parrots, conservation and nature can change dramatically in the course of a single generation.

Conservation per se is never enough. Only in the last decade of the 20th century were parrot conservation education programmes carried out in more than a handful of locations and in a way that had a real impact on local people. If the emphasis in this chapter seems to be on the neotropics, it is because South America and the Caribbean islands have been the focus for conservation programmes.

This is partly because much of the funding came from the United States, due to the proximity of the neotropical countries, and many of its researchers were from universities and conservation organisations there. A major component of expenses are travel costs, which would be very high for Americans outside the continent. In the main, Africa had to find the funds for its own programmes; they were almost non-existent until the foundation of the Research Centre for African Parrot Conservation in 1996. This was based at the University of Natal. Professor Mike Perrin from the university's Department of Zoology switched his attention from mammals to parrots, pointing out that "Parrots are economically far more important and charismatic, and some species are threatened with almost immediate extinction".

In Africa

The Research Centre immediately concentrated on the biology of four species, including the Black-cheeked Lovebird. After conducting fieldwork in south-western Zambia between May 1998 and May 2000, Louise Warburton turned her attention to an education project with local schools, villages, wildlife scouts and village headmen who lived within the range of the lovebird. Information was presented in booklet and poster format and audiences were addressed in the local language. School project ideas were included in the booklet.

The Black-cheeked Lovebird, a near-endemic species to south-western Zambia, has a range of less than 1,000 sq miles (2,500 square km) of mopane woodland. Its distribution is local, probably due to reduced surface water during the dry winter months. Lovebirds need to drink twice a day. The species was down-listed from Endangered to Vulnerable (Birdlife International

2000) because more than 2,500 individuals were known to exist. However, there was little room for complacency with an estimated total population of only 8,000 to 10,000 individuals. The lovebird's range appeared to be shrinking as a result of habitat desiccation and increasing human disturbance at dry season water pools. Illegal capture was another threat.

The education booklet discussed lovebird conservation within the themes of water, soil, trees, climate and bird conservation. It emphasised the importance to humans and lovebirds of these resources and suggested how each could be managed. The small range of the species was explained in terms of river catchments, something with which the local people could identify. They were surprised to learn that this familiar bird was found only in their region. The importance of long-term monitoring of the lovebirds was explained to teachers, who supported the idea of their students making regular lovebird counts at local waterholes.

The people asked why there was so much interest in the *cikwele* (lovebird), as they regarded it as a crop pest. It was explained that, for most of the year, the lovebird was a friend of the farmer as it fed on harmful weed species. Observations of farmer-lovebird interactions from the 2000 crop-ripening season gave little reason for concern. The lovebirds were disturbed from feeding on crops in 25% of all (245) observations when farmers were present in the fields, with no fatal consequences.

Louise Warburton helped to produce an educational video on the Endangered Cape Parrot (*Poicephalus robustus*) and to publish educational posters in English, Zulu and Xhosa. The posters were distributed to all provincial nature conservation permit and law enforcement offices and to international airports.

In South and Central America

When the Blue and Yellow Macaw (*Ara ararauna*) was re-introduced to the Nariva Swamp in Trinidad an education programme was essential to safeguard the macaws' survival. Bernadette Plair, originally from that island but then with Cincinnati Zoo and Botanical Garden's Center for Conservation and Research of Endangered Wildlife, played a large part in the reintroduction in 1999–2000. She also organised local TV and newspaper coverage. Sixteen hundred brochures were distributed throughout the island. Public interest and enthusiasm for the reintroduction was high.

Men from the swamp villages volunteered to monitor the macaws and to report their presence to Forestry Division officers. How times had changed! The local people were no longer trappers: they were guardians. At conservation workshops organised by Bernadette Plair participants distributed information on the wetlands and on the macaw. In the community centre in Plum Mitan, a village close to the swamp, I attended one such workshop and witnessed conservation education first hand. I also learned about the local incentive to develop eco-tourism based on the macaw's presence.

At the village school an environmental education programme had been incorporated into the curriculum in an imaginative way that made it fun. The enthusiastic young teachers

▌*Bernadette Plair at the school in Plum Mitan.*

∎ *The macaw "guardians" at Plum Mitan camp.*

I was elated when I left the school, confident that the young generation of swamp people had such a strong appreciation of the value of the habitat and of the macaw, that its future there was secure. When conservation of the native parrot becomes part of the school curriculum, children grow up with a strong sense of its value, in spite of the fact that their parents considered the parrot solely as an item of food or trade. Many adults were won over by the enthusiasm of their children.

had expended much time and effort. Every morning the assembled 140 children listened to a talk by a guest speaker on the swamp and environmental issues. Competitions relating to these lessons were held weekly and prizes were awarded to "Green Samaritans". Classrooms were decorated with posters and pictures of Trinidad's fauna, including the pupils' paintings of the macaw. The children gave a touching and tuneful performance of their song about the swamp, with one girl playing steel drum and a boy on the keyboard (see photograph above chapter heading).

The environmental programme ran from World Wetland Day on January 29 until World Environment Day on May 31. This programme, in a tiny swamp village with extremely limited resources, was a model for schools throughout the world. The teachers could be very proud of their unique achievements.

Eleven schools participated in conservation education, involving a total of 3,800 children. Four thousand macaw/conservation activity booklets were distributed to schools in nearby villages. Some of the children took part in a carnival competition, in a production that told their story and that of the macaw. Bernadette Plair raised money for low-cost materials with which to make the costumes, including that for their blue and yellow creation entitled "Macaw King".

I visited the swamp camp near Plum Mitan, manned around the clock by a remarkable group of men. Originally unpaid fire fighters, they kept watch, night and day, over the area that the macaws inhabited, preventing entry by strangers. Between January and May 2000 they had clocked up a total of 8,640 man-hours (Low, 2001, 2002). Their dedication brought rewards in the following year when the first young for nearly 40 years left the nest. By 2002 eight young had fledged and in 2003 there were four teams of "macaw guardians", totalling 24 men. Their work was recognised by the payment of small stipends by Cincinnati Zoo.

By September 2005, of the 31 macaws released between 1999 and 2004, 26 had survived. Between 2001 and 2005, 20 chicks hatched (three to five each year). Poaching had almost been eliminated (three eggs were lost from a felled tree in 2002). Conservation education and community involvement took

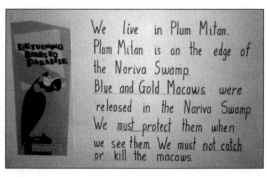

We live in Plum Mitan.
Plum Mitan is on the edge of the Nariva Swamp.
Blue and Gold Macaws were released in the Nariva Swamp.
We must protect them when we see them. We must not catch or kill the macaws.

on a global perspective in 2004 and 2005. Led by Bernadette Plair, students, educators and ecotour groups from the United States visited the release sites and village schools. The macaw guardians served as tour guides while local teachers and students shared their knowledge and enthusiasm for the project.

In Central America, the Belize Zoo educational staff members raised local awareness of the plight of the *belizensis* sub-species of the Double Yellow-headed Amazon. The education programme focussed on the school of La Democracia. In 1999, for example, educational staff sent hundreds of calendars featuring this parrot to schools. The curriculum combined aspects of science, language and social studies relating to the parrot and exercise books contained conservation messages.

Sharon Matola, director of Belize Zoo, was awarded a conservation prize by the Royal Geographic Society in 1998. The prize funds were used for a children's education programme focussing on the Scarlet Macaw in the areas it inhabited. Posters carried the slogan "Keep a poster, not a parrot". Later this dedicated lady wrote a delightful children's book entitled *Hoodwink the Owl meets Mac the Macaw*. Every child who read it surely gained an affection for the macaw that would stay with them for decades.

◼ *Belize: school exercise book.*

The *cyanoptera* sub-species from Central America (arguably the most beautiful, with its extra long tail and yellow wing coverts tipped with blue) had been reduced to only about 250 birds in Belize. In 1997 trapping for trade continued and at least 20 macaws were shot for food. By 1999 the award funds were depleted. In 2000 Loro Parque Foundation supported the project with US$12,000 in order to extend the education programme on a nationwide level. Schools, communities and visiting public at Belize Zoo learned about the natural history of the Scarlet Macaw with posters and brochures.

Caribbean Amazons

In the Bahamas the endemic sub-species of the Cuban Amazon (*Amazona leucocephala bahamensis*) is found on only two islands. One of these is Abaco, where shooting and the theft of chicks from nests threatened the survival of this handsome pink-faced parrot. American researcher Rosemarie Gnam began her project on its breeding biology in 1985, in order to develop knowledge that could be used as the basis of a conservation programme. As a result of two chicks being stolen from a nest, Rosemarie Gnam launched "Friends of the Abaco Parrot" in 1991. The children's colouring book was one of the first steps to increase awareness. This initiative developed into the Bahama Parrot Education Committee. Its campaign commenced in 1992 and resulted in the creation of a national park in southern Abaco that protected most of the parrot's nesting habitat. However, it proved difficult to protect the uniquely ground-nesting Amazons from predatory cats that killed parrots at their nests. Perhaps an education programme should have targeted cat owners who dumped the kittens.

On the Isle of Pines (Isla de la Juventud), Cuba, the Cuban Amazon and the Sandhill Crane were the focus of conservation education. In 1998 an environmental festival was organised by scientists in Havana, with art competitions for children. After listening to talks on conservation, the participants enjoyed a community fiesta. There were thanks for the 400 bird count volunteers, 300 of whom were school children. The populations of the parrot and the crane had risen by 3% and 7.2% respectively since the previous counts in 1995.

❚ *Captive Bahaman Amazon Parrot on Abaco.*

In the Cayman Islands, located between Cuba and Jamaica, protection of the endemic sub-species of the Cuban Amazon (*Amazona leucocephala caymanensis*) was a long time coming. The Grand Cayman Parrot was not removed from the list of game birds until 1990 but in some areas it continued to be shot as a crop pest and trapped. An intensive education programme was inaugurated in 1990 by the National Trust for the Cayman Islands, in alliance with RARE Centre for Tropical Conservation. Throughout 1992 the latter organisation ran a Promoting Protection through Pride campaign to raise local awareness of the parrot. It facilitated the declaration of the Cayman Amazon as the national bird. These campaigns were a highly effective method of conserving endemic species, especially on islands. St Lucia was where it had all started. This was achieved with imagination, determination and the charismatic personality of Paul Butler. Then a young Englishman not long out of college, he was perhaps the first person to turn conservation into a popular cult.

RARE Center was founded in 1973 to conserve tropical wildlife by developing model programmes for use by local, national and international organisations. It focused on areas of urgent need, such as islands where there were precious and declining endemic species in more than 25 countries, mainly in the neotropics, also in the Pacific. Conservation, and Eco-tourism and Community Development were its two major programmes. Practical aspects, such as developing income-producing nature trails and promoting family planning, were included.

Paul Butler never ceased to emphasise that the massively escalating human population was the biggest threat to the survival of wildlife worldwide (Butler, 2000).

He took up the cause of the St Lucia Parrot (*Amazona versicolor*) with an enthusiasm that spread over the whole island of 235 square miles (608 sq km) as, indeed, the parrot had once done. In 1979, when it was confined to 40 square miles (103 sq km) as the result of deforestation, it was declared the national bird. To celebrate its new status, a week of activities included radio and television programmes, children's essay competitions and walks through the rainforest. Information packs reached 20,000 children in biology classes. Paul Butler persuaded rap and rock artists to perform songs about this handsome parrot, he initiated plays in which it was the central character and persuaded local companies to use its picture on their products. In the 1970s this was highly innovative. It was also extremely successful. Hunting and trapping of this handsome blue-faced parrot ceased and the government allocated more resources towards protection of the forest and its sustainable use. At the start of this education programme only approximately 150 St Lucia Parrots were left in the wild. A decade later there were more than 250 and by the end of the century there were a minimum of 350 parrots and perhaps as many as 500.

During the 1990s the World Parrot Trust found a novel way of bringing the plight of endemic Caribbean Amazons to thousands of schoolchildren on St Lucia, St Vincent and Dominica. This was achieved in the form of conservation buses, one for each island. In 1993 I watched the reaction of children of St Vincent to the "Vincie Express" (colour page 16). They

❚ *Paul Butler.*

▌ *Yellow-shouldered Amazon.*

loved the colourful mural on each side of the bus, depicting their native parrot in its natural habitat. Inside they could learn about forest and parrot conservation from the exhibits.

The rough roads of St Lucia finally took its toll of the bus on that island and the exhibits were transferred to a new Interpretative Centre. When the centre opened in 1999 five St Lucia Parrots were resident. The property of the Forestry Department, they were the only captive birds there. Two of them had been bred at Jersey Wildlife Conservation Trust, where the official breeding programme for this parrot was located. At that time 47% of St Lucia was still covered in forest, 18% of that total being primary forest.

Another Amazon threatened by capture for the pet trade was the Yellow-shouldered (*Amazona barbadensis*) from coastal Venezuela and the Netherlands Antilles. On the island of Bonaire it had been "protected" by law since 1952; its capture and export were forbidden. The law was ignored. At the time of my visit, in 1979, there were countless captive birds. The situation changed in July 2002 when a registration programme commenced on Bonaire. Over a period of three months 600 Yellow-shouldered Amazons were ringed and registered – an estimated 95% of those in captivity. Any chicks subsequently removed from the nest could not be ringed and registered and would therefore be identified as illegal. A leaflet describing the "amnesty" was delivered to all houses on Bonaire. The campaign was reinforced with press releases, TV commercials and posters.

Brazilian Amazon parrots

In Brazil there was concern about the future of the Red-spectacled Amazon (*Amazona pretrei*). This beautiful parrot had declined due to deforestation and intense grazing and since the late 1980s had been threatened by trapping. A public awareness campaign commenced in 1991; it was directed at students, professors, ranchers and rural workers, using posters, presentations and published information. An encouraging aspect was the protection of nest trees by landowners. Nest-boxes had been installed in the recently created Carazinho Municipal Park, located in a breeding area with communal roosts (Snyder *et al*, 2001). Corporate industry took an interest and one company sponsored a very attractive children's book about the parrot (see colour page 17).

Elsewhere in southern Brazil's Atlantic forests, the Red-tailed Amazon (*Amazona brasiliensis*) had all the characteristics to promote pride: beautiful, rare and unique to the region (colour page 15). Sadly, it was one of the most gravely threatened parrots in South America. Its number declined due to taking chicks and adults for trade and food, to felling trees for canoe-making and to loss of habitat. An environmental education project was developed for Superagui National Park created in 1989 and covering 21,400 hectares.

In 1997 an education programme was supported in Germany by Dresden Zoo and by a conservation organisation (ZGAPS). A poster, distributed in villages across the range of the parrot, was pinned to every school and church door and handed to customers in bars and restaurants. A car covered in pictures of the Red-tailed Amazon was driven through the villages informing people about the threats to the species and its habitat (Lucker, 2000). More than 500 children from five villages participated in lectures and field trips, the highlight of which was a boat ride to a Red-tailed Amazon roosting site. These activities, plus educational materials, generated so much interest that teachers developed additional activities.

Residents of the community of Vila Barra do Superagüi took part in local art exhibitions, field activities and games, and made and sold craft items relating to the parrot and the Black-faced Lion Tamarin. Their products reached

Europe where the Amazon parrot puppets were available in zoo gift shops. Each one represented two months' pay for the maker, thus bringing economic benefit to the region.

In 2002 Manchester Metropolitan University, UK, was involved in the education programme. Training of wardens and students commenced. An international course in tropical ecology took place on Cardoso Island, with 12 Brazilian and 12 British participants. Six were trained specifically to monitor the Red-tailed Amazon and preparations were made to start environmental education in schools.

Macaws

The macaws were very heavily persecuted for trade and for food. Lear's (see colour page 23) is like a smaller version of the Hyacinthine. Its homeland, a tiny area in Brazil, was unknown until 1978. As mentioned in Chapter 7, the entire population consisted of about 250 individuals. Until the year 2000 about one quarter of all nests were poached annually. It was hoped that raising public awareness and generating pride, with posters in local shops and bars, would play an important role in protecting Lear's Macaw. The wide knowledge that the nest cliffs were continuously monitored was almost as important as the guards actually providing the protection.

Actions to save the Buffon's or Great Green Macaw were described in Chapter 11. As humans occupied areas of the macaws' last habitats, capture for pets, hunting for sport and feathers, and loss of nest sites contributed to their decline. Conservation education became crucial. The removal of chicks from nests was virtually eliminated with education and increased surveillance. Starting in 1998 landowners who safeguarded macaw nests or reported new nests received a cheque for $100 at the end of each breeding season. They were also presented with a trophy of which they could be proud – a statuette of a macaw with their name engraved upon it. Awareness of the problems faced by the macaw was heightened with a colouring book for children and a poster urging people not to buy wild-caught parrots.

A macaw festival became an annual event. In 2002 it was held on the border with Nicaragua and funding was obtained to bring and house 125 people from both countries. More than 500

■ *A colouring book for children and a poster urging people not to buy wild-caught animals were part of the Great Green Macaw campaign.*

people attended. Events featuring the macaw included a craft exhibition, music groups and a play. At the annual prize presentation eighteen local farmers received awards for protecting macaw nests (Chassot and Arias, 2002).

In January 2002 Guisselle Monge and Olivier Chassot started their campaign in Nicaragua and Costa Rica entitled "The Great Green Macaw, Pride of the San Juan River Basin". Three workshops were held with communities, leaders, rangers, the army, young people, local politicians and NGOs. A Nicaraguan biologist was trained with the aim of initiating a similar research project in Nicaragua. Through the Great Green Macaw the people were made aware that their extremely rich natural heritage could no longer be taken for granted. Newspaper articles and national and international television presentations highlighted the plight of the macaw, thus helping to reinforce a growing conservation ethic among Costa Ricans.

Without conservation education some species with small areas of distribution were certain candidates for extinction. One such was the Blue-throated Macaw, apparently restricted to an area of approximately 15,000 sq km in Bolivia. It exists only in the department of Beni where all the land is owned by ranchers. Alan Hesse was the co-ordinator of the 1994 project to try to map the range of this macaw for the Bolivian conservation organisation Armonia. He said: "The great majority of those people who co-exist with the Blue-throated Macaw are blissfully unaware of this species' existence. Those few who do recognise the macaw generally remain unconcerned by its worrying scarcity."

This was not surprising. The Blue and Yellow Macaw occurred in the same area and it was common. These people knew little or nothing about the Blue-throated Macaw. The main focus of the education campaign was the children (and their teachers); the researchers gave them pencils and drawing materials to create their own macaw pictures. Soon, those passing through Trinidad, the nearest town, to see the macaws did likewise. I recall a day spent on a nearby palm island, during which I was fortunate enough to see a pair of these macaws, now the rarest in the wild. We stayed on the palm island until dusk fell and then made our way to the school with our offerings of drawing equipment. It was dark. As we stood chatting to the teacher, the mosquitoes found us and left an impression nearly as deep as those wonderful macaws!

In 2004 Armonia held educational and teacher workshops to raise awareness of Bolivia's other endemic macaw, the Red-fronted (*Ara rubrogenys*). Further workshops were planned for other villages within the macaw's restricted range. Children had the opportunity to watch the macaws at the nest through telescopes donated by the RSPB. It was encouraging that this project was supported by organisations and individuals from four different countries.

Andean parrot on the brink

One of the most critically endangered parrots in South America is the Yellow-eared (*Ognorhynchus icterotis*), a long-tailed parrot like a small macaw. Green above and yellow below, it is a distinctive species, the only member of its genus, and was once abundant throughout the Andes. In 1998 Niels Krabbe, a Danish ornithologist resident in Ecuador since 1990, said: "The decline of the Yellow-eared Parrot has been so drastic, that it might be too late to save the species from extinction." At the Fourth International Parrot Convention that year he showed film of it in western-central Ecuador. It was probably the first ever seen, taken after Francisco Sornoza followed a pair for ten days. It brought a lump to my throat for it seemed likely that we were looking at video of a parrot that was soon to be extinct. Sadly this population (believed to consist of only 19 birds) became extinct in 2000 – but the species lived on. A population of 81 birds was located in a remote valley in the Central Andes of Colombia. Just in time the parrot was brought back from the edge of extinction by a remarkable and dedicated team of biologists from Fundación ProAves, a Colombian NGO, with funding from Loro Parque Fundación.

The Yellow-eared Parrot (see colour page 19) is dependent on wax palms (*Ceroxylon quindiuense* in Colombia and, formerly, *C. ventricosum* in Ecuador) for feeding, roosting and nesting. Mature specimens are the tallest palms in the world. They are very slow-growing. In Colombia this palm, the national tree, is a critically endangered species. At the 2001 Palm Sunday celebration in Antioquia an estimated 100 wax palms were cut down for palm fronds to wave at the procession. Ironically, although the police had been advised of its legally protected status, they too were carrying its fronds.

This demonstrates the kinds of problems that parrots are now facing, especially those with specialised requirements. In many places laws protect their trees or habitats but without conservation education the law is ignored. A campaign funded by Fundación Loro Parque helped to protect the Yellow-eared Parrot and to increase its numbers. The 2002 Palm Sunday event was very different and was indeed cause for celebration. Not a single wax palm was cut down or carried. Over 5,000 people in the procession were given balloons, as well as 2,000 branches from trees and 500 palm fronds from abundant lowland species. More significantly, 600 young wax palms were carried to the church in plastic soil bags and given to people to plant at their homes. In addition, the people who normally cut down wax palms for the procession were paid to plant them across the foraging range of the Yellow-eared Parrot (Salaman, 2002).

In 2003 an intensive public awareness programme was launched. Between January and August community workshops totalled 164 hours and education workshops spanned 617 hours. British ornithologist, Dr Paul Salaman

▌ *In Roncesvalle, Colombia, children wear T-shirts that they painted themselves, depicting the Yellow-eared Parrot. A mural shows this species and other endangered parrots of the Andes. **Above right:** all the street lamps are painted to depict a Yellow-eared Parrot at its nest in a wax palm.*

played a leading part in the campaign, which included local radio broadcasts. The status of the wax palm was emphasised and the people were motivated to use other species for Palm Sunday. Members of the project regularly visited 18 schools and spoke to more than one thousand children. The result was a spectacular population increase (see Chapter 13). The education programme reinforced the ethic that it was wrong to take Yellow-eared Parrots or to rob their nests.

Ironically Colombia's civil conflict benefited the Yellow-eared Parrot and other endangered species. The Andean region was controlled by the FARC guerilla rebels who prohibited hunting wildlife.

Philippine Cockatoo

Parrot conservation education initiatives outside the neotropics were not common. One of the most notable was that for the lovely little Red-vented or Philippine Cockatoo. It had the dubious distinction of being classified as Critically Endangered, one of only 14 parrots in the highest threat category at the close of the century. The principal reason was destruction of 80% of the forests. Illegal trapping was another serious threat. The total population probably did not exceed 1,000 cockatoos with the majority on the island of Palawan.

In 1992 Marc Boussekey from France took up the cause of this small white cockatoo with the red under tail coverts. He persuaded a zoo in France to sponsor a poster. Three

Marc Boussekey.

thousand copies, describing its plight in three languages, were distributed throughout the Philippine Islands. The zoo also sponsored a public awareness initiative, which included a onehour radio programme every Sunday morning. Response from 130 listeners resulted in the location of more than 300 cockatoos and 30 nest sites that were previously unknown to researchers. Even former trappers co-operated. The radio programme continued, resulting in a network of informers and protectors.

On the island of Palawan the human population explosion was highly detrimental to the cockatoo's survival. Trappers knew all the nest sites and removed the young. Their knowledge was put to good use when some former trappers were employed to guard the nests. They received cash incentives, radios, rice and T-shirts and, once again, young cockatoos were fledging from nests with a good chance that they, themselves, would rear young a few years hence.

In 1994 students from Palawan State University formed a movement whose name means "Save the Cockatoo". They helped to set up a protection network in five areas where the cockatoo still had viable populations. Young hatched in protected nests were ringed with stainless steel bands bearing identification codes. The small island of Rasa, off the coast of Palawan, became the main focus for research. In the year 2000 fifteen nests were located and intensively monitored by wardens. Not a single instance of nest poaching was recorded. A fund-raising project was launched. Interested people "adopted" a cockatoo (made a donation) and received information relating to a specific bird, identified by its ring.

Conservation education on Rasa was so successful that in the four years up to 2002 the cockatoo population doubled from 40 to 78 birds. There were 20 nest sites, many of which fledged three or four young, instead of the two that are normal for this species. The eight full time wardens ensured that poaching of chicks and illegal logging did not occur. By August 2003 the population had increased to 89 and four new nest trees had been found. Plans were made to give legal protection to Rasa Island. Loro Parque Fundación was funding the work and, for the year 2003/2004, Chester Zoo in

■ Above left: *A poster in three languages warns against killing or catching cockatoos and,* **right,** *information on the Cebu and Siquijor Hanging Parrots.*

the UK had pledged Euros 30,000. British involvement was welcomed. The cockatoo's numbers on Rasa continued to increase; by 2005 there were 97. Here was more proof (if it was needed) that education is a highly efficient form of conservation.

The population increase resulted in such optimism that in 2002 islands were surveyed to find sites for new populations. They proved to be too ecologically degraded and would need habitat restoration before translocation of cockatoos could occur.

Many other Philippine birds were threatened by deforestation, especially those from the island of Cebu. Seven of the 14 bird species and sub-species from Cebu were already extinct. At the end of the century it was unknown whether the beautiful Cebu sub-species of the Philippine Hanging Parrot (*Loriculus philippensis chrysonotus*) had escaped extinction. Reputedly a few individuals have since been located in a tiny patch of virgin forest in the Central Cebu National Park. However, the sub-species from the island of Siquijor (*L. p. siquijorensis*) was

not located and was believed extinct (del Hoyo, Elliott & Sargatal, 1997).

Indonesia

Indonesia consists of more than 13,000 islands. It might be described as the most disastrous area in the world for parrot survival. Trapping and deforestation were so serious that a number of endemic parrots are likely to become extinct during the first three or four decades of the 21st century. Political and other problems make this a difficult area for conservation workers.

The Red and Blue Lory (*Eos histrio*) was the subject of one of the few education projects. In a remote northern part of Indonesia, not far from the Philippines, are the Sangihe and Talaud Islands. The endemic lory, one of the most beautiful parrots in existence (see colour page 15), was unknown to the outside world until 1992 when trapping and export commenced on a massive scale. In 1994 it was placed on Appendix I of CITES but this was not effective in stopping the export trade. The lory was heading for extinction...

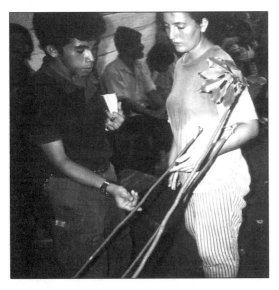

▌*A trapper (left) with branches cut to trap Red and Blue Lories.* **Right:** *Jan van Oosten with two trapped birds, attached to the perch by means of ring and chain.* **Below:** *the branches are placed in a tree with recently trapped lories attached to them to call in more lories.*

Photographs: Jan van Oosten

Then in 1995 the University of York organised an ornithological expedition from the UK, headed by Jon Riley, with the lory as the focal species. By then it was extinct on all the islands except Karakelang. Expedition members targeted six villages known to harbour an abundance of trappers. They visited the headman in each one, held an open meeting to discuss the lory's plight, visited villages and spoke to more than 4,000 children. They used stickers, posters, booklets and leaflets. Their message was clear: the lory had survived only on their island and if they did not cease to trap it, it would soon be extinct. This made sense to the villagers who no longer saw the flocks that were common even four or five years previously. Many people resented the bird trappers who had become rich at the expense of the lory. Jon Riley and his team planned to continue their work there until a law banning trapping was enforced. The Indonesian Government set a zero capture quota for the species. It remains to be seen whether this will operate.

Australia

We associate education programmes with the less developed countries, yet even in Australia they are necessary. One of the most endangered parrots there is Carnaby's Cockatoo (see

Chapter 11), one of the white-tailed black forms. The magnificent, long-tailed black cockatoos are Australia's largest parrots. Between 1970 and 1990 Carnaby's Cockatoo disappeared from more than one third of its range in the south-western corner of Australia due to conversion of habitat for agriculture. In addition, damage to nesting holes occurred when chicks were removed for illegal export.

The education department at Perth Zoo worked to reverse the "indifferent attitude" towards the cockatoos. The zoo produced a brochure and built a Cockatoo Information Centre. Education officers devised a new lesson for schoolchildren entitled "Cockies in Crisis", which was incorporated into the biology curriculum. In a programme linking country and city schools, children collected seeds that form part of the cockatoo's diet. These seeds were germinated at the city schools until the following year when the children returned to the country. They planted the seedlings in areas that the country children identified as suitable by observing the cockatoos

on their properties. At maturity, these seedlings will provide food for nesting pairs and hopefully will prevent further local extinctions of this magnificent cockatoo (Jupp, 2000).

Education projects will have a significant positive impact on the survival of many of the parrots whose future looked bleak at the end of the century. Parrot lovers (individuals and clubs) outside the countries where these programmes are implemented should try to assist them financially, through organisations that support parrot conservation, or by making direct contributions to specific projects. In the UK, Tim Bennets designed a T-shirt that was sold in aid of the Great Green (Buffon's) Macaw.

Local education programmes are important not only to protect the species but also to encourage people to protect the environment and to inform them of the benefits that result. Their community will be the richer, both spiritually and financially, in the long-term and precious parrot populations will be saved – at least for the time being.

■ *T-shirts raise awareness and funds.*

13. CAPTIVE PARROTS FUNDING CONSERVATION

Parrots in captivity have the potential to raise money and awareness for conservation purposes. Unfortunately, that potential has been largely neglected. Manufacturers of foods, cages and toys, for example, also parrot breeders, might have added just 1% to their prices, to donate to conservation, thereby raising large sums as well as improving their own images. All people involved with parrots owe a heavy debt to the millions upon millions of wild parrots that have been captured, and to those that have died in the process. Without them there would be no pets and no industry.

There was a significant development during the 20th century in which captive parrots played an important role in conserving those in the wild. In Chapter 3 I related the story of Loro Parque in Tenerife. It built up the most comprehensive collection of parrots that ever existed. The park never ceased to develop new ideas, while maintaining its high standard of excellence in design, initiative and cleanliness.

Furthermore, it became a school of learning for hundreds of vets and biologists, and thousands of college students. Science and conservation were aspects unseen by visitors yet these disciplines placed the park at the forefront of parrot research. Every four years Loro Parque hosted an international parrot convention (limited to about 700 places), and it organised conferences on avian medicine. It held regular workshops for parrot breeders in German, also occasional workshops in other languages.

In 1994 the Loro Parque Foundation (LPF) was founded. Its mission statement was to conserve parrots and their habitat through education, research and responsible breeding. Legally registered with the Ministry for Education and Science in Spain as a non-profit, non-governmental organisation, it took over the parrot conservation projects that had previously been funded by Loro Parque. In 1995 Dr David Waugh became its Scientific Director. The park's newsletter, which started in 1986, changed its name to *Cyanopsitta* in 1995, became a magazine and gave prominence to the Foundation's conservation work.

The original aim of the park, to attract the public, took second place to that of conservation. About 800 parrots were on exhibit by the end of the century, with more than 2,000 (sometimes nearer to 3,000) housed in a breeding centre away from the park. Wolfgang Kiessling, owner of Loro Parque, took a giant step forward in establishing the Foundation and in handing to it ownership of all the parrots. By the end of 2005 LPF had donated 2.85 million Euros (more than £2 million) to conservation of wild parrots and scientific research, such as funding investigation into nutrition and disease. All the income from the sale of young hatched there went to these causes.

Even in 1994 parrot conservation programmes, and people involved in research on parrots in the wild, were still few but increasing in numbers worldwide. Before conservation action can commence, research needs to be carried out to identify problems faced by certain species. The main setback was usually the lack of long-term funding; some researchers were carrying out valuable work but needed to fight annually for the meagre grants available, casting doubt on future research and spending valuable time looking for funding that might have been spent in the field.

How the Foundation is funded

Loro Parque Foundation took a different approach to that of some funding organisations. It selected a number of projects for threatened species and pledged on-going financial assistance, making an annual allocation for each project. In 2004 alone it donated Euros 437,597, partly from corporate sponsors, individual members and the sale of T-shirts and other items. The remainder of the income originated from the sale of young parrots: 26% of the income in 2001. In 2003 for example, the total number of young ringed was 1,375, of 171 species and sub-species. In 2004 1,400 young were reared, of 184 species and sub-species. Some of the young birds were retained for future breeding purposes; others were sold. Loro Parque met all the overhead expenses of the Foundation, including salaries, allowing 100% of all income to go to the various projects.

The breeding centre

The Foundation's breeding centre is located a few kilometres south of Loro Parque, 200m (650ft) above sea level. It covers an area of 30,000 sq metres (7.4 acres). Here live approximately 350 species and sub-species of parrots. Security is of prime importance and constantly maintained. This collection is priceless, not only for its monetary value but because the breeding pairs,

■ *Loro Parque Fundación's breeding centre.*

and the young birds that are maturing, are like a Noah's Ark of parrots. Virtually all parrots known in aviculture are here (some represented by multiple generations). Exceptions include four Australian species that are not held legally outside their native country: three small lorikeets and the Glossy Cockatoo.

This breeding centre has two distinct sections for parrots from different environments. One area is covered (high above the aviaries) in black mesh. This blocks out 50% of sunlight and is used mainly to house species from rainforest; they need a darker and more humid environment. The second area has a ceiling of a light blue nylon mesh, suitable for housing parrots from more open areas, such as the Australian outback.

The theme of dense planting, palm trees and flowering shrubs, which characterises the park, is repeated here. Rows of aviaries are divided by banana plants, *Schefflera* trees, and flowering lilies and vines that provide shade and shelter. This visual barrier between each aviary gives each pair a sense of security and reduces aggressive behaviour due to the close presence of other males. The lush and generous plant growth gives the impression of a garden city, with the houses replaced by 1,200 aviaries and suspended cages.

Techniques for breeding success

The Spix's Macaw Recovery Programme is strongly supported by the Foundation; it had always been the major benefactor (see Chapter 17). Unlike most of these macaws in captivity, the pair of Spix's Macaws here and their young are the property of the Brazilian Government. The other private owners refused to return ownership to the species' native country, where it is extinct in the wild. The female of the breeding pair was hatched at Loro Parque in 1992. Until the end of 2003 she had been kept with a male who was apparently unable to breed. The park's vet, Lorenzo Crosta, took the male back to Brazil. He examined four males there (under anaesthetic) using a laparoscope and chose the one he believed had the most active testes. His choice was perfect. The new pair nested soon after the male came out of quarantine. Their first chick hatched in June 2004 and was removed for hand-rearing at the age of four days. The female laid again and another chick hatched in November of the same year (see colour page 18). Both were reared and a third chick hatched in December 2005.

Various techniques were used to persuade some of the more reluctant birds to nest or to ensure that young were reared. These included fostering. A Palm Cockatoo was reared to the age of 41 days by a pair of Blue-eyed Cockatoos (*Cacatua ophthalmica*) before being removed for hand-rearing. Two pairs of Leadbeater's (Major Mitchell's) Cockatoos reared Gang Gang Cockatoos (*Callocephalon fimbriatum*) to independence. There is a risk in using foster parents of very different genera but the choice is obviously limited to the species available at the same stage of the breeding cycle.

Some successes could be attributed to special attention to the diet. Fig Parrots are not easy

to breed. Edwards' and Desmarest's (the two largest *Psittaculirostris* species, and of exquisite coloration) produced good results. Chicks survived because no seed was offered to the parents, only a special mixture that included dried insects such as mealworms with baby cereal, plus chopped fruits.

Choice of mate is extremely important in persuading parrots to reproduce. Non-breeding individuals were permitted to choose their own partners in one of several large pairing aviaries containing several males and females. Typical measurements were 39ft (12m) x 11ft 6in (3.5m) wide and high. Nine small cages, each measuring 10ft (3m) long and 33in (1m) wide were suspended along the rear of the flight. In this pleasant environment even the ground was covered with vegetation, such as ferns and flowering shrubs. During the winter of 1994, for example, this aviary was used for groups of the Endangered Red-browed Amazons, and later Cuban Amazons. In the following year both species bred for the first time in the LPF collection. The same pairing method was used to form more pairs of Red-browed Amazons,

▐ *Large aviaries are used to allow parrots to choose their own partners.*

∎ *Young Mercenary Amazon.*

resulting in 15 young in just two years. Smaller planted aviaries, measuring about 24ft (8m) x 21ft (7m), were used in the same way. The first recorded captive breeding of the Mercenary Amazon (*Amazona mercenaria*) took place here. (This Amazon is little known but has been encountered in the Colombian Andes by the members of the Project Hapalopsittaca which is supported by the Foundation.)

Successes were also achieved with a Brazilian Amazon, the Endangered Red-tailed (see photograph on page 187). Held in few collections and difficult to breed (low fertility), one pair produced five young in one year. From three eggs in the first clutch, two chicks hatched and were hand-reared. The three eggs of the second clutch were exchanged with those of a Double Yellow-headed Amazon. Both females reared the chicks that hatched, a result that gave confidence to leave the eggs with the Red-tailed Amazons in the future. This was another species whose conservation was strongly supported by the Foundation (see Chapter 12).

Continuing successes with parrots that are hard to pair are not guaranteed. Male and female might need the stimulation of separation. The Mercenary Amazons were separated in

November, to be reunited in February. Their excitement was then so great that they nested at once. Separation is appropriate because many pairs of Amazons lose interest in reproducing after several years.

Conservation projects funded

Another Amazon that benefited from the Foundation was the Yellow-shouldered (*Amazona barbadensis*) from Venezuela and nearby islands. A consistent breeder in the collection, a good nucleus of about 50 individuals was held by the end of the century. Threatened in the wild (see Chapter 18), the Foundation supported the two parrot species on Margarita, the Amazon and the island sub-species of the Blue-crowned Conure (*Aratinga acuticaudata neoxena*). For several years all chicks had been stolen from active nests. The Foundation's grant of 66,325 Euros (£47,375) paid for nest guards and for censuses. The project team held educational sessions for schools and involved local university students in an education campaign for residents and for tourists. The improvement of the Amazon population was rapid but numbers of the conure had not increased by 2005.

A threatened species which is nearly extinct in Ecuador is the Buffon's or Great Green Macaw (*Ara ambigua*). In the past the Foundation supported the conservation project in Ecuador with more than 5,000 man hours to research nesting and food resources. In excess of 100,000 trees were planted within the macaw's range.

At one stage the three males in Loro Parque's collection were examined by laparoscope by the park's vet who thought that they were unlikely to reproduce. When a 35-year old male was acquired from Basle Zoo in Switzerland he was paired with a six-year old female. The female's first two eggs were given to a pair of Green-winged Macaws who reared two young from the fostered eggs. From her next clutch the Great Green Macaws reared two young in their 36ft (11m) long aviary. In other collections this magnificent macaw was seldom kept in aviaries that permitted sufficient flight.

Young of the large species, such as macaws and cockatoos, were able to mature and socialise in very spacious aviaries. One such enclosure was entirely devoted to Blue-throated Macaws.

Observing them in a large flock, noting their beauty in flight and the intensity of their shimmering almost turquoise blue and golden plumage, was unforgettable for me. These fortunate young birds had a huge space in which to perfect their flying skills. More than 100 had been reared at Loro Parque by the end of the century – a number that was almost certainly higher than the wild population.

Between 1995 and 2005 the conservation of this macaw was supported by the Foundation with 243,681 Euros (£174,060). In 2004 seven researchers visited 21 private ranches in the Beni region of Bolivia (the only locality worldwide where it occurs) and found four new sites where it exists, apparently increasing the number of birds known in the wild by 20 individuals. The researchers published local and national media articles and gave television and radio interviews to highlight the importance of conserving this macaw. They conducted education workshops and gave presentations to small ranches and communities.

The Yellow-eared Parrot

The Foundation started to support the conservation of the Critically Endangered Yellow-eared Parrot in 1996 when a small flock existed in northern Ecuador (see Chapter 12). Three tracts of land were purchased, including the roosting site, and the deforested area was planted with trees. In the Andes of Colombia Fundación Loro Parque works with the Colombian NGO ProAves. A second project to locate and protect the species there met with spectacular and rapid success. As the species is nomadic, even locating it was fraught with difficulties initially. Dependent on the world's tallest palm (the national tree of Colombia), which attains a height of over 130ft (40m), the wax palms were cut down almost everywhere. In October 1999 a flock of 24 Yellow-eared Parrots were observed in central Colombia. Early the following year British ornithologist Paul Salaman instigated and directed Proyecto *Ognorhynchus* on behalf of Loro Parque Fundación.

The first step was a poster campaign, asking farmers to report any sightings. After 11 months fieldwork and 3,500 field hours in the largest surviving palm remnants, the search had proved fruitless. By early 1999 it appeared that the species' traditional haunts had been deforested or mindless hunting had exterminated the last few parrots. (In the late 1980s a farmer in Ecuador had illegally trapped 40 birds from a flock of 60. Half died within one day and the remaining 20 died the next day.) There were no birds in captivity and the worst was feared: that the Yellow-eared Parrot had suffered the same fate as the Carolina Parakeet – extinction.

As the searches were about to end, a report came of its existence from a remote valley in central Colombia. In April 1999 project fieldworker Bernabé López-Lamús went to investigate. Suddenly, descending from the clouds above a breathtaking montane landscape, two flocks of Yellow-eared Parrots swooped down into palm-studded fields. After a year of soul-destroying searching, he was delirious with ecstasy. Sixty-one Yellow-eared Parrots alighted and clambered down the fronds in chattering groups to feed on the palm fruits. The researchers soon realised that few bird species have such complete dependency on a single species of plant as this one has on the wax palm – for feeding, roosting and breeding. Signs of damaged nesting trees and stories of active

■ *A poster played an important role in the rediscovery of the Yellow-eared Parrot.*

Three chicks in a nest in Roncesvalle.
Photograph: ProAves/Loro Parque Fundación

hunting of the parrot for food indicate how it was almost driven to extinction.

Round-the-clock observations of the flock during the following months resulted in a wealth of information. Within a week another flock was located in an adjacent valley. Occasionally all the parrots would gather before roosting together in the palms. It was surely this behaviour that had made this exceptionally social species so vulnerable to hunters. The total of 82 birds included 24 adult pairs. A nest containing a chick was discovered deep within a dead wax palm and in September six more nests were located. By September 2000 this population had increased to 110 individuals, and, in January 2001, two new populations were found totalling 63 birds. By September that year the total number of Yellow-eared Parrots known had increased to 387.

By the beginning of 2003 Loro Parque Fundación had supported the conservation of this parrot with the donation of 100,330 Euros. This was money well spent. The species had been saved from global extinction! The original population of 81 birds in the Central Cordillera (Roncevalles, Tolima) had increased to 312 birds by August 2003 and that in the Western Cordillera (Jardin) to 303 individuals! Furthermore, the survival of this increased Roncesvalles population was safeguarded with 21,500ft (6,560m) of fencing protecting 1,255 hectares of habitat, plus another 3,300 hectares protected.

I was privileged to go to Colombia and to meet the ProAves/LPF team whose dedication and enthusiasm had brought such remarkable results. This unique parrot in its unique habitat was something that I had longed to see. When I saw a pair on a distant palm stump far below the moment was very special. Then a pair flew from their nest to a nearby tree. They perched in the sun, unconcerned by our presence, their plumage gleaming gold and green. How beautiful they were!

Two holes, normally covered, had been made in their nest palm, for inspection and for photography. An extending ladder was placed against the trunk and a member of the ProAves team climbed up to about 11m (33ft) to inspect the chicks and to take photos. He came down and reported the presence of three young. How could I let the moment pass without asking if I could have a look? Yes, of course, was the reply! I climbed up and looked through the hole, at first seeing nothing in the darkness. Then I made out three large chicks, with feathers on the head but still with soft white down, their insulation against the cold nights at 2,800m (over 9,000ft). That was a moment I will never forget!

A roosting site exists high above the town, in an area on farmland, perhaps unique in the world, where many palms still exist. When the late afternoon sun emerged, the wax palms stood with gleaming white trunks like sentinels, closely packed in a small space. I thought they were truly a wonder of nature that should have been preserved for posterity. But naturalists did not know they existed here until the parrot's presence became known.

In Chapter 12 I described how the education programme funded by the Foundation ended the destruction of the wax palms. Palm regeneration then became important. In order to ensure sufficient parrot food resources in future years, palm saplings (which would have been trampled) were transferred from areas used by cattle to protected land. Many thousands were planted. An innovative method of habitat protection was used at Jardin. All the land was privately owned and the owners registered it as private reserves, thus qualifying for tax rebates!

Over more than two decades I have watched the progress of parrot conservation projects with an interested and sometimes critical eye (even before I installed a collecting box for the conservation of the Imperial Amazon in Loro Parque in 1988). Nothing has excited me as much as the events in the Colombian Andes. Such a phenomenal success is unheard of in the history of parrot conservation! It is not cheap, however. By 2006 the sum allocated by the Foundation to the conservation of this species was 269,330 Euros.

Emerging from obscurity

Five little known and globally threatened parrot species are found in the Colombian Andes, including Fuertes' Parrot (Chapter 16). Since 2000 Loro Parque Foundation has helped to finance the search for and conservation of these rare parrots in the Central Cordillera.

By 2004 surveys had been completed at five sites in the Central Cordillera and the second phase of the project, to work with government bodies and others of influence, had commenced. Successes included the protection of 1,500 hectares of montane forest, the El Mirador Nature Reserve, managed specifically by

Fundación ProAves for the Golden-plumed Parakeet (*Leptopsittaca branickii*) and for Fuertes' Parrot. Installed for the latter species were 200 wooden nest-boxes, carefully camouflaged with bark, lichens and epiphytes. Great was the jubilation when five were immediately occupied. Soon, with cameras in the nest-boxes, eggs of this species, believed probably extinct only two years previously, were seen. The rare Golden-plumed Parakeet, also declining rapidly due to cloud forest clearance, also occupied nest-boxes.

The Flame-winged Parakeet (see colour page 20) or Conure (*Pyrrhura calliptera*) survives in only a few fragmented populations in small area of the Eastern Andes. The population (possibly as few as 5,000 birds) is declining rapidly due to habitat loss and persecution as a crop-pest. LPF supported Fundación ProAves to take the necessary conservation measures.

In Ecuador, the endangered El Oro Parakeet or Conure (*Pyrrhura orcesi*), discovered in 1980 (see Chapter 16), has a small geographical range in the Andes. Below 3,000ft (900m) the rate of forest loss in western Ecuador was 57% between 1958 and 1988. The conure's habitat was fragmented and its range and population were declining rapidly when, in 2002, Loro Parque Foundation became the principal supporter of an important conservation initiative. Led by Martin Schaefer and Veronika Schmidt, two biologists from the Ecuadorian NGO Fundación Jocotoco, it revealed much about the breeding biology.

A count of the conure in late 2002 suggested a population size of 120–135 individuals in the Buenaventura valley. Forty to 50 more were located soon after in an adjacent valley. No other individuals were known. During the 2002/2003 breeding season five nests were found. It was discovered that the species has a communal nesting system; incubation duties were shared among individuals, including young from the previous year. Radio-tracking revealed that at

■ *Roosting site of Yellow-eared Parrots at Roncesvalle.*

least three birds were incubating, for periods of three to four hours each. Three out of the five nests were harassed by Crimson-rumped Toucanets (*Aulacorhynchus haematopygus*) and one nest was predated. Toucanets can open nest cavities with their strong beaks. The two successful nests, attended by five and eight individuals, raised only one chick each. Only ten young fledged into the population that year, possibly due to dry weather.

Conservation of white cockatoos

The Philippine or Red-vented Cockatoo (*Cacatua haematuropygia*) is a Critically Endangered species. Captive breeding, generally less successful than with other white cockatoos, was first achieved at Loro Parque in 1988. In the Foundation's breeding centre there were several pairs in aviaries 33ft (11m) long. Two screens, one on each side of the aviary, at right angles, provided visual barriers between male and female. Every precaution must be taken to prevent aggressive behaviour by the male.

▌ *Philippine Cockatoos in the aviaries of Loro Parque Fundación.*

Photograph: Ellen Karhausen

Loro Parque Foundation (LPF) supported the conservation programme, along with several other organisations. Work was centred on the island of Rasa (off the coast of Palawan) where food trees were planted. The cockatoos ignored the nest-boxes erected for them but habitat protection continued with nine wardens on patrol. In August 2003 the highest Philippine Cockatoo count since conservation commenced there totalled 89 birds, a big increase from about

20 between 1998 and 2000. Perhaps one day the cockatoos might colonise the nearby mainland of Palawan.

In 2000 the Foundation donated more than US$11,000 to construct aviaries on two sites in the Philippines. They housed confiscated or donated endemic birds. The location of the aviaries on Polillo Island (off the coast of Luzon), could be important for the endemic sub-species of the Blue-backed Parrot (*Tanygnathus sumatranus freeri*). Possibly even more threatened than the Philippine Cockatoo, the aviaries might be the means by which confiscated parrots could be released back into the wild.

In Indonesia, the Foundation took an active interest in the two endemic parrots of the Tanimbar Islands. It funded re-search on the status, habitat use and trade in Goffin's Cockatoo and the Blue-streaked Lory (*Eos reticulata*). Despite heavy trade in the past, the population appeared to have stabilised. Trade had diminished in the previous two years due to social unrest but sales of the cockatoo and the lory continued – to tourists and for export. The recently acquired autonomy of the archipelago, the precarious economy of the region and the limited qualifications of personnel managing natural resources, suggested an uncertain future for these parrots.

BirdLife International set up a funding proposal for the Foundation to promote protection of Tanimbar's endemic parrots and their habitat. LPF responded with US$20,000 for the year 2002, some of which was used for education campaigns. By the end of 2005, the Foundation had donated US$96,480. Previously the Tanimbarese had little knowledge of their parrots; only about 3% knew which two species were endemic to their islands. Plans for the future include establishing a large protected area on the island of Yamdena to encompass a representative section of the region's biodiversity. This might be the last opportunity.

During the 20th century LPF set a unique example to the world. It demonstrated the enormous possibilities that those responsible for captive parrots have to conserve parrots in the wild. If this theme is not taken up by more collections during the 21st century some parrot species are destined for extinction due to lack of funding for their conservation.

PART III.

DEVELOPMENTS

14. PARROTS AS PESTS

Parrots are perceived in different ways by different people. They might be cherished companions, noisy nuisances, one of nature's miracles when flying free, even a source of food – or the enemy that persistently destroyed your crops, planted in what used to be the parrots' habitat. Their natural food sources were destroyed but they continued to nest in forest remnants.

Seed-eating parrots are more likely to be labelled as agricultural pests, especially those that feed on the ground. (Many parrots are canopy-feeders only.) Fruit-eaters, and those that relish the pips of apples and oranges, can make problems for commercial growers. Worldwide few species cause significant damage; those that do habitually congregate in large flocks, such as the Bare-eyed Cockatoo or Short-billed Corella (*Cacatua sanguinea*) in Australia. They can gather in flocks up to several thousands. In exceptional circumstances such numbers are hugely exceeded. When grass seeds are plentiful the flocks are smaller but during periods of food shortage enormous flocks gather on sorghum crops as these are available year-round. One such flock in Western Australia in the 1970s was estimated to contain 32,000 Galahs.

Worldwide, so-called pest species were often used as food. The poor Galah was used to make Australia's equivalent of pigeon pie among the early settlers. In 1902 the *Truth* newspaper reported: "The sunburnt residents of that God-forsaken outpost of civilisation were subsisting on stewed galah and curried crow." Galah pie was a popular outback dish.

The treatment of cockatoos in Australia was a controversial issue at the start of the century – and equally so at the end. Cockatoo numbers had formerly been much lower because of the limited availability of water. Stock troughs and spilt grain were the means by which cockatoos proliferated to pest proportions.

New South Wales

"The bloomin' cockies are eating me out. There's millions of them down in the crop," reported a farmer in the Riverina area in 1914. According to an article published in *Life* magazine that year, if trappers did not work among the flocks of Galahs, the farmers waged war against them, using guns – or poisoned wheat that killed many other species. At gun-club meetings men shot Galahs instead of pigeons. The trappers were welcomed as friends in need. They took the trapped cockatoos to the city, where they were paid nine pence for each bird. The city dealers sold them to officers of steamers that traded between European and Australian ports. Thousands went to Germany every year where they found a ready sale at the equivalent of five shillings (25p) to £1 each. Occasionally an albino was trapped. It was worth £5 or more.

Victoria

Unusually, Mr D. Le Souef, director of Melbourne Zoo, claimed that Galahs should be protected as the farmer's friend. Their favourite food appeared to be the roots of a native plant, *Microserus forsteri*, and they also appreciated

■ *This albino Galah, described as a "freak of nature", was worth up to 20 times the price of a normally coloured Galah.*

Photograph: *Bird Notes*, **February 1916**

the eggs of grasshoppers (*Bird Notes*, February 1916).

Throughout the century Galahs, Long-billed Corellas and Greater Sulphur-crested Cockatoos continued to be killed in Victoria and elsewhere. In 1980 more than 300 grain farmers attended a meeting west of Horsham to put their anger into words. They told the Fisheries and Wildlife Officers there that they wanted permission to shoot the Corellas and Sulphur-crested Cockatoos. One farmer said that he had given up growing grain because the loss was too large when he had to keep feeding the cockatoos "$2,000 worth of seed at a time". He added: "I have survived floods, fires and drought but the corellas have beaten me."

Another said: "I have employed women to run round and round the fields when the sunflower seeds are ripening and I have had men drive tractors up and down – but nothing works. The corellas won't go away until they have eaten every seed from the flowers."

The Wildlife officers received a hostile reception when they answered that they were looking at ways of eliminating the problem. The farmers wanted an answer – and presented their MP with a 700-signature petition asking for urgent parliamentary approval for an "open season" on cockatoos. Eventually shooting was permitted. However, in 1981 a West Wimmera

farmer appeared in Nhill Magistrates Court to face 11 charges of killing wildlife and using poison. Shooting had failed because the cockatoos were too cunning and flew too high. In April 1999, the Minister for Conservation in Victoria gave permission to use poison to control Corellas causing crop damage. This was allowed because despite the use of traditional control measures, the level of damage to crops in Victoria continued to increase. In 2000 a new Government was elected in Victoria and poisoning under permit was no longer legal. Trapping and gassing continued. In 1999 about 5,000 cockatoos had been poisoned, assessed as 1% to 2% of the population in Victoria.

Legislation regarding killing pest species varied from state to state. In South Australia, shooting was approved. The National Parks and Wildlife Act (1972) and the Prevention of Cruelty to Animals Act (1985) allow hunters licensed under the Firearms Act and using a 12 gauge shotgun, to destroy Corellas "humanely" and during daylight hours.

Ray Ackroyd has been a cockatoo trapper for many years but by the end of the century he preferred to operate wildlife tours. He told me: "The government does not issue trapping licences without a hefty payment. To obtain a licence to trap one has to go before a wildlife committee to prove expertise. There are very few trappers today because government royalties, strict conditions and limited markets have forced trappers into other fields."

Export or death?

Many parrot lovers outside Australia considered the Australian policy of not exporting their cockatoos (and other "pest" species of parrots) to be wrong in view of the fact that thousands were killed. The "pest" species were the Galah, Long-billed and Bare-eyed Corellas and the Greater Sulphur-crested Cockatoos. Those people who thought export was preferable had not considered certain issues. I believe that cockatoos suffered less from a quick death by gassing than by being exported as adults after knowing life in the wild. Of course poisoning can never be condoned in any circumstances. I explained my reasoning at length in my book *Cockatoos in Aviculture* and believe that it is worth repeating extracts here.

"... it would be necessary to capture and export several million cockatoos annually to have any impact on wild populations. Could avicultural and pet demand worldwide really absorb such immense numbers? The answer to this question is undoubtedly 'No'."

"Between 1981 and 1985 the minimum total of Goffin's Cockatoos exported from the Tanimbar Islands was 24,147. Supply soon exceeded demand and Goffin's were commonly seen in pet shops where they might spend many months. As the smallest of the cockatoos it might have been considered suitable as a companion bird. I was breeding this species at the time but it was always with difficulty that I could find homes for the young.

"If a five-year average of less than 5,000 per year resulted in supply exceeding demand, what would happen when millions of Australian cockatoos were suddenly unloaded on to the markets? Just because they were exported *en masse* they would not be cheap. Air transport of all birds must adhere to the regulations of the International Air Transport Association (IATA), and each bird must be contained in a box of specified dimensions... If this was not done the death rate would be high and export would quickly be criticized and halted. Add to this the high cost of airfreight and the expenses of the mandatory quarantine period, plus various other expenses, including taxes and handling charges, the cost would at least equal that of the Indonesian cockatoos...

"... adult birds do not adapt to the close confinement of a cage. If mass export was allowed, many would die of stress, boredom and neglect – a long, slow torture for relatively few people have the sympathy, patience and time needed to give cockatoos the companionship they crave in the absence of a mate."

Written in 1993, when rescue centres were unknown, these words proved to be prophetic. Now there are usually more abandoned and abused cockatoos in rescue centres than any other parrots. Adding to these numbers with wild-caught Australian cockatoos does not bear thinking about.

In addition, the Greater Sulphur-crest is one of the most intelligent of all parrots. It always disturbs me to see them in captivity; they are simply too intelligent to be caged. Because of the great strength of their beaks, few people can provide suitable and spacious housing for these extraordinary wonderful parrots.

South Australia

Some areas of South Australia have been under permanent cultivation since the start of the 20th century. At the beginning of the 1970s few parrots were found in the Adelaide Hills area. Then Adelaide became a garden city filled with flowering trees that attracted lorikeets and other parrots. As commercial fruit-growing increased, the parrots became a serious problem. In order of importance, grapes, apples, cherries and apricots were the main crops. Starlings (European), Silvereyes, Rosellas and Regent Parrots (Rock Pebbler Parakeets), in that order, were eating the grapes. Rosella parakeets were the worst enemies of cherry growers, eating the flower buds. They also relished apples and their pips, especially the new varieties that had double the number of pips compared with the traditional kinds. The total bird damage to traditional apples, mainly by Rosellas and to a lesser degree by Musk Lorikeets, was about 1%.

■ *Short-billed Corellas and Greater Sulphur-crested Cockatoos.*

Yellow Rosella – shooting was permitted.

In May 1999 the South Australian Government passed legislation that allowed commercial horticulturists to shoot Adelaide and Yellow Rosellas and Rainbow and Musk Lorikeets without a permit. This could be done to protect their orchards. According to one report, after the first 12 months the Department of Conservation surveyed 231 orchardists. At a conservative estimate they had killed 45,000 Rainbow Lorikeets. Sharon Blair, of the Bird Care and Conservation Society said: "South Australians are proud of our wine but distressed that so many parrots are being destroyed to produce it." In March 2001 this regulation was revoked.

Farmers and fruit growers took the law into their own hands when they believed that their livelihood was at risk. They illegally killed parrots when they could have solved the problem in a different way. In many countries fruit crops are grown under large areas covered in fine mesh to keep out birds. Ultimately it would make economic sense (and common sense!) to follow this practice.

Lorikeets must contend with loss of nest-sites due to destruction of trees and lack of food as a result of prolonged droughts. Shooting and persecution due to increased fruit-growing in the last years of the 20th century added to the threats to their survival. Nomadic birds that often congregate in large flocks where food is available, lorikeets appear numerous but their populations could suddenly crash. The colourful, playful and loquacious flocks of Rainbow Lorikeets seem to symbolise eastern Australia. And tourists love them! Their loss would leave a void that could never be filled.

Cockatiels rising from a field of sorghum.

Queensland

In the last decade of the century farmers were growing a crop that was very attractive to black cockatoos. In the rich volcanic soil of Lakeland, in southern Cape York Peninsula (in the north-east of Australia), peanuts (a legume that grows in the ground) do well. Red-tailed Black Cockatoos have probably been visiting this area for hundreds of years to eat the seeds of the bloodwood trees. Then they found peanuts left on the ground to dry after harvesting. Eventually they learned to pull the plant from the ground to discover the soft, oily "nuts" growing below.

From the early 1990s the Red-tails came regularly, working methodically from the edge of the crop or from any patch where the crop was thin. Between feeds they exercised their beaks on the huge pivot irrigators, shortening the wires so that one wheel would go faster than the others until the whole expensive contraption tripped and twisted and was rendered useless. One property lost more than AUD$50,000 per year to the cockatoos; others lost entire crops.

In their frustration the farmers aimed high-powered rifles at the cockatoos but when the birds were approached within shooting distance they floated up into nearby trees on those lovely big wings, then drifted across to another paddock. It was rumoured that farmers then resorted to illegal poisoning. They used scaring devices or patrolled their crops all day. The Queensland Parks and Wildlife Service was generally held responsible for the damage because they would not issue permits to shoot more than 30 cockatoos at a time. The Wildlife Service could only suggest leaving part of the crop for the birds. (They did not suggest how the birds could distinguish the paddocks set aside for them!)

I find it interesting that Cockatiels can descend on a field of grain in their hundreds, even in their thousands, yet they are not persecuted by farmers. They simply are not perceived as pests, perhaps because they are less conspicuous than cockatoos, due to their smaller size, or because they are nomadic. I once watched a flock estimated at 2,000 birds (a large flock for this species) whose members were alternating between a field of sorghum and the surrounding trees. It was an awe-inspiring sight, probably my most memorable bird-watching experience in Australia. I couldn't help wondering if the Cockatiels were just as guilty as the much-maligned Corellas.

Indonesia

The Tanimbar Islands are situated 300 miles (480km) north of Australia and consist of more than 60 islands. The largest is Yamdena; it covers nearly 2,000 sq miles (5,000 sq km). Here and on some of the other islands of the group occurs the endemic Goffin's Cockatoo (See Chapter 13). It is a lot like Australia's Bare-eyed Cockatoo (Short-billed Corella) and closely related to it. Yamdena's eastern coastal area is where crops are grown, mainly maize and rice, beans (including peanuts), papaya, ba-nana and cassava. In April and May 1993 a survey was carried out by a team from PHPA (CITES management authority for Indonesia) and BirdLife International. The aim was to assess populations of significantly traded species, in this case Goffin's Cockatoo and the Blue-streaked Lory and to evaluate the damage caused by the cockatoo to the maize harvest. Farmers reported that on agricultural land the cockatoos spent approximately 80% of their time feeding on maize and 20% on rice.

The team observed the cockatoos in the maize fields and found that a single cockatoo destroyed an average of 1.69 maize plants per day. An average flock of 148 birds would destroy an average maize field (of only 1,200 plants) in three days. Maximum damage occurred if a flock

▌ *Goffin's Cockatoos.*

moved to a new field after it had damaged 50% of the crop; the farmers would then abandon the crop. A conservative estimate of the maize season was 30 days. In this period the average flock would eat their way through 7.5 fields. The study concluded that Goffin's Cockatoos destroyed approximately 1.7% of the maize crop in the south-east region of Yamdena. Village leaders who were present at five of the seven villages surveyed said that cockatoo damage to these crops was not a serious problem and was insignificant in relation to other factors – probably climate and soil infertility (Cahyadin *et al*, 1994).

It was a problem for the cockatoos, however, as they were easily trapped in the maize fields using leg snares. This species was almost unknown in aviculture prior to 1972 and probably was not trapped. It was of no interest to the people of the Tanimbar Islands until bird dealers in Indonesia alerted them to the fact that they could make money from them. In the seven years up to 1989 an average of more than 11,000 Goffin's per annum were reported as imports to CITES. This was believed to be less than 5% of the Yamdena population (however, it does not account for numbers imported by non-CITES countries and for mortality before importation). In 1992 this cockatoo was placed on Appendix I of CITES (the Appendix for species that would be threatened with extinction by commercial trade).

Goffin's is a charming little cockatoo. It is also an escape artist, seemingly capable of taking aviaries apart and picking padlocks. A significant percentage of captive birds probably escaped from their cage or aviary, never to be seen again.

New Zealand

In New Zealand's South Island there is a very different kind of pest: the Kea (*Nestor notabilis*). It is possibly the most intelligent, inventive and destructive parrot that ever lived. There is no doubt that it is the most inquisitive. An olive-green mountain parrot with a long, curved bill and glorious orange under wing coverts, it has clashed with humans for years. Quite fearless, it runs around among tourists at ski resorts and other places where people leave food and cars. These items are consumed and/or destroyed with equal relish. From cars Keas rip off the windscreen wipers, from open-air diners they steal food, and on houses they damage the roofs.

Always in the news, a typical newspaper report about these parrots read as follows:

"The trouble really starts when they decide to hit town. They are gangs of marauding juvenile kea birds, New Zealand's native mountain parrot, fuelled on high-energy food from the dump and out for a good time. Fun in kea terms can mean anything from tearing open the seat of a motorbike left in an unlocked garage to pulling out nails or shredding building paper at construction sites" (*The Independent*, August 25 2000).

While tourists generally look on Keas as lovable nuisances, not everyone tolerates their antics. One man, kept awake in a mountain hut by the noise of Keas sliding

▌*Left: A Kea enjoying playing in water. Above: Sign at Arthur's Pass: Do not feed the Keas.*

down the tin roof, went out next morning and shot the miscreants. But this crime pales into insignificance compared with the result of them being declared as sheep-killing pests in the late 19th century. Over an eight-year period, 29,000 were killed; there was a bounty on their beaks. In fact this bounty operated from early in the 19th century until the 1950s. It has been estimated that as many as 150,000 of these wonderfully playful and inventive parrots were killed. By the end of the 20th century only an estimated 3,000 had survived. Man was to blame; he invaded their territory, the sub-alpine areas of South Island, farming sheep in their rightful habitat.

New Zealanders, presumably the farmers, must have been quite without sentiment. Keas are such endearing birds, with a *joie de vivre* unequalled by any other parrot. They love to play. Who could fail to smile at their inventive games or at the sight of one sliding down a snow-covered slope *on its back*?

Asia

One of the most numerous parrot species is the Indian Ringneck (Rose-ringed) Parakeet (*Psittacula krameri manillensis*). It usually occurs in small flocks but at concentrated food sources hundreds of birds, or even thousands, might gather (Forshaw, 1989). At an experimental sunflower seed crop at the Punjab Agricultural University Farm at Ludhiana, Ringnecks were responsible for a loss of about 22% of the production. In the same area guavas were the favourite cultivated crop, maize was eaten from September to December and peanuts from November to June. In other areas the parakeets attacked grain stored at railway sidings, even tearing open bags (like cockatoos in Australia) and causing serious losses through spillage.

In the UK this species is a "naturalised" immigrant with its headquarters in Surrey (see Chapter 15). Ringnecks have caused problems at Painshill Park, near Cobham, by feeding on grapes. One year the estate produced only 500 bottles of rosé instead of the 3,000 bottles anticipated. In the following year there was some success in keeping the parakeets at bay with explosions and bird scarers.

The closely related Moustache Parakeet (*Psittacula alexandri fasciata*) sometimes congregates in numbers judged to be several thousand strong in the rice fields of Thailand. In Burma (Myanmar) in the early years of the century Moustache Parakeets were called Banded Parakeets. They descended "when the paddy is ripe in immense numbers... cutting the stems of the rice with their bills, and then eating the half-ripened grains" (*Birds of British Burmah*).

Africa

In South Africa some parrots that were once agricultural pests have now declined in numbers to the degree that this is no longer the case. For example, in Transvaal orange groves Meyer's Parrots (*Poicephalus meyeri*) were formerly considered to be a nuisance. The Cape Parrot (*Poicephalus robustus*), found only in South Africa, was approaching extinction by the end of the century with a rapidly declining population in the region of 500 birds. Nevertheless pecan nut farmers persecuted and killed parrots that ate their crops.

▌*Evidence that Cape Parrots have raided pecan crops.*

Photograph: Louise Warburton

In eastern Africa Masked Lovebirds (*Agapornis personata*) caused considerable damage to cereal crops, especially sorghum. The threatened Black-cheeked Lovebird, considered a pest on millet crops, was studied from 1998 to 2001 by English researcher Dr Louise Warburton in Zambia. She found that 18% of seed heads suffered more than 20% damage during the ripening season. These small lovebirds also fed on sorghum (colour page 15).

Caribbean islands

The Critically Endangered Puerto Rican Parrot survived precariously in the wild, with fewer than 40 individuals at the end of the century. Its population had been decimated by deforestation yet these parrots were still plentiful enough in the early years of the 20th century to be considered as agricultural pests. Children were used to drive them from the corn crops.

Haiti is one of the poorest and politically most unstable nations of the Caribbean. The economic embargo declared against the military government in 1991 left people desperate for food. The Hispaniolan Amazon was shot and poisoned as a crop pest. It fed on bananas and maize, because so much of the natural forested habitat had been destroyed. Impoverished people struggling to feed themselves in a country of poor soil, erratic rainfall and civil unrest did not appreciate the parrot's rarity. Its numbers were so low that it was approaching extinction there and had survived in viable numbers only on the eastern part of the island, the Dominican Republic.

∎ *Hispaniolan Amazon.*

In Jamaica both the endemic Amazon parrots, the Black-billed and the Yellow-billed (*Amazona agilis* and *A. collaria*) are classified as Vulnerable. Vin Helwig grew up there. He recalled of the three parrot species (including the conure, *Aratinga nana*): "All have a liking for commercial crops and can make substantial inroads on ripening corn, Congo peas and Seville oranges. In normal times farmers are able to control their numbers by scaring them off from the crops with shot guns, killing some, which they find good for the table" (Helwig, 1989). During the 1970s the government enforced a moratorium on hunting of all animals.

Chile

The Slender-billed Conure is unmistakable, being the only parrot with a long and hardly curved upper mandible (see colour page 18). It was once very common with roosts numbering 2,000 birds or more. There is something very endearing about this highly sociable green parakeet. By the end of the century it was classified as Near Threatened, mainly due to forest clearance in central Chile, the only area where it occurs.

In 1895 it was a very different story. "These parrots are met with in large flocks; which may number hundreds or thousands of individuals, and keep up an incessant screaming. For a part of the year they inhabit the forests, but from October to April they make their appearance in the cultivated districts of Valdivia, for the purpose of feeding on the crops. At this season they appear every morning in large flocks flying from the northward, and returning in the evening. With their long beaks they extract the grains of maize and wheat from the growing crops, and also dig up roots of grass, which form their staple food" (Lydekker, 1895). According to A. W. Johnson in *The Birds of Chile*, while the flock fed sentinels took up their positions high in nearby trees and sounded the alarm long before a hunter came within range. Nevertheless, Johnson gave "excessive shooting" as one of the reasons for its decline.

Argentina

In Brazil, Quaker Parakeets "multiplied explosively" as the result of the planting of crops on which they fed and eucalyptus plantation in which they nested. A decline in predators

(Sick, 1993) had aided their increase. In the neotropics forested areas were widely destroyed to grow food. The forest margins where crops were planted provided good foraging and nesting areas for many parrot species. Examples included the citrus groves in valleys between mountains in north-western Argentina and in the semi-arid Chaco savannahs of Argentina, Paraguay and Bolivia. During the middle of the century, the Argentine Government declared all parrot species, large and small, to be national pests. There was a long history of conflict between parrots and farmers. A bounty was given for each pair of legs collected by local government agents.

By the mid-1990s several Argentinian provinces had passed laws to control Quaker Parakeets. In Entre Rios landowners were required to destroy or poison nests (see photograph on page 197) on their property, and in Buenos Aires province nest destruction "sweeps" were made every five years. The parakeets were unpopular because they fed on crops of wheat, barley, millet, rice, sunflower and sorghum, as well as maize, the main crop. Researchers found that crop damage was usually related to, or entirely due to, poor agricultural practices by farmers, rather than by aggressive foraging. The motivation for killing the birds was often political.

In Argentina the Patagonian Conure (*Cyanoliseus patagonus patagonus*), also called the Burrowing Parrot, had been persecuted for decades. It was officially declared an agricultural pest in 1963. During the last 20 years of the century its populations declined dramatically and it became extinct north of Buenos Aires and in the province of Córdoba. Much of its steppe habitat has been converted for agricultural use. The largest breeding colony was in El Cóndor, in north-eastern Patagonia. Until the 1980s this colony was sprayed with DDT by local authorities to kill the birds. Not only was this a painful death, resulting in young also dying in the nests, but some surviving birds were unable to fly, the result of genetic deformities caused by DDT. These beautiful parrots (spectacular in flight) continue to be shot and poisoned. One farmer claimed that a flock of 20,000 wiped out half his wheat crop. He called the bird a plague and said the government should do more to reduce its numbers. The government did too

Patagonian Conure.

much by giving an export quota of 10,000 birds per annum (see colour page 8). Conservationists knew that persecution and export could drive this parrot to extinction.

The local government of north-eastern Patagonia received claims of thousands of dollars for compensation against crop damage by Patagonian Conures. Patagones was the area that claimed the most serious damage. In 2004 a study of the diet of this species and its potential interaction with local agriculture was carried out near El Cóndor. A questionnaire on crop damage was distributed to local farmers and 70 farmers were interviewed. The results showed that damage (to maize, sunflower and oats, also millet and almonds) by these parrots was overstated. Some farmers pointed out that other birds, including Quaker Parakeets, thrushes and flickers were responsible, or they apportioned the blame between Burrowing Parrots and geese. In Patagones only 11 of the 30 farmers questioned reported bird damage and of those only 8 implicated Patagonian Conures. However, most would not answer questions regarding the size of affected areas, and the validity of their claims was doubted.

Shooting of birds in general and parrots in particular was the method used most commonly to control crop damage. The use (illegal) of poisoned baits was also mentioned. Farmers admitted, however, that these methods were ineffective and expensive. Some farmers used non-lethal deterrents such as dense sowing of crops, or sowing and harvesting at times of low risk of damage. Others sowed unattractive crops around the main one, such as rye surrounding wheat (Perez *et al*, 2005).

Corn, sunflower and, to a lesser extent, wheat and sorghum, were the most frequently affected grain crops in Argentina, attacked by Burrowing Parrots, Maximilian's Pionus, Blue-crowned Conures and Quaker Parakeets. Noisy, conspicuous and gathering in flocks, their presence never went unnoticed and damage caused was generally exaggerated. Other causes of crop losses such as viruses or fungi were less obvious but generally more serious. Parrot damage at the regional level was usually minimal. This generally made the implementation of large-scale control campaigns uneconomical because costs were higher than losses (Bucher, 1992).

Argentina's system of defining "pest species" was corrupt. The studies were carried out by university students to determine the quotas for so-called pest species such as Patagonian Conures and Blue-fronted Amazons. And guess who paid for these studies? The exporters, of course...

Solutions

"Individual farmers in Victoria, Australia, have experienced losses of their entire crops to corellas resulting in severe economic hardship," wrote Kevin Love, Assistant Secretary of Resources and Infrastructure to the Director of The World Parrot Trust in May 1999. He stated: "The Victorian Government welcomes your input on this issue, particularly in relation to alternative measures to minimise crop damage by birds."

There were alternatives to the inhumane practice of using poison – a slow and very painful death, for cockatoos and for non-target species that took the bait. In North America scientists developed non-lethal chemical deterrents to repel bird species from crops. Perhaps these could have been used in Australia or chemicals developed that caused temporarily infertility. The solution should have been in population control (and better crop management), not in poison and other expensive and time-consuming methods of killing. If destruction was permitted, surely humane methods could have been used? In Adelaide, National Parks and Wildlife Service Officers used hypnotic drugs in the drinking water to capture flocks of corellas. The cockatoos were then given a lethal dose of carbon dioxide.

Minimising crop damage

In many cases poor agricultural practices are to blame; damage could be greatly reduced. Obvious solutions like enclosing fruit crops within netted areas are often ignored in Australia. The initial outlay would be expensive but in terms of increased yield, and time and/or ammunition saved in deterring or killing parrots, there would ultimately be a big gain.

Grain crops are more difficult or impossible to protect. Should farmers consider growing a sacrifice crop of the most favoured food item? After losing his peanut crop, Queensland farmer Martin Garate was convinced that this was the only way to control cockatoo damage. In 1999 Mr Garate made available 40 acres of land where he had planted his crop previously. A peanut company provided seed peanuts at a reduced price and another company prepared the ground. A local farmer lent seeding machinery and another put one ton of seed peanuts in the ground. Truly a co-operative effort, two brothers took care of the crop, spraying weeds and applying thousands of dollars worth of fungicide donated by Bayer Chemicals.

It was so successful that a local shooter, who had been employed to keep cockatoos off commercial crops, could fine none to shoot. When he visited the sacrifice crop, the reason was evident. Five hundred Red-tailed Black Cockatoos rose from the ground. The cockatoos stayed on this crop for the duration of the peanut-growing season. For relatively little outlay and with much community goodwill, the farmers saved their peanut crops and were able to get on with other farm work, instead of shooting or deterring cockatoos (Garnett, 1999). However, this was probably a one-off effort and it only side-stepped the real issue. It had saved the farmers' time but it might also have increased the black cockatoo population.

Crop damage by parrots was often the result of poor agricultural practices such as plots with excessive open spaces and low plant density, or crops left too long between ripening and harvesting. Unsuitable locations were also a problem. In northern Rio Negro province in Argentina wheat crops were damaged by Patagonian Conures (Burrowing Parrots). However, the area was so unsuited to wheat-growing that it was discouraged by the local Ministry of Agriculture (Bucher, 1992).

It seems likely that in future the farming industry will find ways to minimise crop depredation. In New South Wales there was significant damage to growing sunflowers (*Helianthus annuus*). Choosing sunflower

▌*Patagonian Conures in Rio Negro province, Argentina.*

hybrids with pendulous heads was suggested as a means of reducing damage. On one farm two sunflower crops were grown in one season: one with flowers with pendulous heads and the other a commonly grown hybrid. It was found that sunflower heads that were taller and larger were more susceptible to damage than down-facing heads. Early damage occurred near the field margins but later the whole crop was attacked. Early harvesting, reducing the edge to area ratio of the crop, and planting hybrids of uniform height and with down-facing heads, would have reduced damage by cockatoos.

In 2002 Birds Australia Parrot Association issued an information sheet (No. 10) on the subject. It stated: "... much reported damage is small-scale and localised. Individual farmers and orchardists, as well as bowling and golf club managers, may be hard-hit on occasion but, at a national level, the economic costs of parrot and cockatoo damage to agriculture are trivial compared with the effects of weather, insect pests, plant and animal diseases, and fluctuations in world commodity prices."

In Argentina damage to crops in the orange groves was substantially reduced by growing a variety with a small number of pips. This was less attractive to the Blue-fronted Amazons that formerly arrived in large numbers. They were (so I was told in Salta) frightened from the fields with the explosions of gas bombs set to detonate at intervals. Apparently, another tactic was the use of scarecrows. I found this somewhat

difficult to believe. Amazons are too intelligent to be fooled on a regular basis.

Taste repellents were widely employed to protect crops from various species of birds. They were used experimentally against Quaker Parakeets but with mixed results. Research and developments of new repellents were limited because the requirements on environmental safety were so costly. Recorded distress and alarm calls might deter some parrots – or have the opposite effect. In Quaker Parakeets and Patagonian Conures distress calls actually attract other members of the species.

In Australia the use of decoy grain crops and food dumps worked well in some situations. Other suggestions were scare tactics, reinforced by selective shooting of individuals, and an insurance or compensation scheme that would recompense farmers for significant damage. However, there are problems with accurate damage assessment as early damage to crops might be made up in later growth so that there is little or no decline in yield. Common sense should dictate that crops are not planted along tree-lined watercourses – the preferred habitat of many parrots.

The farming community needed to accept that small-scale crop damage is one of the hazards of agriculture. More research is needed into crop damage and non-destructive control methods, along with education of the wider community with the facts to counter irrational anger and sentimental misperceptions.

■ *Ringneck Parakeet in the Canary Islands feeding on* Kniphofia.

15. THE INVADERS: INTRODUCED POPULATIONS

The official attitude to the introduction of non-native species underwent a significant change during the course of the century. In the 1930s an American called Eastham Guild was living on the island of Tahiti. Because native birds were few, he decided to import small birds from other tropical climates and release them. He imported hundreds of birds from Africa, South America and, in one shipment, 500 finches from Australia. All these were released – and many were never seen again. However, he reported: "The French Government has been very sympathetic in my experiments, giving me the necessary permits to import birds and has passed local laws prohibiting all shooting and trapping" (Guild, 1938).

By the end of the century it was highly unlikely that government advisors anywhere would have permitted the release of non-native species; indeed, the reaction would have been one of horror and, in most countries, a reminder that it would be illegal to release such birds.

Non-native species became established in most countries worldwide through accidental and intentional introductions. High numbers of introduced bird species were found in the Hawaiian Islands, North America, New Zealand and Europe. Many such birds had a harmful impact on native species, because they competed for food and/or nest sites. Some were widespread, such as the House Sparrow, whereas others had small populations. Some became established for a short while only. In 1906 Madagascar's little grey-headed lovebird

(*Agapornis cana*) was introduced to the Seychelles, to the main island of Mahé. By the 1930s the lovebirds were common, with huge flocks in Gordon Square. Numbers declined rapidly, for unknown reasons. By the end of the century the lovebird was seen only on rare occasions.

Certain factors increased the likelihood of parrots becoming established in areas or countries to which they were not native. These were:

1. The population was founded from wild-caught parrots (better able to survive in the wild).
2. There were suitable suburban areas to inhabit. In such areas parrots were protected from shooting, avian predators were present in lower numbers and bird tables and exotic planting provided good food sources.
3. There were regulations that protected exotic bird species and, in the USA, even fines for removing their chicks from nests.

Some introduced species were not known to do much damage to the ecosystem, especially where they live in the artificial environment of suburbia. *Aratinga* conures (parakeets) in the USA (such as the Red-masked) might even have colonised areas formerly inhabited by their extinct cousin, the Carolina Parakeet. Little investigation into the possible impact of these invaders was carried out, except some preliminary studies in California and Florida, and in southern England on the Ringneck Parakeet.

Budgerigars: short-term successes

One of the first members of the parrot family to attract attention as an "invader" was the Budgerigar. It could be seen in the St Petersburg area of Florida in 1940, possibly before, the population apparently having originated from escaped birds. In the 1970s there were large flocks in Florida, reputedly as many as 10,000 individuals! In 1978 one roosting site in Pasco County attracted between 6,000 and 8,000 birds. Some Budgerigars had been released to increase flock sizes as the big flocks were considered to be a tourist attraction. In due course the natural colour of the species, light green, predominated.

Eventually the Budgerigars were established along the Gulf coast from southern Hernando County to Sarasota County. They nested in cavities in pine trees, cabbage palms and even in streetlights! However, they needed human habitation to survive. Residents loved them and hung up bird feeders and nest-boxes in their gardens. They seemed to be thriving. Then, in the early 1980s, Florida was hit by severe freezes. Previously it was almost unknown for the orange crops to be ruined. The cold weather was believed to be an important factor in the Budgerigars' decline. Lack of sufficient nesting sites, especially as the Budgerigars were in competition with European Starlings, must also have played a part, as Starlings increased their range and numbers. Strangely, during the winter they often flocked with the Starlings. One observer believed that the population might have approached or exceeded 20,000 birds in a five-county area of west-central Florida by the late 1970s. By 2003 it was reduced to two small declining populations located ten miles apart.

For a short period Budgerigars had thrived in the mildest climate of the USA. Simultaneously, the same was occurring in the mildest climate of Britain, in the Scilly Isles, off the coast of Cornwall in the south west of England. In 1969 the Queen Mother suggested to the Lord Lieutenant of Scilly that he should introduce free-flying Budgerigars to the estate on the island of Tresco. Four pairs were duly acquired from the royal aviaries at Windsor Lodge. In 1970 six more pairs were added to their aviary in the abbey gardens. In 1972 the aviary was opened; the Budgerigars reared their young away from it but visited it for food. At first they nested in holes in cordylines and palms, but later they used elms, sycamores and other tall trees.

In 1974 about 35 nests were in use and there were 30 or more non-breeding birds. During the summer they separated into two flocks that came together to roost. One flock of 20–30 birds consorted with starlings in the fields and neither they nor House Sparrows showed any aggression towards the little parakeets. The Budgerigars were fed by a lady who left the island in 1974 and by 1975 their numbers were greatly depleted. They probably died out that year.

Ringneck Parakeets

The Budgerigar was a short-term invader, not invasive like the Indian Ringneck Parakeet (*Psittacula krameri manillensis*). An invasive species is defined as a non-indigenous one that becomes an abundant and influential invader of communities of native species. The best-known introduced parrot in Europe was the Ringneck Parakeet. It has received much press coverage in the UK. One rumour had it that the large population in the south originated from a pair given to rock icon Jimi Hendrix by Keith Moon of The Who. The birds were apparently liberated when the guitar-playing legend died in 1970. Another strange tale is that the ancestors of the flock escaped from Shepperton Studios in 1951 during filming of *The African Queen* with Humphrey Bogart and Katharine Hepburn!

■ *After some years, the Budgerigar population in Florida consisted primarily of birds of the natural light green colour.*

Reputedly, Ringnecks bred in Norfolk as long ago as 1855. In *The Gardeners' Chronicle* for October 11 1930, Sir William Lawrence referred to a threatened plague of "green parrots" in Epping Forest, Essex, resulting from the sighting of seven birds! They had been identified as either Ringneck or Alexandrine Parakeets.

Fred Stoker from Loughton, Essex, described how a single bird had arrived two years previously. The male Ringneck lived alone through the "dreadful" winter of 1928–29, finding some protection in dense hollies. In the spring he discovered a captive female whose cage was placed in the open during fine weather. One eventful day the owner was astounded to find the bars of the cage forced apart and the female gone. The pair lived together. Then an outbreak of psittacosis spread alarm through the land and probably resulted in people liberating parrots, for two apparent exiles joined them. The four birds took up residence in old elm trees. There they bred and their numbers increased to seven. Their favourite diet was crab apples which they split open to extract the seeds. On winter days they ate holly berries while swinging on a branch. Then two or three disappeared – feared shot by vandals.

After hearing a rumour that they had feasted on a neighbour's plums, Fred Stoker commented (*Avicultural Magazine*, December 1930): "Personally I would allow them very considerable latitude in the matter of food for the joy of having them in the garden, and I feel sure that if Sir William Lawrence could view their tricks, their gambols, and their radiance, he would be the last to virtually bracket them with that undoubted and unrepentant villain, the grey squirrel."

In 2002 the British Trust for Ornithology published a paper that suggested that in 1998 the population of Ringneck Parakeets from Ramsgate, Kent to Esher, including the colony at the 65-acre Hither Green Cemetery, numbered more than 2,000 individuals. In 2003 Pete Forrest, Kent Wildlife Trust warden in the Sandwich area said: "In the past four or five years the Ringneck Parakeets in Thanet have spread out quite a lot and they are doing very well, probably due to a succession of warm winters and more people feeding birds

▌ *Ringneck Parakeets using a building in Germany. Inset: Young looking out of their nest in a ventilation duct.*

Photographs: Michael Braun

■ *Ringneck Parakeet feeding on palm fruits in Tenerife.*
Photograph: Rafael Zamora Padron

In New Zealand

Generally, the attitude towards introduced parrots was one of tolerance. This was not the case in New Zealand when escaped Rainbow Lorikeets (*Trichoglossus haematodus moluccanus*) started to increase in 1999. Many of this country's endemic birds have become extinct. The introduction of predatory mammals such as rats, cats and stoats were usually to blame, along with introduced food competitors such as deer and brush-tailed possums. Since 1840 more than 80 alien species of mammals, birds and fish have become established in New Zealand. Ironically, no law prevented introduced predators such as rats, ferrets and weasels being bred in captivity and released into the wild yet, when a few introduced Rainbow Lorikeets started to breed, the Department of Conservation (DOC) designated them as "unwanted organisms" so that unlike rats and stoats and other bloodthirsty predators, they were covered by the Biosecurity Act (1993). This meant that if you bred one of these "infamous" creatures and let it go, you could be jailed for one year.

during the cooler months. They are confined to suburban areas and often nest in colonies quite close to each other."

Peanut feeders in gardens are a greatly appreciated source of food for these elegant birds. In autumn and winter they feed in small flocks but congregate at roosting sites. As many as 200 to 300 birds could be seen flying in to some roosting areas, including Ramsgate station and Hither Green. As numbers increased apple growers in the Thanet area became worried.

A report in the *Sunday Times*, September 19 2004, indicated that concern was more widespread. The Royal Society for the Protection of Birds said that the parakeets could displace native hole-nesters such as owls and Lesser Spotted Woodpeckers. Dr Chris Butler, a zoologist at Oxford University with a particular interest in the wild parrot population, said there were already too many to control and that Ringneck numbers were increasing by 30% every year. By 2005 the colony at the edge of the rugby ground in Esher, the largest in the country, held an estimated 7,000 Ringnecks. It was calculated that the British population could reach 100,000 by the end of the decade – a figure that hardly seemed credible.

It is not surprising that Ringnecks thrive in northern Europe. In the Himalayas they occur up to 4,000ft (1,200m). The altitudinal record for this parakeet is said to be 12,000ft (3,600m) above sea level!

In a "fact" sheet issued by DOC to justify their action, they made various claims. They stated that they might carry avian diseases. So might any bird – yet in 1999 when DOC trapped and killed 17 Rainbow Lorikeets in Auckland, not one of them showed any trace of disease or parasites. At that time the estimated lorikeet population was 200. DOC claimed that they were prolific, rearing as many as three broods in one season. More than two broods would be unusual and, in any case, the clutch size is only two. DOC claimed that six or seven Rainbow Lorikeets that escaped from aviaries in Perth, Western Australia, in 1968 had expanded their range and by the 1980s had become a nuisance. The same could happen in New Zealand, they said. In fact in Perth the Rainbow Lorikeets live in mature suburbia full of winter-flowering trees.

■ *Rainbow Lorikeet – an "unwanted organism" in New Zealand.*

fruit bat damage. In the Adelaide Hills area of Australia, crop damage reported by apple and pear growers averaged about 5%. Rosellas were the worst pests, followed by Musk Lorikeets. Yet in Auckland, the very area where DOC had allocated NZ$245,000 to trap and kill Rainbow Lorikeets, introduced Rosellas were ignored by DOC.

Finally DOC claimed that because of their ability "to travel", Rainbow Lorikeets posed a threat to endangered species that survived only on the Hauraki Gulf Islands which had been cleared of predators. DOC overlooked the fact that the lorikeets could not live in these islands of native bush because there were insufficient flowering plants.

By 2002 their numbers had reached at least 10,000, according to one report, yet no attempts had been made to eradicate them. There was not enough food for them to live in the new suburbs or in native bush but exotic species of eucalyptus had played an important role in their success there. According to Professor Recher of Edith Curtin University, the effect of the Rainbow Lorikeet on the local avifauna was nil. Furthermore, no fruit growers had complained about them.

DOC claimed that Australian horticulturists regarded them as a significant pest and that in Darwin 80–90% of some tropical fruit crops were lost to Rainbow Lorikeets. In fact, tropical fruit losses to flying pests in the Northern Territory averaged 2% to 3% and this included

The situation in the Auckland area was akin to that in Hawaii. It abounded with introduced birds (mainly European) and with many of the 1,600 species of introduced plants that thrived in New Zealand. It was not an area of native habitat! If Rainbow Lorikeets had infiltrated island reserves and threatened endangered native birds, eradication would have been justified, but this was not the case. Furthermore, DOC was proposing to spend scandalous sums of money on eradicating a few lorikeets while deciding not to trap stoats where endangered Kakas were nesting until two females had been killed by stoats! The budgeted salary for the position of Rainbow Lorikeet Project Manager was in the region of NZ$58,000 (£17,575) per year for the two year contract. In addition, nearly a quarter of a million dollars had been budgeted for killing the lorikeets! Apparently they resulted in the eradication of the Rainbow Lorikeet in 2002.

Engaging conures

Conures are the noisy parakeets from South and Central America that are often found in large flocks in the wild. Some very successful

■ *The endangered Kaka.*

species can thrive in a variety of habitats and are therefore candidates for colonisation of non-native lands. Because of their engaging ways and colourful plumage, they proved to be popular aliens in some parts of the USA. Harmful aspects of introduced populations include the possibility of carrying the seeds of invasive weeds over great distances, and of the introduction of avian diseases to the endemic bird population. Both these potential problems were suggested in the case of a flock of Mitred Conures (*Aratinga mitrata*), a 15in (38cm) parakeet from the Andes.

In 1987 a pair was allowed to fly free from their aviary in Huelo on the island of Maui in Hawaii. They could come and go as they pleased. They nested – and by 1993 the flock consisted of at least 13 birds. By 1995 there were 28 or more. In 2001 an animal rescue organisation aimed to capture the red and green conures to prevent them being killed by state officials who said that their growing numbers posed a threat to native ecosystems. Considering that by 1981 an estimated 98% of the fauna and flora of the Hawaiian islands were said to be introduced, their concerns over a few conures seemed out of all proportion to their threat. Twenty-seven species and sub-species of birds are included among the one thousand plus species of plants, animals and insects that have become extinct there since Polynesian explorers arrived 1,500 years ago.

The conures nested in the cliffs at Huelo. In 2001 they were reported to have increased to between 50 and 200 individuals. The reputedly

■ *Blue-crowned Conure.*

deleterious effects of in-breeding seldom seem to surface in the wild (often not the case in captivity). There are several instances of a species being reduced to the last one or two females yet the population has bounced back to number in the hundreds or thousands. In 2003 their numbers were estimated at between 120 and 200. Wildlife officials there asked the federal government for $52,000 to trap or kill them. (The outcome is not known.)

The larger conures are resilient birds that can adapt and survive in alien environments. These include a London suburb. Another conure, the Blue-crowned (*Aratinga acuticaudata*), is common and widespread in many parts of South America. It was first reported in Bromley, Kent, in 1997 when two birds (probably aviary escapees) came to a garden feeder. In 1999 a flock of 15 birds was observed. In April 2001 a nest with four eggs was found in a park in Lewisham (not far from Bromley). The nest was abandoned and the eggs were missing; possibly the culprit was a grey squirrel (another alien!). Although it seems improbable that the numbers of this conure that originates from arid habitats will grow to Ringneck proportions, it does illustrate how certain parrot species can quickly reproduce in suburbia where there are no farmers to feel threatened by their existence – only householders who delight in seeing something different at their bird feeders.

In San Francisco a flock of about 50 parrots included Red-masked Conures (*Aratinga erythrogenys*). These noisy, handsome birds, with scarlet heads, are much loved by local residents. One householder who fed them on a balcony, attracted flocks of 20 or more. In fact they became the most celebrated conures alive when Mark Bittner wrote a book about them entitled *The Wild Parrots of Telegraph Hill*. (Their fame increased when the film of the book was released in 2005.) The total population in California was believed to be in the region of 300 by the end of the century. In Ecuador these conures are threatened by loss of habitat – and formerly by trapping. Large numbers were imported into the USA. The day might come when populations established in California are the only means of ensuring the continuation of the species.

Another conure, more common in its native southern South American than its red-headed counterpart, is the Nanday (*Nandayus nenday*), with a Californian population in the region of 200 birds. When some moved out of suburbia into canyons to the west of Los Angeles, and nested in native sycamore trees (*Platanus racemosa*), it was suggested that their benign exotic status might be changing to invasive (Garrett and Mabb, 2004). However, the Nandays were still close to residential areas, having invaded the canyon to find nest sites.

Quaker Parakeets

Quaker (or Monk) Parakeets (*Myiopsitta monachus*) are unique among parrots in constructing huge twig nests. They carry the twigs to the site one by one and cleverly weave them together. These parakeets occur in dry, semi-open lowlands in the southern part of South America where there are few trees large enough to offer nesting holes, thus they evolved to solve this problem in a very satisfactory way. They are colony nesters; the huge structures accommodate many breeding pairs.

One of the reasons why conures and Quakers colonised other countries was because they were exported in massive numbers from countries such as Argentina and Bolivia. The purchasers in far-off countries quickly tired of their loud, harsh calls and, I suspect, opened the cage door and let them go. There are now naturalised populations of Quakers in countless countries worldwide. In Belgium a colony of these grey and green parakeets was responsible for destroying a factory chimney. The first pair arrived in 1979 and their numbers increased to 60 or so. When the company who owned the factory in Ukkel moved, the people living nearby liked the parakeets so much they asked the company to leave the chimney intact. The twig nests had grown, over the years, into a huge "apartment block" 20ft (6m) high. The weight brought the chimney crashing down.

In the USA stable populations of the Quaker Parakeet were established in at least 14 states. Records showed that during the late 1960s and early 1970s more than 64,000 were imported into the USA. They became established as the result of releases, intentional and unintentional. In colder areas such as Illinois they survived in winter by feeding at bird tables. In the 1970s these parakeets started to grace the Brooklyn

skies. For some years they kept a low profile, nesting in cosy places, such as near the powerful lights that shine on the playing fields of Brooklyn College or around the warm transformers at the tops of utility poles. One local man whose house faced a nest noticed that even in the most violent windstorms, when trees come down, their nests stayed intact. Residents seemed to like them.

But their nests were causing problems by blocking the ventilation ports on transformers, thus creating fire hazards and disrupting local power supplies. In New York City Quaker Parakeets were implicated in what became known as Blackout 2003. One August day the whole city lost its power source. When one power company arrived with cherry picker vehicles and dismantled five nests some local residents wept! The explanation that people on life support could die if the power supply was lost did not satisfy them.

Due to its alleged potential as an agricultural pest, the Quaker Parakeet was banned in some states of the USA. Ownership and selling were not permitted in California, Georgia, Kansas, Kentucky, New Jersey, Pennsylvania, Tennessee, Wyoming and Hawaii. In Connecticut you could own them but not sell them or breed them. Residents of New York and Virginia had to register their Quakers with the state. The amount of legislation enacted in connection with this species in the USA was nothing short of amazing. You would think that they had posed a threat to national security!

Quaker Parakeets were persecuted as agricultural pests in the 1970s in the Central Valley of California. However, according to Todd S. Campbell of the Institute for Biological Invasions, the US Fish and Wildlife Service's attempt to eradicate them in the 1970s failed. Despite the small sizes of all the feral populations at that time, they could not be wiped out. This parakeet did not wreak havoc on agriculture as predicted by its behaviour in its native countries in southern South America. It truly was a survivor. Campbell states: "Its endearing qualities and status as a persecuted underdog have brought many local citizens, politicians, birders, and even professional biologists to the defense of this invader."

People enjoyed these cheeky characters! They were fun to have around! When I lived in Tenerife Quakers would visit daily, feeding on the seed from my own aviaries. I came to know some of them as individuals. There was, for example, "Longbeak" who had a greatly thickened and overgrown upper mandible, probably the result of a beak injury. I can understand how Quakers would add joy to the lives of many city dwellers.

Amazon Parrots

In the USA, released and escaped Amazon parrots became firmly established in the southern states. They were thriving in southern California due to the profusion of tropical plants and trees (perhaps even their natural food plants) that bore fruits and blossoms the year round. In addition, mature trees offered roost and nest sites. These intelligent birds with long memories were not slow to utilise these resources.

While the purist is aghast at the thought of thriving introduced populations of any species, in the case of the Green-cheeked Amazon (*Amazona viridigenalis*) there could be conservation benefits. Biologist Karen Mabb believed that southern California held about 25% of the world population. By 2003 their numbers were estimated at 2,800 birds.

■ *Green-cheeked Amazon.*

Amazingly, they represented more than 40% of the state's estimated free-living 6,600 parrots of 13 species! Furthermore, the wild population of Green-cheeked Amazons in Mexico (the only country to which they are native), which declined dramatically due to habitat loss, was estimated as being as low as 3,000 birds by the end of the century.

Karen Mabb began to study the Californian population in 1996. Her observations indicated that they were creatures of habit, commuting to feeding sites via a set route in flocks of up to 20. Sometimes they returned with their plumage covered in fruit juice. During the period from spring to autumn they roosted in ash, sycamore and liquidambar trees, enjoying the fruits, buds and bark. In winter they wisely moved to trees that retain their leaves, such as fig, eucalyptus, oak and Indian laurel. Winter roosting sites contained as many as 500 Green-cheeked Amazons.

Predators were few. Karen Mabb saw crows taking eggs and chicks. When a hawk tried to attack ten parrots it was harassed by them from above, causing it to fly off. Even the smaller Mitred Conures would mob a hawk. As usual, man was a threat; some chicks were removed from nests. In the San Gabriel Valley Karen Mabb found that food and nest sites were plentiful; the area was so disturbed by human activity that competition with native animal species was limited. In her opinion, roost sites were the limiting factor in the parrot's numbers.

According to Kimball Garrett, of the Natural History Museum of Los Angeles, the introduced parrots were a symptom of how residents modified and destroyed the native habitat of lowland California. It was inevitable that exotic species would move into areas of exotic vegetation. By 2003 at least seven parrot species had populations in excess of 100 individuals. Four species that exceeded 500 individuals were Green-cheeked and Lilac-crowned (Finsch's) Amazons (*Amazona finschi*, Mitred Conures with more than 1,000, and Ringneck Parakeets with a population of about 900 birds in the San Joaquin Valley.

Amazons enjoyed the climate of coastal California. A resident of San Diego, near Ocean Beach, reported a flock of eight to ten Green-cheeked and an occasional Lilac-crowned, a threatened endemic species in Mexico (added to

Appendix I of CITES in 2005). He followed the group and watched the parrots feeding on date palms. They made a lot of noise while feasting on the sticky fruits and dropping some on the cars below.

It was rumoured that these Amazons originated from a local woman who would cross the Mexican border into Tijuana and "rescue" parrots from street vendors. When her house caught fire in the 1960s the fire fighters opened the cages and set the parrots free, to save their lives. Some were later recaptured. Others were thriving in the Ocean Beach area due to the abundance of food trees, such as macadamia, silk oak, pine and pecan. They nested in palm crowns. Many young fell out of these unstable nests and were tended by local vets.

Other introduced Green-cheeked Amazon populations existed in Texas and Puerto Rico, also apparently on the Hawaiian island of O'ahu. If this Amazon became extinct in its native country, something that, alas, is not beyond the bounds of possibility, it might still be numerous elsewhere. Even in Mexico there are feral populations; I saw them in the city of Monterrey in the north-east from where the species was extirpated in the past. It seemed to be re-establishing itself from escapees.

Free-living Amazons also existed on the eastern side of the United States, in Florida. In the 1980s the curator of Miami Metrozoo, Ron Johnson, took me to the roosting locality of a mixed flock: a small stand of casuarina trees by an apartment building in Miami. It was at the side of a busy road. Across the road was a park

▮ *White-fronted Amazon.*

with plenty of trees – but the Amazons found the casuarinas more appealing. We arrived just before dusk. Through binoculars we watched the parrots coming in to roost. Orange-winged and White-fronted (*albifrons*) predominated. There were also Yellow-fronted, Blue-fronted, Finsch's and one Double Yellow-head.

Two days later we returned at 6am to watch them leave and to try to estimate their numbers. As the sky lightened the first squawks and calls were heard from the roosting parrots. Soon many were calling excitedly before departing to their feeding grounds. At 6.40am the first small group flew out. Other Amazons were preening and chattering and groups took off in various directions. By 7.20am, when all the parrots had left, our count was approximately 120.

Where had they come from? At that time Miami was a hotbed of livestock importers. Some of the Amazons might have escaped from their premises but perhaps the majority had escaped or been released from their cages. Wild-caught adult birds do not make good pets.

A flock of Amazon parrots numbering about 150 birds in 1997 lived in and near the grounds of the famous Breakers Hotel on Palm Beach Island. Amazons were first seen there in the late 1950s. The mature trees provided a plentiful harvest of fruits, nuts and seeds. It was rumoured that they originated from the private collection of an eccentric millionaire, who instructed that on his death the parrots should be liberated. They included a number of Green-cheeked Amazons – and notably several cinnamon specimens that were breeding. (One private aviculturist in Florida maintained a breeding stock of this high-priced mutation which perhaps originated from the introduced population.)

The climate of the Caribbean islands, natural home of 11 Amazon species, is of course also to the liking of non-native Amazons. These could threaten endangered native species. According to a report made in 1996, on Puerto Rico, Yellow-naped Amazons, Quaker Parakeets, conures, Cockatiels and cockatoos had been released or escaped At least three species had established breeding colonies. It seemed unlikely that they would make their home in the relatively inhospitable habitat of the Luquillo forest, where the remnant population of the native parrot was found.

Introduced populations provided the opportunity for parrot lovers to observe their favourite birds living free without going to the countries of origin. The island of Barbados once had a native Amazon, according to reports that referred back to the 16th century. In 1998 a local bird lover took me to the Belville area on the south-west coast. Cabbage palms in the heart of this residential area formed the favoured roosting site of a small group of Amazons. At 5.30pm we heard their distant calls. It was a few minutes before three broad-winged silhouettes winged their way above us to land in the top of a palm – and instantly disappeared from sight. The Amazons were quiet for a while. Soon more groups of three to five birds arrived. They perched high in the trees, stayed for a few minutes then flew, calling loudly, to nearby palm crowns. At least 15 had come in. The light was fading but through the binoculars I had identified Orange-winged and Yellow-crowned Amazons.

At least five sites were used, with approximately 20 birds in each location. They had not colonised the northern part of the island because they would not fly over the extensive cane fields. Breeding occurred but their numbers had not increased because the young were removed for pets, by cutting down the palm trees in which the Amazons nested. They bred unmolested in the grounds of the Prime Minister's residence.

In California, where there were perhaps more naturalised parrots than anywhere else by the end of the century, they were not considered to be ecologically invasive, even although some were abundant. Their overlap with native birds was mainly with adaptable species such as Crows, Band-tailed Pigeons and Acorn Woodpeckers that inhabited suburban and urban areas.

Introduced Amazons in other locations might have deprived some native birds of nesting sites but their numbers, even after a couple of decades, had not increased to pest proportions. This was probably because they were inadvertently controlled by people who took young from nests. On balance, the pleasure these parrots gave to local people far outweighed any nuisance value. And, in my view, the conservation potential of the Green-cheeked Amazons in California should not be overlooked. Although it seems unlikely, it is not beyond the bounds of possibility that the parrots in California and Florida, where introduced populations are thriving, might be used to re-establish wild populations of some endangered species. The case of the Green-cheeked Amazons shows that they might actually be better protected in California than in their natural habitat.

■ *Dhani Papuan with a Yellow-capped Pygmy Parrot* (Micropsitta keiensis) *

16. "NEW" SPECIES IN THE 20TH CENTURY

In the 1750s the Swedish naturalist Carl von Linné (Linnaeus) devised a system of binomial nomenclature (genus and species) for plants and animals. It still operates today as the only form of classification. At that time relatively few birds were known to scientists. The only parrots classified in this way were the Ornate Lorikeet, the Red Lory and the Chattering, Purple-naped and Black-capped Lories, the Moustache Parakeet, the Blue-crowned Hanging Parrot, the Red-faced Lovebird, the Lesser Vasa and the Grey Parrot, the Scarlet Macaw, Hahn's Macaw, the Sun, Petz's and Brown-throated Conures, Green-rumped Parrotlet, Black-headed Caique, Hawk-headed Parrot, the Sordid Pionus, and seven species of Amazon: Cuban, Yellow-billed, Black-billed, Red-lored, Red-tailed, Festive and Blue-fronted. Almost certainly other parrot species were known, but without an international system to name them, they had not been recorded scientifically.

Between 1820 and 1890 about 300 more species were added to this list but it was not yet complete. In far-off days many were described from skins rather than from living birds. During the first two decades of the 20th century thirteen more parrots were described as new to science. Four of these were small species of island lorikeets that would have been difficult to detect in the little visited regions they inhabited.

Meek's Lorikeet (*Charmosyna meeki*) is tiny, 6in (15cm) long and all green. A canopy-dweller in the high, misty forests of the Solomon Islands,

it is no wonder it remained undetected for so long! The game was up in 1901 when it was detected on the island of Kolombangara during an expedition led by Albert Meek.

Lorikeets and Pygmy Parrots

Meek was the son of a London natural history dealer. In 1889, at the age of 17, he sailed to Australia where he worked on sheep and cattle stations for five years. In 1894 he went to New Guinea. This journey marked the start of his career as a collector. He spent 20 years in New Guinea and the Solomon Islands, seeking bird specimens, mainly for Lord Walter Rothschild (1868–1937), who amassed the second largest (to the British Museum) zoological collection in Britain. Among the new species he obtained was Meek's Lorikeet and, later, Meek's Pygmy Parrot (*Micropsitta meeki*), named in his honour by Lord Rothschild (see Chapter 3), his museum curator in 1914.

Small parrots in remote places are difficult to detect – and none are smaller than the Pygmy Parrots. Ranging in size from 3 ½ in to 4in (8.5–10cm), they climb about tree trunks and branches using their stiffened tail feathers for support, while they nibble at lichen. Found in New Guinea and the Solomon Islands, they have long aroused the imagination of parrot lovers. It is believed that they cannot be kept in captivity because they feed mainly on lichens.

Seldom is the exact moment of a species' discovery recorded but we have to thank Walter

---

* Photographed by Christian Krause in the Baliem River region of Irian Jaya in 1977.

■ *Lord Walter Rothschild.*

Goodfellow for one such moment, graphically described. Born in 1866, Goodfellow was an intrepid explorer and a member of the Avicultural Society. In 1903 he went to the island of Mindanao. Mount Apo, the highest peak of the Philippines, was covered in dense jungle to a height of about 8,500ft (2,800m). A white stony slope rose above this with crumbling cliffs, intersected with burning fissures and an incessant noise as of colossal machinery working underground. The white slope of the volcano, viewed from a distance, conveyed the impression of a snow-capped summit. The upper forests were dark and gloomy and depressing.

Early one morning Goodfellow stood for a while looking up at the crater when he was surprised to hear the unmistakable chatter of small lorikeets. He traced these sounds to an isolated tree. A flock of 30 or more lorikeets flew out, circled around at a great height and re-entered the tree. He recorded: "Beyond noticing the yellow undersides of their wings flash as they turned in the sunlight, it was impossible to gather any idea of their appearance. I was convinced this must be a new species..." (Goodfellow, 1906).

One can imagine how his heart quickened at the thought, the excitement that surged through

him! In the name of science he had to obtain a specimen. This he did. Then he could see what a pretty bird it was with its brick pink forehead and throat, brown-maroon band from the lores through the eyes to the nape, and yellow and green underparts. He named the new species Mrs Johnstone's Lorikeet (*Trichoglossus johnstoniae*) after a well-known aviculturist for whom he was a collector. He acquired four live birds, three of which he landed in England in 1905. Appropriately, Mrs Johnstone became the first person to keep and, in 1906, to breed this species. It later became known as the Mount Apo and, more recently, as the Mindanao Lorikeet (see colour page 6).

Two more small lorikeets were subsequently named. In 1911 the Striated Lorikeet (*Charmosyna multistriata*) from the main mountain ranges of New Guinea was described. It remained a little known bird, in nature and in aviculture.

■ *Striated Lorikeet.*

On Henderson Island

Members of the genus *Vini* are tiny, short-tailed jewels, confined to the Pacific region. Stephen's Lory (*Vini stepheni*) has the most easterly distribution of any lory, being confined to Henderson Island, an ancient coral reef in south-eastern Polynesia. The island measures only 6 miles by 3 miles (9.6km x 4.8km). As the Pitcairn Islands, of which Henderson is the largest, are extremely remote, with no major landmass within 3000 miles (5,000km), few ornithologists visited this outpost. The little scarlet, green and blue gem (see colour page

20) was not named to science until 1908. In the previous year an Australian by the name of Alfred Ernest Stephen visited Henderson while directing prospecting expeditions in the Pacific. He shot two lories. They were preserved in spirit and forwarded to the Australian Museum.

Henderson Island is the world's best remaining example of an elevated coral atoll ecosystem with few exotic species of plants or animals. It is densely vegetated with tangled scrub and scrub forest, the tallest trees being screw pine (*Pandanus tectorius*). Pigs and goats were introduced early in the 20th century but fortunately died out.

The island's four species of endemic land birds include the lory. Few parrots have a smaller area of distribution. The Pitcairn Island Group is a Dependent Territory of the UK. If the government had allowed it to be settled this little lory would be long gone. The island can be visited only with a licence issued by the Governor and, since 1995, by payment of a significant fee. If only this desirable state applied to other islands with endemic birds, how much more secure their futures would be! Long may Stephen's Lory remain almost unknown!

In the early 1920s, the Dutch lepidopterist Toxopeus was collecting on the Indonesian island of Buru when he received seven live specimens of a small lorikeet. It was entirely green, darker above, with an orange bill. Extraordinary as it may seem, this is the only time the species has been positively identified. Buru is a mountainous island of 3,000 sq miles (8,000 sq km); after 1965 it was used as the main internment camp for thousands of Communist prisoners. Some areas were clear-felled. The Red Lory and the Green-naped Lorikeet, two widespread and adaptable species, survived there. If the Buru Lorikeet (*Charmosyna toxopei*) still exists, it must be extremely rare.

Racket-tailed Parrots

Unique among parrots, the six species of Racket-tails (*Prioniturus*) have the two central tail feathers elongated into a shaft terminating in a spatule. The tail is otherwise square and of medium length. These parrots are found in the Philippines, also in Indonesia, including the island of Buru in the southern Moluccas to which island the Buru Racket-tail (*P. mada*) is

endemic. It was not described until 1900. In 1903 when Goodfellow discovered the lorikeet on Mount Apo, he was unaware that further down the mountain lived another parrot unknown to science. It was the Mindanao Racket-tail (*P. waterstradti*). In the following year it was located at 3,000ft (about 1,000m) by a Danish professional collector, Johannes Waterstradt, who made many expeditions to the region.

Africa

The last African parrot to be named was the Black-cheeked Lovebird. Found only in river valleys in mopane woodland in south-western Zambia, it has the most restricted range of all the lovebirds. Although Zambia (to become Northern Rhodesia in 1911) had attracted many European adventurers and explorers, including David Livingstone, not until 1906 was the lovebird formally identified. The first specimen was collected by Dr A. H. B. Kirkman in September 1904, and described by W. L. Sclater in *The Bulletin of the British Ornithologists Club* (1906, vol. 16: 61–62. Regrettably, the Black-cheeked Lovebird quickly became an endangered species during the 1920s, due to over-trapping. (See Chapter 5.)

South America's conures

This great continent produced more surprises during the last two decades of the century than could ever have been imagined. In the first two decades the *Pyrrhura* conures, pretty small parakeets, were still being counted. Two more species were added to the 23 already known. In 1913 northern Colombia's Santa Marta Mountains gave up its best-kept secret, the Santa Marta Conure (*P. viridicata*), with its orange shoulders and primary coverts. The presence of drug operators in the area deterred people from going there. It was found above 6,500ft (2,000m) and much of the original habitat had been cleared to grow marijuana. Only 77 square miles (200 square km) of suitable habitat had survived to the end of the century, making this little known *Pyrrhura* vulnerable to extinction.

In the year after *viridicata* was named, another *Pyrrhura* was discovered in the mountains of Ecuador. The White-necked Conure (*P. albipectus*) is distinctive, with a broad white collar and a plain yellow breast. (Most members of the genus have the breast feathers heavily scalloped with a contrasting colour.) Not until 2002 was this species recorded from extreme northern Peru – the first record for that country. An uncommon bird with a small population and a small area of distribution, it was at risk from forest clearance – even in the Podocarpus National Park.

In September 1939 a *Pyrrhura* conure was collected in south-western Ecuador, reportedly at about 1,000ft (300m). Its skin lay, unrecognised, in a drawer in the Natural History Museum (first in London, then at Tring in Hertfordshire) for four decades. In August 1980 an unidentified *Pyrrhura* species was seen at a higher elevation than that collected in 1939, at Piñas in the province of El Oro. Five years later Robert Ridgely, eminent specialist in neotropical avifauna, and Kenneth Berlin of RARE Center (the American conservation organisation), verified it as a new species: the El Oro Parakeet (*Pyrrhura orcesi*).

In 1981 RARE Center had sent a small expedition to Ecuador to survey the western slopes of the Andes. On the very first day of field work the conure was sighted in a new area, west of Naranjal in the Province of Azuay. At an altitude of 3,000ft (900m) two flocks numbering 18 birds were feeding in fruit trees in a heavily cut-over valley. This sighting extended the known range by 62 miles (100km) north of the original site. This, apparently, was the entire extent of the range – in an area only three to six miles (5-10km) wide. Due to the small range and rapid habitat decline, the conure was immediately described as Endangered. By the early 1990s, only 4% of the original forest cover remained – on the most inaccessible slopes.

From pre-dawn the forest is enshrouded with cloud for several hours, at both locations. Here the trees and the dense understory are laden with epiphytes and the branches are hung with mosses. The El Oro Conure (see colour page 20) is a bird of the high forest where clouds roll in from the coast. Five sites between 2,000ft (600m) and 3,900ft (1,200m) were investigated without any sign of the species. In the Bolívar Province most of the montane forest had been replaced by orange groves, some of which were 70 years old. The conure's habitat had nearly disappeared. Large trees were being removed daily from accessible tracts of forest.

Above 3,000ft (900m), deforestation was less severe due to the steep terrain. It is a sobering thought that this conure nearly became extinct without knowledge of its existence.

In 2002 the Loro Parque Fundación (see Chapter 13) joined forces with Jocotoco, a major conservation organisation in Ecuador. In the first months of their fieldwork it was estimated that 120 to 135 El Oro Conures lived in the Buenaventura valley and 40 or 50 more inhabited an adjacent valley 2km to the north. During the 2002/2003 breeding season five nests sites were found, all in tree cavities at an elevation above 3,280ft (1,000m). Researchers Martin Schaefer and Veronika Schmidt discovered that this parakeet has a communal breeding system. It nests in groups of from three to nine birds. Incubation duties were shared among several individuals. Radio-tracking revealed that in three nests at least three birds incubated and incubation periods lasted between three and four hours. Two nests were successful but only one bird was reared in each. In captivity *Pyrrhura* conures are prolific breeders, rearing four to six young in a nest. In 2003 only ten young were reared in the entire valley, perhaps because of dry weather during the breeding season.

The El Oro Conures in Buenaventura generally avoided lower altitude forest, even although they fed and roosted on pasture and one pair bred on a cattle ranch. They preferred forest patches with large trees, where they feed on figs. Usually only 20–30 used the reserve, which was not large enough to protect the species. Then Jocotoco purchased two adjacent priority areas that encompassed the home range of three or four flocks. Disused cattle pastures were the focus of a reforestation programme using seedlings grown from fruits collected there. Seeds were collected to establish a nursery and 1,300 tree saplings donated by the Ecuadorian Ministry of the Environment were planted.

In 2002 an education project was launched, with Loro Parque Foundation as the main sponsor. Project members took classes of children into the reserve where the basic principles of montane forest ecosystems were explained. They also visited schools to explain the consequences of habitat destruction and hold talks with local politicians and landowners (Waugh, 2004). The discovery of this small

▌ *Charles Munn.*

conure could have a long-term beneficial impact on its forests.

All field workers dream about "discovering" a new species, one that has never featured in any field guide, which has never been noticed before by scientists. In October 1985 Charles Munn saw and photographed a tiny parrot in the Manu National Park in Peru. He did not know what it was. In 1986, while working 19 miles (30km) further downstream on the river Manu, Munn and his assistants repeatedly observed flocks of the same species eating the fruits of a vine, a member of the fig family. Macaws were his main interest, so he passed the information on.

A "new" parrotlet

John O'Neill is a great American ornithologist who has discovered more bird species unknown to science than anyone alive. In July 1987 he was working in the eastern Peruvian rainforest, east of the city of Pucallpa (near the Brazilian border). Two members of the expedition, Tony and Pete, had seen some small parrots every day in a tall stand of bamboo close to the Rio Ucayali. The parrots were difficult to observe in the flowering bamboo so one afternoon they decided (in the name of science) to try to obtain a couple of specimens. They each came back into camp clutching a very small green parrot. Tony handed one to John O'Neill, commenting: "It looks like a *Forpus* parrotlet."

John O'Neill exclaimed: "There's no blue in the wings. And look at the blue on the forehead! It's something new!" Then he realised: "This is the same small parrotlet that Charlie Munn has seen at Manu" (Stap, 1990.)

Only 6in (14cm) long and green with a powdery blue crown, this inconspicuous little bird was soon hailed as a major ornithological discovery. It was formally named the Amazonian Parrotlet (*Nannopsittaca dachilleae*) in a paper published by John O'Neill, Charles Munn and another ornithologist in 1991. It occurred locally in south-eastern Peru and north-western Bolivia, with a question mark over adjacent western Brazil. Its habitat was relatively intact, mainly due to inaccessibility. But all that changed with developments such as mining, road-building and human colonisation. The parrotlet soon became another entry on the long list of Near-threatened species.

Rare parrots of the Andes

In August 1911 two bird collectors from the American Museum of Natural History in New York climbed to 10,000ft (3,000m) in the Central Cordillera mountain range of Colombia. Leo Miller and Arthur Allen had scaled the slopes of the snow-capped volcanoes of Tolima and Santa Isabel. They spent several months in the inhospitable and desolate high Andean páramo and stunted forest

▌ *Amazonium Parrotlet depicted by renowned ornithologist and artist, John O'Neill.*
Reproduced by kind permission of John O'Neill

wilderness to explore the bird life. They were rewarded by discovering a distinctive species. It was described the following year and named the Azure-winged Parrot (*Hapalopsittaca fuertesi*). Nothing more was seen of this parrot and it was feared extinct.

The genus *Hapalopsittaca* is perhaps the least known of all neotropical parrots and contains some of the most endangered species. These small green parrots from the Andean region are about 9in (23m) long, green and prettily marked with contrasting colours on head, wings and tail. They are unknown in aviculture.

Opinions vary regarding the number of species that exist. Forshaw (1989) gave only two while other authors give specific status to forms that Forshaw recognised as sub-species, making four species. The Azure-winged Parrot, or Fuertes' Parrot (see colour page 20), from the Central Andes of Colombia, was feared extinct. The American bird artist, after whom the parrot was named, Louis Agassiz Fuertes, did not have much luck either. He was killed in New York when his car was struck by a train.

In 1989 came very exciting news. More than 70 years after the first sighting of Fuertes' Parrot an unidentified member of the genus was seen in the area. Smithsonian Museum ornithologist Gary Graves described a new sub-species (*velezi*) of the Rusty-faced Parrot (*Hapalopsittaca amazonina*), a species previously known from the Eastern Cordillera range of Colombia to Venezuela. It differed from the other sub-species, also from *fuertesi*, in having the hind-neck and nape golden olive.

The rich soils and lush vegetation of the volcano, where these two closely related parrots had lived, attracted colonists who ravished its natural resources and denuded its steep hillsides. The designation of "Los Nevados National Park" had only marginally stopped colonization. What little forest remained was plundered for firewood and cleared for potato fields and pasture. Despite Miller and Allen providing accurate details of where they originally found it, subsequent searches over nine decades had failed to locate Fuertes' Parrot. Its plight had not gone unnoticed, as national and international conservation and ornithological authorities, such as BirdLife International, had listed the species as Critically Endangered. It was the harsh environment and difficult access that

■ *The chilly cloud forest habitat of* Hapalopsittaca amazonina velezi. *It is most easily accessible on horseback.*

had been a deterrent to searching the species' possible range.

Then a team from Fundación ProAves (partly funded by Loro Parque Fundación) made a determined effort to rediscover it. In 2000, Jorge Velasquez, then 20, was a student at Colombia's National University in Bogotá. With initial help from the American Bird Conservancy, a series of preliminary searches were launched throughout the Colombian Andes for both species of *Hapalopsittaca*. You have to know the habitat to realise that looking for a needle in a haystack might be easy in comparison.

Jorge rapidly located several new populations of the Endangered Rusty-faced Parrot and collected vital ecological data useful for its conservation, but Fuertes' Parrot eluded him. Was it already extinct? One day Jorge and another ornithologist, Alonso Quevedo, ascended over 10,000ft (3,000m) through a mosaic of pastures to a small patch of cloud forest. Shrouded in a dense mist that swirled around the forest canopy in the afternoon winds, the silence was ominous. Suddenly, a sharp cry pierced the gloom and a single parrot was joined by others in the mist. "The ghostly silhouettes of fourteen parrots tumbled from the cloud, drawing nearer, as if released from the heavens," said Jorge. They spiralled downwards in tight vortexes to alight in nearby trees. In those few seconds, brilliant emerald greens, cobalt blues and scarlet flashed before Jorge and Alonso. They thought they were witnessing a miracle, as one of the world's rarest birds – Fuertes' Parrot – materialised before their eyes. July 28 2002 would forever live in their memories.

■ *Female Fuertes' Parrot looks out of her artificial nest site.*

After a long night celebrating with local people, Jorge and Alonso spent several days studying the flock, taking detailed notes, sound-recordings, photos and video to document the discovery and to provide vital information on the species' ecology and biology. It seemed incredible that the 14 birds, which included three juveniles, had survived in just a few dozen hectares of forest. The critical requirements of the species appeared to be tall mature trees, where they fed on berries amongst the epiphyte-laden canopy branches and found vital nesting cavities.

Jorge and Alonso's elation faded when they encountered a young parrot lying dead near the forest, perhaps killed by a hawk. As Alonso reflected: "The flock survives in a tiny forest island in a sea of pasture and cattle. My team's task has only just begun. We must commence the vital job of protecting the species with great urgency."

In 2003 they were elated to discover a nest containing young with the entrance 8ft (2.4m) from the ground. At an altitude of 10,500ft (3,200m), it was in a cut tree, in a locality where trees had been felled. The researchers had identified an area of 700 hectares of good habitat for this parrot and, furthermore, had ensured its protection under written contract with the local mayor. By forming a "friends of the parrots group" and giving talks to the local community, they had taken important steps to secure the parrot's future. Protection could only be successful with the full support and commitment of the local people who unwittingly were the parrot's greatest threat.

The Fundación ProAves team erected more than 200 natural wood nest-boxes, covered with bark. In April 2004 came wonderful news! Five boxes were occupied by breeding pairs, which were then incubating eggs. In 2005 an astounding 21 nests were monitored in artificial boxes (underlining the lack of suitable nest sites) as well as 12 in natural nests. Of these 33 nests, young fledged from 83%.

Brazilian surprises

Closely related to the *Hapalopsittaca* parrots are the *Pionopsitta* from the same region. One member of this genus, the Vulturine Parrot (*P. vulturina*), is often given a genus to itself, *Gypopsitta*, because adult birds differ in having

Photograph courtesy REFAP S.A.

42 A picture book about the Red-spectacled Amazon (*Amazona pretrei*) taught children in Brazil about the need to protect this parrot (CHAPTER 12). **43** There are probably more Blue-throated Macaws (*Ara glaucogularis*) in the aviaries of **Loro Parque Fundación** than exist in the wild. All these were hatched there (CHAPTER 13).

44 Pair of Spix's Macaws (*Cyanopsitta spixii*) in Loro Parque's former breeding centre.
45 Young Spix's Macaw hatched in the Foundation's breeding centre at La Vera (CHAPTER 13).
46 Slender-billed Parakeets (*Enicognathus leptorhynchus*), a declining species formerly classified as a pest (CHAPTER 14).

47 A pair of critically endangered Yellow-eared Parrots (*Ognorhynchus icterotis*) in the Andes of Colombia (CHAPTER 13). **48** One of the few Yellow-eared Parrots to have survived captivity. Photographed by Thomas Brosset in the UK. **49** A poster highlights the plight of the beautiful Cebu Hanging Parrot (*Loriculus philippensis chrysonotus*) (CHAPTER 12). It might already be extinct. **50** Green-winged Macaws at the clay lick at the Heath River, Peru (CHAPTER 18).

Illustration: Bernd Gerischer

Bernd Gerischer

51

51 Stephen's Lory (*Vini stepheni*) was not described to science until 1908 (CHAPTER 16).
52 Flame-winged or Brown-headed Conure, a threatened Colombian species, assisted by
Loro Parque Fundación. (CHAPTER 13). **53** The critically endangered Fuertes' Parrot
(*Hapalopsittaca fuertesi*) was believed extinct until 2002 (CHAPTER 16).

Photo: Fundación Loro Parque/ProAves

52

Photo: Alonso Quevedo/LPF

53

the head bare of feathers. However, this is not reason enough!

In 2002 a new species, *Pionopsitta aurantiocephala*, was described from Brazil, distinguished by its bare, bright orange head. It was claimed that in the past specimens were misidentified as the Vulturine Parrot. In the Vulturine Parrot the head is black and the bare skin extends only to the occiput; in *aurantiocephala* the nape is also bare. The Vulturine Parrot does not have a stage in which the bird is bare-headed without the black skin colouring. The newly described parrot is so far known only from a few localities encompassing the Lower Madeira and Upper Tapajos rivers. It is sympatric with (found in the same locations) as the Vulturine Parrot on both sides of the middle and lower Tapajos.

White-faced or Kawall's Amazon

Another discovery from the Amazon region concerned a member of a very well-known genus: *Amazona*. At first called Kawall's Amazon (*Amazona kawalli*), in scientific circles it is now called the White-faced Parrot, as this is the translation of the common name used by the local people where it occurs. The species remained undescribed partly because it was confused with the Mealy Amazon and partly because it inhabited a fairly remote region. The unique feature that distinguishes it from all other members of the genus is the naked area of bare skin (white) at the sides of the mandibles.

Nelson Kawall was born in 1928. He kept and bred Budgerigars as a child and received his first parrot, a Blue-fronted Amazon, when he was 12. He became a commercial breeder of parrots who, at one period, kept 50 different neotropical species. In 1968, when visiting Jose Xavier de Mendonça in Santarem, Kawall saw for the first time an Amazon that he believed was an undescribed species. This proved to be true and Kawall

■ *Nelson Kawall, after whom Kawall's Amazon was named.*
Photograph: Roland Seitre

■ *Kawall's or White-faced Amazon.*

considered Mendonça to be its true discoverer. He acquired the bird and found another in the aviaries of Alcides Vertamatti. I saw this species in Kawall's aviaries in Brazil in 1988 – but not for the first time (see Chapter 3).

In 1995 Tony Pittman and Joe Cuddy from England discovered in the Natural History Museum in Berlin a specimen of this Amazon labelled as *Amazona farinosa* aberr. *rubricauda* (= red-tailed). It carried a tag with a literary reference. The museum librarian found the reference – a report published in 1924 by Stresemann, the museum's curator. Stresemann stated that this Amazon had been in Berlin Zoo from 1910 to 1923. He described the bird, pointing out that the tail was shorter than that of *farinosa* and that the tail feathers were red at the base. The two outer feathers were margined with blue. A loose feather in an envelope that accompanied the skin highlighted the vivid colours of its tail. The museum curator agreed to send this specimen to the British Museum (Natural History) so that a comparison could be made with the specimen there, discovered in the collection by Nelson Kawall. The result was that Nigel Collar from BirdLife International and Tony Pittman co-authored a paper (in the *Bulletin of the British Ornithologists' Club*) in which the species was formally named.

Apart from the two twentieth century zoo birds, it is unknown in aviculture outside Brazil.

In the wild it has been located only in Brazil, from a few areas of lowland forest in the Amazon basin, from the northernmost Mato Grosso to as far south as the Serra dos Apiacas. These areas span 1,050 miles (1,700km). Further locations will almost certainly be discovered.

Kawall's Amazon was not the only "new" species of parrot hiding in the aviaries of Brazilian parrot collectors. Several were unaware that they kept an unnamed conure. In 2005 a species closely related to the Sun Conure was described for the first time. Called the Sulfur-breasted Parakeet (*Aratinga pintoi*), it was found on the northern bank of the lower Amazon River in the state of Pará. The excellent photograph by Roland Seitre (colour page 21) shows how little it differs from the Sun Conure. One of its distinguishing features is the green mantle and wing coverts, suffused with pale yellow.

Australian discoveries

In the early years of the 20th century W. McLennan worked in a farrier's shop in Victoria. He struck up a friendship with a man who taught him how to skin birds, preserve specimens and make field notes, and who introduced him to Dr William MacGillivray. The latter commissioned McLennan to collect birds in northern Queensland from 1909 to 1915.

In 1913 McLennan decided to investigate reports of a strange parrot in the rainforest of the Pascoe River on the Cape York Peninsula. While journeying up the river to look for a campsite, he saw what he was searching for – an unknown species of parrot, unlike any other in Australia. The male was an exquisitely beautiful bird with soft violet and rose-red head feathers. The *Geoffroyus* from Indonesia, New Guinea and the Solomon Islands are square-tailed green parrots varying in length from 8in to 10in (21cm to 25cm). In Australia this parrot remained undetected until the 20th century but this was explained by the fact that it inhabited rainforest in a little-known region. In those far-off days it would have been difficult to reach Cape York, on Australia's north-eastern tip.

McLennan had discovered the presence of the Red-cheeked Parrot (*Geoffroyus geoffroyi*) which was first described in 1811 from New Guinea and Indonesia. It was certainly worth the effort as the Australian sub-species was named after him: *maclennani*. His impact on Australian ornithology did not end there. He added four new genera including a parrot finch and a honeyeater. Yet another parrot skin he sent to Dr MacGillivray turned out to be a species not previously recorded in Australia – the Eclectus! The Australian sub-species was named *macgillivrayi* after the ardent collector.

From 1915 until 1922, with a break of two years when he fought in the first world war, McLennan worked for another collector. Then he turned his talents to prospecting for gold. Whether he was successful is not recorded but he had certainly been in the right place at the right time as a bird collector.

Name changes

Examination of the parrot literature from the start of the century and of that at the end, could give the impression that there were one hundred new species! The author of each new reference work on parrots invariably alters a substantial number of common names. This might be to keep in line with names accepted in the American ornithological world or because naming species after people is now discouraged (except when they are wealthy benefactors funding fieldwork!).

Sometimes it is considered more correct to use the name of the island to which a species is endemic. For example, Kuhl's Lory becomes the Rimatara Lorikeet. This helps to promote pride among local people that on their island exists a bird that is found nowhere else in the world. It has conservation benefits. The St Vincent Parrot used to be known as Guilding's Amazon because the naturalist who originally named the species did so from two specimens acquired by Lansdown Guilding, an accomplished Vincentian naturalist. Today his name has no significance and calling it the St Vincent Parrot is more logical.

Altering long established common names without good reason can cause much confusion. For example, one author used the name Black-crowned Parrot instead of Black-headed Caique and Maroon-faced Parakeet instead of White-eared Conure. These names will never find favour with aviculturists!

Language is constantly evolving and during the 1980s the spelling of parrakeet in English was gradually dropped in favour of the American parakeet. This seems illogical. Will we one day be referring to parrots as parots?

17. TWENTIETH CENTURY EXTINCTIONS

Even Gilbert White, the most renowned naturalist of his age, shot the sparrows and owls on his property. When he died, in 1793, two Indian Ocean species had recently become extinct, the Broad-billed Parrot (*Lophopsittacus mauritianus*) from Mauritius and the Rodrigues Parrot (*Necropsittacus rodericanus*) from the island of that name. The cause was almost certainly hunting. The beautiful Cuban Macaw (*Ara tricolor*) (see Chapter 11) survived until 1864 when the last known bird was shot close to the Zapata swamp.

In the 20th century, when firearms were so readily available, shooting was blamed for the extinction of the Carolina Parakeet (*Conuropsis [Aratinga] carolinensis*) in the United States. Its range was extensive – from the east coast south from Virginia and west to Nebraska and Texas, and north to New York, Indiana, Ohio and Illinois and even, apparently, as far as Wisconsin. This area covered about 1,200 miles (1,920km) from east to west and from north to south. As Errol Fuller recorded: "This unusual distribution did not long survive the systematic colonization of North America, however. As European influence upon the land became increasingly felt during the nineteenth century, so the area occupied by parakeets was steadily pegged back – in the west towards the Mississippi River; in the south towards Florida" (Fuller, 2001).

Noisy and colourful, the Carolina Parakeet favoured woodland habitat along rivers.

Christopher Cokinos wrote poetically, its "neck and head shone yellow, like the sawtooth sunflower, and its forehead shone the red of blood-oranges, the red of distant, slowly dying stars" (Cokinos, 2000).

As its habitat was destroyed by the settlers and gave way to orchards and other cultivation, the parakeet found new sources of food. Flocks covered fields of corn like a brilliantly coloured carpet. They had become pests. In 1831 Audubon made the most famous painting of this species, accurately showing seven birds feeding on cocklebur. As with all Audubon's paintings, it seemed to have an element of fantasy about it, in this case because of the unnatural positions of some of these birds. It somehow made it hard to envisage the Carolina like any other parakeet. My first sight of a photo of a living bird made the species real. It was not behind bars in a zoo but in a pet situation, as one might find a Sun Conure today. The photograph was taken in 1906 by Paul Bartsch, the owner of a tame Carolina called "Doodles". Nestled up to his friend, a Mr Bryan, Doodles is about to give him a kiss. If ever a photo depicted the poignancy of extinction, it was this one. (I am indebted to Shirley Briggs who rescued it from a tangle of brittle old negatives left by Paul Bartsch.)

To make his painting, Audubon had "procured a basketful at a few shots" from his gun. If one could have transported a competent 20th century aviculturist into the past and given him the "basketful", there would be a fair chance

■ *"Doodles" the Carolina Parakeet with his friend Mr Bryan.*

Photograph by Paul Bartsch, courtesy of C. Cokinos and Daniel McKinley

1917. The male, Incas, died in February 1918; he was the last known living representative of his species. Rumours persisted into the 1920s that the species existed in Florida and Carolina.

Although shooting accounted for the deaths of hundreds of thousands of Carolinas, some nature historians believe that it was loss of habitat that was the real cause of its extinction. In the 20th century the Quaker Parakeet established itself in many regions of the United States (see Chapter 15), including some once occupied by the Carolina.

If the Quaker could survive, why did the Carolina die out? The Quaker can breed anywhere, as it builds its own nest, so was the real reason for the demise of the Carolina lack of nesting sites? There is another theory. Often living in close contact with humans, this parakeet might have been exposed to disease from poultry, for example – a disease to which it had no resistance.

that the species would have been saved from extinction! But in 1831 the breeding in captivity of exotic birds was a very rare event. The Carolina was quite close to a Jendaya Conure (*Aratinga jandaya*) in appearance, except for the light-coloured beak. It differed from the typical *Aratinga* in two minor details: the cere was feathered and it lacked the attenuated (long and narrow) fourth primary. However, neither feature is important enough to place a species in a separate genus.* In 1826 the Carolina Conure was classified with the *Aratinga* species, then the name of the genus was changed to *Conuropsis* before it reverted to *Aratinga* again. The Carolina's generic name became stuck in a time warp – the time it became extinct in the wild.

During the 1880s Cincinnati Zoo received 16 Carolina Conures at the price of $2.50 each. A number of zoos kept the species and knew that it was approaching extinction in the wild. Perhaps the belief existed that captive breeding could not save a species reduced to little more than a handful of birds. Whatever the reason, the Carolinas gradually died until only one pair survived in captivity, at Cincinnati Zoo. The female, called Lady Jane, died in the summer of

The Glaucous Macaw

While the very day of the passing of the last Carolina Parakeet is part of ornithological history, by the time it was suggested that the Glaucous Macaw (*Anodorhynchus glaucus*) was extinct it was almost certainly long gone. References to these macaws being kept as pets make fascinating reading. In 1908 Wesley Page, editor of the magazine *Bird Notes*, visited Mrs Anningson of Cambridge and congratulated her on so rare an acquisition as a Hyacinthine Macaw – almost unknown outside zoological gardens. I read his account – at first incredulous, then with mounting excitement for, "more rare if anything than the preceding which it closely resembles" was a Glaucous Macaw! Could it have been a Lear's – wrongly identified? No – the description made it clear that it was a Glaucous: "... of a greyer hue, and the head and neck of a decided greenish tinge; cheeks, throat and crest slightly tinged with brown." In any case, Page had seen Lear's Macaws in Hubert Astley's collection, so he knew the difference. The Glaucous was in "faultless condition" and was perfectly gentle with its fortunate owner. In 1913 it was still alive, and was said to be a male.

---

* For example, only some members of the lorikeet genus *Charmosyna* have attenuated primaries and only one sub-species of an Amazon parrot has the cere feathered.

■ *Carolina Parakeet: museum specimen.*
Photograph: David Alderton

When Wesley Page saw it in that year, the maid took it out of its cage, caressed it, and held it in her arms (*Bird Notes*, Nov 1913).

Its existence overlapped with one at London Zoo whose records indicate that it arrived in May 1898 and died in 1912. Another entered the collection in 1906 and lived until 1916. It seems likely that they were correctly identified for Lear's Macaws were fairly well known. The Glaucous differed in its blue-grey head, dull grey cheeks and lores (tinged with blue) and brown-grey throat (see colour page 22). An obvious difference was the brownish underside of the tail (blackish in Lear's) and the brown tail feather shaft. In the same era, J. W. Marsden of Harrogate, who kept a large and varied bird collection, mentioned (without comment) the Glaucous in the list of macaws he had kept (*Bird Notes*, May 1915).

The British Museum (Natural History) at Tring had two Glaucous specimens, both collected in Paraguay in 1883. The late Helmut Sick, who spent his life studying the birds of Brazil, examined most of the few *glaucus* skins

in museums. That in the Paris Museum was from Corrientes. Sick stated that the only two skins in the American Museum of Natural History were received from London Zoo in 1886 and 1912. Both these birds originated from Paraguay. The earlier record indicates that the zoo had three specimens over the years. In Volume III of *Parrots in Captivity*, W. T. Greene referred to Eclectus Parrots whose "maddening shrieks were not much less terrible than those of the neighbouring Glaucous Macaw and the Orange- and White-crested Cockatoos." How sad that the Glaucous was deserving of comment only because it was loud!

Amsterdam Zoo also had three specimens (Sick, 1993). One died in 1862 and another was acquired in 1863 (and died in 1867). A third arrived in 1867. Nothing further was recorded about it. It might be no more than coincidence, but the continuity of deaths and arrivals suggests a reliable source of supply. Berlin Zoo also kept a Glaucous in 1892. The great French aviculturist Jean Delacour told Sick that between 1895 and 1905 he found one in the zoo in Paris (Jardin de Acclimatisation). It lived for several years and was the only Glaucous ever seen by Delacour (who died in 1985 when in his nineties).

Unlike the Passenger Pigeon and the Carolina Parakeet, in which the deaths of the last zoo specimens were recorded down to the hour, there was no realisation that the Glaucous was approaching extinction. A lot has been written about this macaw in recent years, and when its extinction might have occurred, yet the existence of captive birds is never mentioned. The Glaucous was also known in the United States. In May 1925, Louise Washington from New York, recorded: "I have 2 Hyacinthine Macaws and 2 Glaucous Macaws that play and roll on the ground with us and the dogs in perfect confidence." (*Avicultural Magazine*, August 1925).

During the 1960s and the 1970s the Italian aviculturist Paolo Bertagnolio corresponded with a friend in Brazil. Guiseppe Rossi dalla Riva was passionately interested in keeping and breeding the rarer Brazilian parrots. By 1971 he had moved to Miracatu, 87 miles (140km) south west of Sao Paulo. In 1970 he wrote to Bertagnolio that the Glaucous nested not far from where he lived. He would not reveal the locality as collectors "would immediately send

▮ *Elizabeth Butterworth's comparison of Lear's and Glaucous Macaws.*

their hunters and trappers", he wrote. On November 14 1975 he wrote to Bertagnolio that his birds included two pairs of Spix's Macaws and one Glaucous Macaw. On January 12 1976 he listed the Glaucous as being among the birds that had died from an "alimentary intoxication". A trustworthy source in Brazil suggested that I should be "very careful with this information". It is interesting that in 1966 dalla Riva gave the body of a Diademed Amazon in his collection to the Sao Paulo Museum. If he really had a Glaucous Macaw he might also have presented the body of this great rarity. The museum's only skin was collected by Vieillot during the 19th century, so perhaps it is the type specimen from which Vieillot described the species in 1816.

For a decade from the 1980s there were intermittent rumours about the survival of the Glaucous Macaw. These rumours were strong enough for it to be listed as Critical rather than Extinct when *Threatened Birds of the World* was published in 2000. It stated that the species was formerly widespread but very locally distributed in northern Argentina, southern Paraguay, north-eastern Uruguay, and Brazil from Paraná state southwards, along the middle reaches of the major rivers. The macaw became rare before or early in the second half of the 19th century. Only two acceptable records exist for the 20th century, it claimed, one direct observation in Uruguay in 1951 and one based on local reports in Paraná in the early 1960s.

The Glaucous Macaw would have fed on palm nuts, like the other members of its genus. The only palm species in its range were the yatay (*Butia yatay*) and, in Paraguay, the 10–13ft (3–4m) high yatai (*Butia paraguayensis*). Most of these palm groves were destroyed, either through clearance or lack of regeneration due to cattle grazing. The presence of these palms apparently indicated good quality soil, ideal for agriculture. The renowned French ornithologist D'Orbigny (who travelled in the area between 1827 and 1835) described vast *blue* expanses of palms. (This must be the explanation for the blue plumage of the *Anodorhynchus* species.) He prophesied that Glaucous Macaws would soon disappear. Alas! The macaw's numbers declined to extinction along with its habitat.

Bearing in mind that the range of its sister species, Lear's Macaw, was not discovered until 1978, it seemed remotely possible that the Glaucous might have survived into that period. Perhaps, somewhere, there was a tiny relict population. After all, South America kept many of its ornithological secrets well hidden. But in the last years of the 20th century at least one expedition was mounted to search for this now almost mythical macaw – but without result.

In June 1991 the species hit the headlines in a *Mail on Sunday* article. The author stated that the Glaucous Macaw was "supposedly driven to extinction by man's greed". Can agriculture be interpreted as greed? Another arguable statement concerned Carlos Lazaro Fraga, an Argentine arms dealer whose activities were exposed "after two years of intensive investigative work by a small team of British wildlife enthusiasts ..."

Fraga also trafficked in rare and endangered parrots and boasted about the ease of bringing them into Europe. It was feared that he had found the last existing colony of Glaucous Macaws in Paraguay. This could lead to it being "wiped out within two years", the report stated. The investigators had infiltrated a network of Amsterdam bird dealers to obtain Fraga's price list. He offered two pairs of Glaucous Macaws at $1900 per pair (just over £1,000). This story is not convincing. If the man really had a presumed extinct species, the price would not have been so low! Fraga told the newspaper's investigator that the Glaucous were quickly sold. It seems unlikely that Glaucous Macaws could have surfaced and not been seen or photographed by someone, somewhere.

It is probable that the Argentine province of Corrientes was the centre of distribution of this macaw. In 1767 Sanchez Labrador published a book on the birds of Paraguay. He stated that the blue macaw was rare along the River Paraguay but common in the woods along the eastern banks of the River Uruguay, along the eastern boundary of Corrientes (Pittman, 1997/1998). Steam-powered shipping in the 1830s resulted in rapid settlement of Corrientes province and the destruction of the yatay palm groves. The settlers would have considered any large bird as game. Indeed, one of the saddest references to this species is that by D'Orbigny whose expedition navigated the Paraná River in 1837. He wrote that the crew had tried to use the meat of this macaw – but it was so leathery it could not be eaten.

In 1997 two English macaw enthusiasts, Tony Pittman and Joe Cuddy, visited areas that were previously associated with yatay. These localities had suffered enormous disturbance and the palm was almost extinct, except in a national park established in 1965 to save it in Argentina. They visited the historic nesting sites on the river banks at Ita Ibate on the Paraná – but no habitat had survived.

Tony Pittman journeyed on to Argentina to investigate unconfirmed reports, including that of two Japanese ornithologists who claimed to have heard a macaw in the wetlands to the east of Corrientes province. He went on to Paraguay to become a member of an impromptu expedition to investigate reports of the macaw's presence in the south-west of the country. All these investigations drew a blank; however, when conversing through an interpreter with a 95-year-old cotton farmer who spoke only Guarani, he acquired some worthwhile information.

Ceferini Santa Cruz was born in the village of Lomas in 1902. The old man had seen only the red macaw (Green-winged). His father had moved there in 1875 and had told him about the Glaucous Macaw. It fed on the cocos palm (*Acromonia totai*), on the fresh green fruits on the tree; the fallen fruits were too hard to consume. The old

man's reminiscences suggested that the macaw had become extinct in that region at the end of the 19th century.

Tony Pittman met an important Argentine ornithologist, Professor Julio Contreras. He had travelled extensively in the province of Corrientes for 15 years, while compiling an atlas of birds. Contreras related that the local people had hunted and shot the macaws. He knew of three sightings. In 1919 his uncle had seen a Glaucous Macaw near the city of Corrientes. An employee of his uncle (who had died recently at the age of 90 years) claimed he saw the macaws in the forests of Riachuelo, until about 1930. Finally, a neighbour told him that a pair nested in a huge, ancient tree, an *Enterolobium contortisliquum*, just north of the city of Corrientes. In 1932 they disappeared (Pittman, 1997/1998).

Two different sources in the Corrientes region stated that the Glaucous Macaw had survived into the 1930s. So when did the last one die? Did it pass its final days in a zoo, like the last Carolina? This might have been the case. In 1938 Sydney Porter wrote about his visit to South America. He especially liked Buenos Aires and its zoo. The parrot house there was "an amazing structure, resembling some Eastern Mosque, with towers, domes and minarets" with aviaries that seemed to be an "afterthought". Despite its architectural shortcomings, it housed some interesting birds, the rarest of which was a Glaucous Macaw.

▌*Glaucous Macaw in Buenos Aires Museum.*
Photograph: Tony Pittman, www.bluemacaws.org

Porter wrote: "It was the first time I had seen an example of this very rare bird." He was told that it had been in the collection for more than 20 years and was known to be over 45 years old. Its plumage was in good condition but it was suffering from "senile decay" (Porter, 1938). The zoo's species' records do not extend that far back so there is no further information.

The Glaucous Macaw was represented in European zoos almost continuously from 1862 until 1916 and in the USA until at least 1925 if the single report is accurate. The dates of acquisition coincide with the reliable wild sightings that suggest the macaw became extinct in the early 1930s. The Buenos Aires bird that was apparently trapped in the early years of the 20th century and lived until at least 1938 was possibly the last living representative of its kind.

The Paradise Parrot

Thousands of miles distant in Australia, the Paradise Parrot (*Psephotus [Psephotellus] pulcherrimus*) was on the verge of extinction. The word pulcherrimus means "most beautiful". The male was the real contender for this title, with his bright red forehead, wing coverts and abdomen, mantle, back and wings of brown (an unusual colour in a parrot), black crown and nape, and turquoise and emerald green elsewhere. The female was less brightly coloured, with buff-yellow and pale blue on the underparts (see colour page 21).

The cause of its extinction was almost certainly loss of habitat exacerbated by drought. Formerly locally common from central Queensland to northern New South Wales, it fed on seeds of various grasses, also of herbaceous plants. When Europeans arrived, with their sheep and cattle, these lovely birds were pushed into unfarmed areas. The introduction of the prickly pear cactus (*Opuntia vulgaris*), thick and impenetrable in some areas, was highly detrimental to the Paradise Parrot.

Some birds were trapped, but the numbers taken were unlikely to have contributed to its demise. In the 1880s, W. T. Greene wrote in volume I of *Parrots in Captivity*: "The Splendid Parakeet is not a difficult bird to keep, so that the £10 pr so given for him is much more safely invested, than if risked upon a couple of pairs of Paradiseas, or Many-coloured Parakeets." It was

a lot of money, several times that of the weekly wage of a working man.

The parrot's numbers declined dramatically between the 1880s and the 1920s. In 1882 it had been described as numerous in the Fairfield area but in 1915 one resident stated that he had not seen the species since the drought of 1902. In 1926 Neville Cayley received a letter from Florence Irby describing her momentous sighting of five Paradise Parrots in November of that year, a pair with three young. This is often described as the last sighting in New South Wales. The weather had been hot and dry and the surrounding area from 25 to 50 miles away was on fire. She described her avian visitors as looking tired, calling as though lost and nibbling at half-dead leaves in their vain search for food. They stayed for ten minutes, and then flew away. She painted a poignant scene: "...with a dense haze of smoke hanging over everything the five birds with their beautiful colouring made an unforgettable picture. One male in particular was especially beautiful..."

The tiny remnant populations had experienced loss of their feeding grounds, fire, drought and perhaps, finally, starvation.

These lovely birds nested in terrestrial termites' mounds. In 1922 C. H. H. Jerrard

∎ *Paradise Parakeets.*

photographed a male at his nest in Queensland. This famous photograph has been reproduced in several books (including *Australian Parrots* by Joseph Forshaw). Taken many years before colour photography was developed, who can look at even the black and white reproduction without feeling a pang of sadness? Jerrard had followed the birds for several months and built a rough hide. The historic and unique photos he obtained were perhaps the first and probably the last. In 1927 he saw the pair for the last time.

However, rumours of the Paradise Parrot's survival persisted for several decades. In 1965 Alan Lendon revised Cayley's famous book *Australian Parrots in Field and Aviary*. That year he visited the upper Burnett River in southern Queensland, where Jerrard's photos were taken. This was probably after he had been shown a *colour slide* of "an obvious male Paradise" said to have been taken in the 1960s. He thought it was "convincing evidence that the species is not extinct". Joseph Forshaw did not agree. In 1974 Forshaw had visited an aviculturist in Sydney who had paid a high price for what he believed was a pair of Paradise Parrots. Forshaw identified them as Golden-shouldered x Many-coloured Parakeet (Mulga Parrot) (*P. varius*) hybrids, the females of which bear little resemblance to Paradise Parrots. These captive-bred hybrids might have been the source of some of the rumours regarding the species' continued existence, and the male might have been the bird depicted on the slide. Many aviculturists knew the elegant closely related species, the Golden-shouldered (*P. c. chrysopterygius* and the Hooded (*P. c. dissimilis*[*]) parakeets.

Since 1989, an Australian friend who resides in New South Wales, has told me of events which convinced him that Paradise Parrots existed in 1971 in Goondiwindi. In that year my friend travelled there on August 16 with the late Alan Lendon to investigate the claim that two pairs of Paradise Parrots had been seen. Copies of correspondence to him from Alan Lendon, dated July 1971, testify to the truth of this (not that I would ever doubt his word). No Paradise Parrots were seen.

However, on his way back from Goondiwindi, the front tyre of his vehicle blew. He set out

in search of Eric Boreham, the postmaster at Warrumbungle (Lendon noted in his letter "*not* the Warrumbungle National Park, but further west"). Lendon asked Boreham if he had ever seen the Paradise Parrot. Boreham replied: "Yes, six birds on one occasion, in very rough, hilly country behind Croppa Creek and one, I think, on another occasion near Mungindi, on the Queensland border."

Sadly, Alan Lendon became ill on the trip and died several months later. (He did not live to see his book, *Australian Parrots in Field and Aviary*, in the shops.)

The unsuccessful search was not the end of the story, as told to me by my friend. A man who shall be nameless had committed what we would now see as a ghastly wildlife crime, one that hastened the extinction of a species already presumed extinct. On August 23 1967 in the Goondiwindi District, southern Queensland, he collected the eggs of the two pairs whose rumoured existence led to the search.

The egg collector recalled that in one nest that he robbed there were four eggs and incubation had not commenced. The nest was located in flat, grassed, lightly timbered black soil country, running into occasional sand ridges of approximately 100 acres, forested on the sides with large eucalypts, bloodwood and carbeen. The nest was in a reddish terrestrial termitarium, 3ft (91cm) in diameter and 2ft (61cm) high, one of a number scattered about 50 yards apart on a dark red soil belt.

Attracted by their calls, the collector discovered two isolated pairs of Paradise Parrots. The termite country in the area was very limited and, by following both pairs, he secured five clutches during 1967. These comprised 4,4 and 5 from the first pair and two clutches of four from the second pair. The parrots fed on marthaguy [?] flea grass, 500 yards from the nest site and near a small dam, ¼ mile from the nest; the dam ultimately dried up during a dry spell. Then the parrots disappeared. This is a heart-breaking account. Egg-collecting was (and is) an obsession that is difficult to understand, especially in the case of pure white eggs. It could not be proved that they were laid by Paradise Parrots and the collector had no intention of

---

[*] Now often regarded as separate species.

selling them. He took them to blow them and add to his cabinets, purely for the satisfaction of possession.

The collector gave one clutch to a friend – the same person who extracted the above account from him. The friend wrote: "His wife, a nice, average-educated person, did his letter writing for him... The parrots were real enough, without doubt, for she had ideas of stuffing a specimen and borrowed a book on taxidermy from me."

The friend (not my friend), a copy of whose letter of September 7 1971, I have before me, stated that the collector gave one clutch of eggs to his brother in law, another clutch to someone else and a third clutch to him. His eggs were slightly damaged by falling chips as the collector excavated the nest. The collector kept a clutch of five eggs from one pair and a clutch of four from the other. Some time later the friend offered the collector a clutch of eggs from the Powerful Owl (*Ninox strenua*) for another clutch of the Paradise eggs – but the collector refused to make the exchange. This surely demonstrates that the Paradise eggs were genuine. Had they been those of, shall we say, Redrump Parakeets, the collector would surely have exchanged them for a clutch from the Powerful Owl.

Some writers have made the naïve claim that the Paradise Parrot never existed, stating it was a naturally occurring hybrid between the Golden-shouldered Parakeet and the Mulga Parrot. They seem to have overlooked the fact that their ranges do not meet and are separated by hundreds of miles. In the early 1990s there were several reported sightings from south-eastern and south-central Queensland, also in north-eastern New South Wales. Joseph Forshaw suspects that they arose from misidentification of Mulga Parrots in districts where formerly they were scarce or unknown (Forshaw, 2002).

From the time it was first seen and named, in 1844 and for most of the 19th century, very little was known or published about the natural history of the Paradise Parrot and yet its captive history in Europe, from the 1870s, was well documented. Breeding successes were achieved by Count Celle de Sprimont in Belgium, Princess Gustavus of Croy and Prince Ferdinand of Saxe-Coburg-Gotha. In his book *Foreign*

Cage Birds G. W. Gedney described them as "undoubtedly the loveliest of the parakeet tribe, combining the most vivid and varied colouring of plumage with an extremely graceful outline, and a temperament remarkable for great gentleness of disposition and attachment." Gedney commented that he knew of no other parakeet that would "die upon such short notice and insufficient grounds".

In England, in the early years of the 20th century, the well-known aviculturist Canon Dutton called it "surely the most beautiful Paroquet that ever existed" but the beauty of his pair did not prevent him sending them to London Zoo. He complained of their "annoying habit" of trying to burrow into the wall of the room in which they were housed. That statement perhaps summed up the attitude that most bird keepers had to breeding, even when the species was rare and expensive. Dutton only needed to make them an artificial termites' nest to burrow into and they might have produced young.

In a more enlightened era, could the Paradise Parrot have been saved by captive breeding? The answer is yes, quite possibly yes, as the closely related Hooded and Golden-shouldered became established in captivity. One might also ask: What would have been the point? The environment in which the Paradise Parrot evolved and lived for thousands of years had been destroyed. If this most beautiful of parakeets had survived solely in cages and aviaries, by now cinnamon or lutino mutations would have obliterated the true gem that it was.

The Night Parrot

Australia is vast. It keeps secrets, such as when the Paradise Parrot breathed its last. It has long-running mysteries – and mystery has always surrounded the Night Parrot (*Geopsittacus occidentalis*). A small ground-living green

❚ *Night Parrots.*

and yellow parakeet, genetically it is closest to the Budgerigar and the Ground Parrot (*Pezoporus wallicus*). It inhabited shrublands and grasslands, it was nocturnal and, if it survived, it was in places where men seldom go. Some writers state that there were only a couple of sightings of Night Parrots during the first nine decades of the 20th century, including one at Cooper's Creek, South Australia, in 1979. Others insist that there were sightings from inland regions in all states except Victoria during the 1980s. The regions it might have inhabited were searched on countless occasions – but as they cover several million square kilometres, the searchers might have been described as optimistic!

The optimism arose from an event in 1990 that evoked worldwide interest. The desiccated corpse of a Night Parrot (perhaps killed on the road) was found in a remote part of north-western Queensland, near Boulia. The story attracted even more attention when a man called Dick Smith presented the Australian Museum with $50,000 towards further research and a big reward for anyone who found the bird. An awareness campaign was launched to encourage travellers, such as long-distance road-train drivers, to look out for Night Parrots in remote regions. There followed reports from people who were convinced that they had seen them. These included seven "sightings" in 1992 and 1993 near Cloncurry, north of where the body was found and, even more convincing, in 1996 a pair of Night Parrots landed 10ft (3m) from trained observers at Newhaven in the centre of Australia.

It is extremely likely that this ground-dwelling species survived to the end of the century. But can it exist much longer in a habitat populated with feral cats and foxes and grazed by 13 million cattle and 18 million sheep, and overrun with rabbits? Will it survive in a land where 54 species of birds, mammals and frogs became extinct between the coming of European man and the end of the 20th century?

Extinct in the wild

Extinction is deemed to have categories. They relate to birds that are truly extinct, such as the Cuban Macaw, and those deemed "extinct in the wild". Two examples of the latter are the Spix's

Macaw, which has no known wild population but exists in captivity, and the Kakapo whose entire population is intensely managed at freedom on offshore islands.

Some people consider that captivity is a fate worse than extinction. However, with the scientific advances of the 20th century, captive birds could hold the key to the future reintroduction or survival of a species in the wild. DNA technology might be used. In another scenario, perhaps some remote and secure Brazilian habitat might be found into which Spix's Macaws (*Cyanopsitta spixii*) could be reintroduced.

A slender distinctive light-blue macaw, it became extinct in the wild in the year 2000. All species are unique but some stand out as being of very special interest. This is one such. In appearance it bears no resemblance to any other parrot. Vocally and behaviourally it differs from other neotropical macaws.

Everything about its history is extraordinary. Almost nothing was recorded about it in the wild until only one was known to survive. The vast country that is Brazil did not easily give up the secret of its location. The first known sighting occurred in 1819 when an Austrian naturalist called von Spix shot a specimen. The second reported sighting occurred in 1903 by naturalist Othmar Reiser, near Parnagua, southern Piaui. A few years later there was another sighting from Juazeiro, 56 miles (90km) west of the spot where the first bird was shot. Juazeiro was the location of the next report in 1922. The next sighting occurred on Christmas Day 1974. Helmut Sick saw seven birds at Formosa do Rio Preto. Finally Swiss biologist Paul Roth found the site that was the last recorded – Melancia Creek, near Curaçá, where the first bird was shot. Dr Roth had made 11 arduous expeditions across remote and poverty-stricken north-east Brazil in search of this elusive macaw. He found it only at Melancia Creek. Until 1989 several Spix's had existed at Riacho Vargem, 74 miles (120km) east of Melancia. In that year that population was totally depleted by trappers.

Spix's Macaw apparently needed to nest in gallery woodland dominated by caraiba (*Tabebuia caraiba*) woodland. No regeneration had occurred due to grazing by goats, sheep and cattle. At the end of the century it was claimed that only 11 square miles (30 sq km) of such woodland had survived, and these were in three fragments. Although loss of habitat dealt the species a terrible blow, it was illegal trapping which sounded the death knell. Probably wealthy Brazilian bird collectors (with one exception, they were not breeders) had taken the majority of the captured birds. But overseas there were a few people prepared to pay very large sums for such a rarity.

The last Spix's Macaw existed at a traditional nest site at Melancia Creek. It was to become one of the most studied and protected birds in the world, monitored daily over a large area by about one hundred families of local ranch workers, known as the "Spix's cowboys". It soon became apparent that the lone survivor was paired with an Illiger's or Blue-winged Macaw (*Ara maracana*), a much smaller species.

Loro Parque's attempt to aid Spix's Macaw started in August 1987 when it hosted a meeting of scientists, conservationists and owners. A document was drawn up with recommendations for a captive breeding programme. Alas, it proved impossible to influence private owners to work together. In 1990 the Permanent Committee for the Recovery of the Spix's Macaw (CPRAA) was founded, of which the principal financial supporters were Loro Parque and later Loro Parque Fundación, in Tenerife. All holders were invited to enter their birds into a globally managed population. The Spix's Macaws were not being taken away from them. In 1995 a large aviary was built within the habitat of the last wild bird, by then identified using DNA as a male. The last Spix's known to have been taken from the wild, a female then in captivity in

▌ *Illiger's Macaws.*

Brazil, was placed in a large release aviary. Then she was liberated. Reputedly, male and female consorted closely for a month, then separated and were said to use adjacent areas. The male returned to the Illiger's (Blue-winged) Macaw to whom he was paired. Given the strong pair bond that exists in most macaws this could have been foreseen. Trappers might have been asked to catch the male Spix's and to place him in the big aviary with the female. Release should not have been carried out until the two Spix's had formed a bond. The experiment went tragically wrong when the female disappeared. Three or four years after her death a campesino admitted that he had seen her body. It lay beneath a power line with which, it was suggested, she had collided.

In 1999 the last Spix's surviving in the wild was still paired to the smaller species of macaw. Fertile eggs were produced but failed to hatch, although successful hybridisation was possible. In January 1999 the pair was given two three-day-old chicks from the nearby nest of a pair of Blue-winged Macaws. They were successfully reared and fledged. It was reported: "The experiment provides evidence that the hybrid pair is capable of fostering young." This was something that many parrot breeders could have confirmed. The experiment wasted precious time in which eggs from captive birds might, if laying times synchronised, have been placed in the nest. What was the point in Blue-winged Macaws fledging from this nest when they might have been desperately needed Spix's? Or if the eggs had been removed, the smaller macaw would have laid again, increasing the possibility of synchronisation of laying, or perhaps producing hybrids whose presence in the wild could have been beneficial, especially if they resembled their male parent. They would have been an incentive to protect the habitat and to maintain the interest and pride in conservation, perhaps until captive-bred Spix's could be released.

The captive population increased but the gene pool was dominated by the young from one prolific pair. They were in the Philippines, in the care of Antonio de Dios, owner of the world's largest parrot collection (counting individuals – Loro Parque still had the most species). In 1995 six young Spix's were reared there, four of them much needed females. At that time the studbook population was 23 males and 14 females.

▌*Young Spix's Macaw hand-reared at Loro Parque in 2004.*

In 1996 a further decree was issued by the CPRAA to encourage holders of undeclared Spix's to come forward. After October 30, undeclared birds would be confiscated. If there were any more holders, they did not make themselves known. Outside Brazil, Spix's Macaw was held in only three *known* collections, two in Switzerland and Loro Parque in Tenerife. Young had been reared in three locations – but with consistent and outstanding success only in the Philippines. By 1997 the captive population had reached 40 birds and climbed to 60 by 1999. Those originally in Switzerland, apparently numbering at least 17, had been sold to two private breeders. One of these, Roland Messer, produced one young one in the year 2000 and two in the following year.

In early 2001 the CPRAA collapsed after a disastrous meeting. It was learned that four Spix's Macaws from the Philippines had been "transferred" to the private collection of Sheikh Saud Bin Mohammed Bin Ali Al-Thani in Qatar. Reputedly he had also acquired Spix's from another source. This transgressed the agreement that transfers would take place only between breeders or zoos approved by the committee. It made a mockery of the whole concept if the macaws were to be sold to the highest bidders. Loro Parque Foundation's funding of the committee's field programme was suspended. During the 1990s it had poured nearly $600,000 into trying to conserve Spix's Macaw in the wild. But its hands were tied; the politics became ugly.

A new Working Group for Spix's Macaw recovery was formed in 2002 and the foundation was again funding the recovery attempt. It continued to work closely with IBAMA, the Brazilian environmental agency. Plans (to date unfulfilled) were made for a breeding centre in Brazil for the nine Spix's there, also for land purchase and habitat protection. By 2004 the captive birds numbered approximately 70, of which only nine were managed by the Working Group; however, these nine represented more than 90% of the gene pool – and were set to increase (see Chapter 13).

The strange and endearing Kakapo

New Zealand's Kakapo is described as extinct in the wild. Technically this is true because it is extinct in its mainland habitats and on Stewart Island (its last stronghold). It was necessary to remove the last few survivors to small offshore islands where they live totally natural lives, without cages or bars. Supplementary feeding and unseen teams of people guarding nests night and day against predation are essential.

The Kakapo is arguably the strangest and the most endearing parrot that ever lived. Forty-seven per cent of New Zealand's land bird species have become extinct since the arrival of man and 55% of the survivors are in danger of extinction. This, the heaviest of all parrots, weighs between 4 ½ lb and 6lb (2 to 3 kilos) – and is flightless. One might also say that it is "fightless" since it has nothing with which to defend itself except its plumage, an effective camouflage in the era in which it evolved. Ground-dwelling mammals were unknown. Then came man, with his cats and dogs and introduced pests, the rats and stoats. The Kakapo was a sitting target. Furthermore the introduced deer, and later the possums brought from Australia for the fur trade, ate their way through tons of vegetation, including the Kakapo's food.

This nice fat trusting parrot was the principal food of Ngatau natives before the potato was introduced to New Zealand. The Kakapo was even used as dog food by early settlers. During the gold-digging era of the 1860s and 1870s this tame and appealing parrot was apparently the main item on the miners' menu. What a lot man – so lacking in compassion – has to answer for...

However, the Kakapo was the subject of what might have been the first ever parrot conservation project. In 1890 a small island called Resolution was designated as a bird sanctuary. Several hundred Kakapo were released. It was a sanctuary only until stoats reached the island. The parrots were wiped out.

Between 1958 and the mid-1970s New Zealand's Wildlife Service made regular expeditions to South Island to search for Kakapo. Only eight birds were located, all males. Incubating females were so vulnerable to predation they had all been killed. When helicopters were used to search, 18 more of these precious parrots were found. Alas, not one female was among them. The Kakapo was effectively extinct! Or so it was thought.

During this period much more was discovered about the biology of this strange species. Not only is it nocturnal and unusually solitary, it is also (uniquely among parrots) a lek species. There are only about 80 such species worldwide but the Kakapo is the only flightless lek species. The term lek denotes that males gather together and perform courtship displays on traditional mating sites. In the case of the Kakapo, males attract females by making a far-carrying booming sound by inflating the thoracic air sacs.

The year 1977 was a momentous one for the Kakapo. Off the tip of South Island lies Stewart Island. There a population of 200 Kakapo was discovered. They included the first females seen for many years. A reprieve for the Kakapo? Only just... The population was being depleted by feral cats at the rate of 50% per annum. In the nick of time were cats prevented from causing the Kakapo's total extinction. Dogs were used, in 1980, to find the secretive parrots in order to fit radio transmitters to their backs. By the end of 1981 they had caught 23 males and 11 females. In March 1981 two nests were located and a chick was seen for the first time. At last, in 1982, it was decided to transfer 11 males and seven females to Little Barrier Island. This was the start of a programme to remove predators from offshore islands, to make them safe habitats for Kakapo. All the known birds were caught and transferred, although probably 20 or so were left behind because they could not be located. All the birds at new sites were fitted with transmitters so that they could be radio-tracked.

For the next decade Kakapo numbers almost stood still. Breeding successes were rare and chicks were killed by predators. It was a

Don Merton.

frustrating situation for those working with this endearing parrot. Their hands were tied by bureaucratic protocol. Finally Don Merton and his team were allowed to implement all the conservation measures needed to turn around the plight of a parrot fast heading for extinction.

Gideon Climo radio-tracking Kakapo.

■ *Kakapo learned to use these feeders.*

Eggs or chicks were moved as necessary and underfed chicks were removed for hand-rearing. These efforts culminated in an exciting record-breaking breeding season in 2002, with the hatching of 26 chicks and the survival of 24. (Previously, the best breeding season was in 1999 when six young were reared.)

The good news did not end there. Females were desperately needed. DNA sexing confirmed that 15 (62%) of the 24 young were female! Until then there had been a preponderance of males. Manipulation of female weights prior to breeding (to increase the ratio of females at conception) appeared to have been effective. There was evidence that heavy females produce

mainly male young and that light females produce more females. However, the balance must be precise because if females are too light they are unlikely to breed. Supplementary feeding in previous years might have been a factor in the disproportionate number of males produced. Nine of the 11 young hatched by supplementary-fed females during the period 1991–1999 were males. The number of females in the population had increased from 26 to 41 (54%). This gave enormous hope for the future.

The world Kakapo population had increased from 62 to 86 in one season and Codfish Island, only 1,390 hectares in extent, had become overcrowded. The transfer was therefore made in 2003 of 14 birds to Chalky Island (Te Kakahu) in the Fiordland area of South Island. This was a significant milestone in the epic Kakapo recovery story. The object was to expose birds to a greater range of masting plant species in an effort to induce more frequent breeding. The Kakapo selected for the move included the old male Richard Henry, captured in 1975. Don Merton caught this famous bird (named after a Kakapo conservation pioneer) with the help of a specially trained dog, high on the south wall of Gulliver Valley in Milford Catchment. Don took him to Maud Island soon after.

In 1982, when stoats invaded Maud, Don took Richard Henry, with the other three

■ *View from Maud Island.*

Kakapo on Maud, to Little Barrier. Soon after, the whereabouts of Richard Henry became a mystery as he was not wearing a transmitter. One day in 1992 he was miraculously recaptured by DOC employee Terry Greene who was trimming a track in a remote part of the island. In 1996, after 14 years on Little Barrier, the old male was unable to compete successfully for a place in the lek so Don moved him back to Maud. Just 18 months later he bred successfully – for the first time in at least 23 years. The female known as Flossie raised his three offspring, Gulliver and Sinbad, two males, and Kuia a female, thus perpetuating Richard Henry's precious Fiordland genes. So, after 27 years, he returned home to Fiordland. Sadly, all other mainland Kakapo had died by about 1987, probably killed by stoats. Don Merton told me: "I see the return of the Kakapo to this, their homeland, as an exceedingly significant and symbolic event."

Department of Conservation (DOC) staff had cleared Chalky Island (about 500 hectares) of stoats – a remarkable achievement. The aim was to maintain it permanently stoat-free through trapping, and to manage a small population of about 25 Kakapo there. Soon Kakapo were feeding heavily on the kernels of fallen miro nuts (high energy winter food) which were plentiful on Chalky and Codfish. Although the Kakapo was officially "extinct in the wild", the promising developments were propelling the new and younger population of Kakapo towards a natural lifestyle.

Unseen for decades

To our certain knowledge, three parrot species became extinct during the 20th century; the Carolina Conure, Glaucous Macaw and Paradise Parrot. The total number of extinctions might be greater as two species of tiny *Charmosyna* lorikeets have not been seen for decades. The mainly green 6in (16cm) Blue-fronted Lorikeet (*C. toxopei*) from the Indonesian island of Buru (see Chapter 15) was unknown in trade on an island where parrots were heavily trapped. The sighting in 1997 of two groups of six and five birds, possibly of this species, gave some hope for its survival.

The New Caledonian Lorikeet (*C. diadema*) is a mysterious bird, known only from the type specimen, collected in 1859 and from another collected in 1913 but not preserved. Mainly green, with violet-blue on the crown and thighs, red around the vent and black, red and yellow on the tail, the female must have been very pretty. The male was never described. This is indeed an unusual case of a species in which evidence for its existence rests on a single skin. Unconfirmed sightings of small lorikeets in flight in 1953 and 1954 and again, by the same observer, in 1976 of two small green parrots, suggests that the New Caledonian Lorikeet might still survive in the cloud forests of this volcanic Pacific island.

We will never know if unrecorded parrot extinctions occurred during the 20th century, that is, species that were never known to science. The El Oro Parakeet (see Chapter 15) narrowly escaped that category.

How does the minimum of three parrot extinctions during the 20th century compare with the 19th century? During that period at least five species breathed their last. They included the *Cyanoramphus* parakeet (Kakariki) from Tahiti. Called the Black-fronted, its loss in 1844 might have been due to introduced rats. The Mascarene Parrot (*Mascarinus mascarinus*), akin to a Vasa, from Réunion Island in the Indian Ocean, was not seen after 1834. Hunting was probably to blame, as it was for the extinction of the Norfolk Island Kaka (*Nestor productus*) during the 1850s. The extinction of the Cuban Macaw has already been mentioned, as has the near-extinction of the Echo Parakeet from Mauritius. Two Indian Ocean island species closely related to the Echo, did not escape this fate. Newton's Parakeet (*Psittacula exsul*) from Rodrigues was last seen in 1875, but the passing of the last Seychelles Parakeet (*Psittacula wardi*) went unnoticed. It probably occurred in the last years of the 19th century or very early in the 20th, due to deforestation and shooting. It was too fond of raiding maize plantations. Much like the Alexandrine Parakeet, the male differed in lacking the neck ring. At the time of its loss it was given sub-specific status only but this has since been revised to species status.

A century from now, how many more parrots will have become extinct? Some of those now judged to be Critically Endangered, with very small populations, are unlikely to survive. Other critical species that are currently closely monitored, might survive as tiny remnant populations. However, the species for whose survival I fear most are those with populations that were fairly high numerically at the end of the century but which had been heavily trapped. Popular Amazons, such as Yellow-naped and Double Yellow-headed, whose every nest is robbed if located, will have ageing populations that will crash very suddenly when the adult birds cease to reproduce.

Some parrots classified as sub-species, distinctive in appearance and isolated by range and/or habitat, were declining almost to extinction, yet were ignored by conservationists. Endangered sub-species seldom attract much conservation concern although research using DNA is increasingly showing that many sub-species are in fact full species. One example might be the Greater Patagonian Conure (*Cyanoliseus patagonus bloxami*), found only in Chile. It nests exclusively in cliffs and many such sites have been destroyed.

Another conure awaits either rediscovery or the conclusion that it is extinct. Originally classified as a sub-species of the Painted Conure, the Sinú parakeet (*Pyrrhura picta subandina*) had not been seen for some years. Known from only 17 specimens, it was confined to the lowland Rio Sinú valley of Colombia. In 2002 it was given the status of species and declared Critically Endangered.

In the future, lack of nest sites will cause parrot extinctions. In Australia, for example, the early settlers destroyed so many trees, of species that can take 100–200 years to form cavities suitable for parrot nests, that by the end of the century some parakeet species were declining and small lorikeets were also affected. Many parrots are very adaptable and some might learn to accept artificial nests. Even if they do, my prediction is that significantly more parrot species will become extinct in the 21st century than in the preceding two.

∎ *Greater Patagonian Conure.*

18. Macaws and the Eco-tourists

The great naturalist Peter Scott wrote: "In the crazy world of today, when the human race seems so little able to control its destiny, when crises and depressions follow each other in mad succession, the need for escape is more urgent and the call of the wild places more insistent than ever."

This might be especially true of people who live with parrots. Many have a longing to know the places where their parrots originated. By the last decade of the 20th century it was possible to visit such locations and to hire bird guides. All you needed was time and money!

Ecotourism in South America started to make an impact in the 1980s. The number of overseas tourists visiting Manaus in the heart of the Brazilian Amazon increased from 12,000 in 1983 to 70,000 in 1988. During the 1982–83 winter season only one cruise ship called at Manaus; by 1989–89 the number had increased to 21. The income of one small ecotourism company in Peru, with a 25-bed lodge, increased from $7,000 in 1985 to $240,000 in 1989. In northern Peru, in 1988 tour lodges were the fastest growing and most lucrative businesses in Iquitos on the banks of the Amazon. Sixty thousand visitors went on jungle trips in the area (Munn, *in* Beissinger and Snyder, 1992).

It was the flamboyant macaws that were most likely to inspire such travel. Few more spectacular sights exist in the natural world than large macaws in flight, their long tails trailing or fluttering behind them. What could be more rewarding to the tourist, even if he or she has no special interest in birds, than such a

memorable glimpse? Macaws seem to epitomise the tropics. To watch their distinctive silhouettes as they leisurely flap overhead sends a shiver of satisfaction down the spine of even the "been-there-done-that" type of tourist.

But macaws and other parrots are notoriously difficult to observe. Despite their bright colours their camouflage is extremely effective. They land in a tree and instantly disappear; then they are hidden from predators, especially man, their enemy of many centuries. Wary and usually silent when perched, their habits are frustrating to the parrot lover and field worker. In South America there is one special kind of location where they can be observed in all their glory, in the open and for prolonged periods: the clay lick. This is a bank or cliff of clay visited by parrots and other animals for its beneficial properties. Watching parrots at such a site is perhaps without rival as a scene of colour and activity than is not man-made. Furthermore, it can be used to protect huge areas of habitat and the birds within it.

Parrots and mammals, including monkeys, peccaries and tapirs, dine on leaves and seeds that could kill them. Many tropical plants contain toxic compounds to ward off seedeaters. Unfortunately for them, the seedeaters learned a trick or two – that the consumption of clay would prevent these toxins from entering the bloodstream. Possibly the clay contains beneficial minerals and also protects the mucus film of the gastro-intestinal tract, preventing chemical irritation. Some clay seams are of particular interest and are mined with enthusiasm by macaws, while other clay faces are ignored by all animals.

Charles Munn, the well-known American conservationist, promoted macaws as the flagship species to protect and preserve thousands of acres of habitat. Manu National Park in Peru covers 1.5 million hectares. Tourism is centred on clay licks, of which there are probably about one hundred in Peru. Charlie searched for years to find them – and privileged people from all over the world are experiencing their fascination. The first was the now legendary Tambopata Research Centre, established in 1989 and featured in many television documentaries. In the south-eastern part of the country where the Andean foothills meet the Amazon basin, it is located on the banks of the Tambopata river. The lodge can be reached by an eight-hour journey by motorised canoe from Puerto Maldonado.

Just 980ft (300m) away from the centre is the largest clay lick yet discovered in South America, extending for 1,640ft (500m) along the river. Macaw lovers come here from all over the world to see nine species of their favourite birds. Most numerous are the Green-wings and the Scarlets. They put on an impressive and unforgettable show when they visit the high reddish cliffs.

It started in Peru

In 1990 the Tambopata-Candamo Reserved Zone was created, bounded by the Bolivian border and extending over 3 million acres (1.2 million hectares). It surrounds the Rio Heath sanctuary which I visited with Charlie Munn in 2003. He told me that in the combined Tambopata-Madidi Protected areas, which are about 20% the size of the UK (and reach from lowland rainforest up to 19,000ft glaciers), there are many thousands of pairs of Green-winged, Scarlet, and Blue and Yellow Macaws. Nowhere else in South America has such a rich biodiversity and so many macaws. Eco-tourism will help to maintain both by protecting huge areas of forest. (Biodiversity diminishes as forested areas become smaller.) Protection of clay licks and their environs will be vitally important for the future of the macaws. Munn believed that each lick required a minimum of 58 square miles (150 sq km) of intact, protected, forest to guarantee parrot visits.

Opened in 1998, the 23-bedroom Posada Amazonas Lodge is reached after three hours on the river. It was the pilot scheme in community and private enterprise partnerships. The local community had benefited little from the Tambopata Research lodge: this time it would be

❚ *Blue-headed Pionus and Weddell's Conures at the clay lick on the Rio Heath, Peru.*
Photograph: Priscilla Old

❚ *Mealy Amazons at the Rio Heath clay lick.*

Photograph: Priscilla Old

different. Rainforest Expeditions and the Eseieja Native Community drew up a 20-year contract. It defined the profit proportions as 60% for the community and 40% for Rainforest Expeditions. Decision-making was to be equally divided. At first this was not easy as community members had difficulty understanding the concepts of vacation, tourism and lodge. However, soon 65 families produced 10,000 woven palm fronds for the roofs and 15 families cut wood and collected cane for the walls. Two years later this lodge, with its en-suite bathrooms, hot water, bar and lounge, had become one of the most popular in Peru.

The next project was located on the Rio Heath, on the forested Bolivian border, near a remarkable clay lick. At 6am on the August morning I visited it, the lick was already bustling with parrot activity. The cries of Mealy Amazons (*Amazona farinosa*), circling around above a large tree, filled the air. We disembarked from the canoe on to a floating, palm-thatched hide. Inside seats were positioned around the sides, with a ledge for our cameras and binoculars and just above it observation slits in the thatch. As I sat down excitement surged through me! About

to unfold was one of the most colourful and exhilarating spectacles of the tropics.

The lick consisted of an exposed bank of yellowish clay about 15ft (4.5m) high, topped with tall straggly white-barked trees and low vegetation. The branches of some of the straggly trees were bare, no doubt stripped over the years by visiting macaws. First came the small parrots, the little Weddell's or Dusky-headed Conures (*Aratinga weddellii*), inconspicuous and grouped closely together on the lower face. This species is common and widespread throughout the Amazon region.

The Blue-headed Pionus were also early arrivals, unmistakable with their brilliant head coloration and red under tail coverts. They, too, kept together on the lick face, more manoeuvrable and flighty than the big Mealy Amazons that descended after perching to survey the scene. How beautiful are Mealies in their natural habitat! They have a *joie de vivre*, an exuberance that is rarely seen in captive birds. The sun lit up their silvery backs as they dropped down on to the lick face. Known in Ecuador as *loro real*, they are indeed the kings of the mainland Amazons, big, bold and boisterous. I watched one holding a piece of clay in his foot, then striking out with his foot at another Mealy trying to take it. I watched another swinging on a palm frond close to the clay face.

Four Green-winged Macaws flew over and others were perching in the trees above the lick. More and more Green-wings landed, shrieking and dropping into the trees, playing on the wind. It was not long before fifty or sixty were present (see colour page 19 and photograph on page 242). Very cautious at first, they took their time to assess that it was safe, then dropped down directly on to the clay, or hung on a branch of a tree in front of the bank, swinging there playfully. The volume of their calls filled the air. In front of me was a constantly changing scene: macaws flying down, feasting on the clay, taking off, circling around in pairs emitting their deep, throaty calls, then coming back for another feed of clay. Amid the clamour of their calls, you could *feel* their exhilaration.

Early on, among the Pionus, two little parrots were gleaming emerald in the sun, their red under wing coverts briefly visible in flight, their faces with striking contrasting markings of orange and black. These were the Barraband's or Orange-cheeked Parrots (*Pionopsitta barrabandi*) (virtually unknown in aviculture). Three other species were present in small numbers: Yellow-fronted (Yellow-crowned) Amazons, Severe Macaws and a group of eight or more Golden-crowned (Peach-fronted) Conures (*Aratinga aurea*).

In dry weather clay licks provide almost guaranteed and unparalleled sightings of macaws and other parrots. By the end of the century the licks at Manu, Tambopata and other sites in Peru, drew more than 6,000 tourists annually, providing an incentive to preserve the birds for local people who might otherwise hunt or trap them. From 1984 up to the end of the century the licks generated approximately one thousand jobs at rainforest lodges.

In 1992 Charles Munn wrote about the value of each major macaw lick that is accessible and promoted by locally-owned tourism companies. He suggested that they might be worth as much or more than the two biggest earning lodges of Tambopata which were then taking $300,000 and $700,000 per year. If these licks were visited by 150 to 400 macaws, then each wild macaw would be worth between $750 and $4,700 per year as a tourist attraction. There are clay banks in Peru in remote places where tourists never go. They could be made accessible for a more exclusive kind of tourist who was willing to spend big sums on a private tour, reached by a weekly flight from Lima. According to Charles Munn, there were "massive numbers" of parrots, including Blue-headed Macaws, at these sites.

Scarlet Macaws in Costa Rica

In Central America Costa Rica is the most popular holiday destination, especially with Americans. Many go there only to watch birds and others are more specific, their main aim being to observe the spectacular Scarlet Macaw. In 1988 in Central America, the tourist industry was in third place in generating foreign capital behind the traditional export crops of coffee and bananas. Sadly, in general, nature tourism had not helped to maintain the economic integrity of visited areas or met the economic needs of local people who traditionally had exploited wildlife resources.

In Central America all the large macaws have suffered serious declines due to loss of habitat and illegal trapping. In January 1991 a paper was presented at the First Mesoamerican Workshop in Honduras on the Conservation and Management of Macaws. Christopher Vaughan and Jill Liske had studied the economic value of the Scarlet Macaw at the Carara Biological Reserve, created in 1978. The only other significant population in Costa Rica was in the

■ *The floating hide.*

Corcovado National Park in the south-west where about 50 macaws had survived. This location is less accessible. The Carara Reserve had more visitors due to the availability of hotel rooms and its proximity to the popular beach at Jaco. A study carried out in March and April 1990 showed that most visitors saw macaws within one hour of visiting the reserve, and some found them within 170ft (50m) of the car park. During the wet season (June to November) macaws are usually seen only at sunrise and sunset when they fly to and from the mangroves where they roost.

I visited this reserve in November 2000, staying at Tarcol Lodge, situated on the Tarcol estuary with a view over the mangroves. After only a few minutes on a newly-cut trail that led to the beach, a pair of Scarlet Macaws flew quite low above me, shrieking. Then they flew back silently to observe the three humans on the trail. To our surprise, one bird landed not far away to observe us. No visitor to the reserve could fail to be thrilled by the proximity of such an inquisitive macaw!

Although ecotourism generated a substantial income in Costa Rica, little of the money stayed in the country. Airlines and most hotels were foreign-owned, also some tour companies. The local community around Carara hardly benefited from tourism. Unless it benefits, there is little reason why the people should be interested in macaw conservation. Some people earned money by stealing macaw chicks from the nest to sell, on occasions even felling the nest tree. Poaching was, of course, illegal, but worth the risk because each macaw chick was said to equal a month's salary and the fine was less than the value of the bird (Vaughan and Liske, 1991).

In the 1990s Costa Rica ranked fourth among the world's nations for its high rate of deforestation. Its forests were being cut by 3.9% annually, despite the fact that they are its major tourist attraction and the Scarlet Macaw is the flagship species. In Belize the Scarlet Macaw is drawing tourists to the village of Red Bank, in the Stann Creek district. Local economy has been strengthened in this way.

Ecuador's Yasuni National Park

The first clay lick visited by a parrot lover cannot fail to make a lasting impression. My first was in Ecuador. It lacked macaws yet the impact it made on me was enormous. This experience was part of a holiday organised by an eco-tourism

▌ *Tarcol Lodge in Costa Rica.*

▌ *Sacha Lodge in the Ecuadorian rainforest.*

company. My group flew to Coca, the gateway to Ecuador's Amazon region, and then travelled by motorised canoe for two and a half hours down the Rio Napo. After gliding by canoe across an ox-bow lake Sacha Lodge came into view. Built of bamboo and thatch and surrounded by jungle, the lodge was set within a 5,000-acre private reserve. Dusk was approaching and Orange-winged Amazons were calling noisily from the tops of trees.

At 5am next morning we travelled half an hour downstream to the Yasuni National Park in the eastern Napo region. As we reached our destination Amazon parrots were circling around and calling. From a hide close to the steep clay bank Weddell's (also called Dusky-headed) Conures were landing on nearby trees, then Amazons and Blue-headed Pionus. A few minutes later the Pionus, twenty or thirty or more, descended on the clay bank, together with the conures. A crescendo of calls was building as more Amazons flew around excitedly. The Pionus kept on coming, sixty in all, with a smaller number of Yellow-fronted Amazons.

Mealy Amazons were flying into the trees and surveying the scene. Then one flew down onto the lick. He was joined by eight or ten more. The smaller parrots were on the left and the Yellow-fronted Amazons in the middle. Some of the conures, subordinate by virtue of their size, took clay by climbing up the left side of the bank. The other parrots favoured the area around a depression that had undoubtedly been made over many years by busy beaks. Only a relatively small area of clay seemed to be attractive to the parrots – but what a picture it made! My senses were overwhelmed by the colour and the movement and the flurry of wings of 200 or 300 excited parrots.

Different licks attract different parrots. At one, located far inside primary forest south of the Rio Napo, thousands of little Cobalt-winged Parakeets (*Brotogeris cyanopterus*) have been seen. Their use of these sites varied throughout the year, perhaps due to ingesting foods that are hard to digest, and to weather conditions.

Hyacinths in Brazil

From the United States Priscilla Old and her husband travelled to Brazil to see macaws. "We were thrilled each time we saw the birds fly with such effortless beauty and grace. We wanted to see what their natural habitat and activity included to help us understand our own pet macaws at home," she said. "We did not expect the emotional impact these observations would have on us. We are much more sensitive to the possible extinction of these wonderful birds for having observed them first-hand."

The realisation spread throughout the neotropics that macaws and other charismatic parrots could bring more tourists, and earn more money, than trapping and trading them, or cutting down the forests and selling the timber. The first step towards using parrots as a tourist attraction was protection of their habitat. In many countries reserves were encroached by local people. They resented being kept out of areas where they could graze their cattle or grow their crops. Creating reserves was a philosophy that was difficult to comprehend.

Habitat protection of a charismatic parrot species was a task that went hand-in-hand with educating local people regarding the intrinsic value of birds. When tourism became reality, they realised that they could make more money, over a longer period, as guides, drivers and builders of tourist accommodation, than they could make as trappers. However, this was dependent on the economic benefits being controlled by local people and not by a national or foreign source.

In several South American countries men who were once trappers were hired as bird guides. Priscilla Old recorded of the former trappers of Hyacinthine Macaws: "Their knowledge is impressive and very valuable to tourists who pay to see these creatures in the wild. Our three field guides could hear the birds, know the species, the number and which way they were flying, by the time we started to hear the calls ourselves."

One of the best known macaw eco-tourist facilities was created in the north-eastern Brazilian state of Piauí. BioBrasil Foundation's camp (called Hyacinth Valley) was situated near Sao Gonçalo do Gurgueira. Twenty miles away were caves in the red clay cliffs where the magnificent blue macaws nested. A hide built 85ft (25m) from a cave allowed visitors to watch the comings and goings of a breeding pair who nested 20ft (6m) inside. Elsewhere a large hide was reached via a 40ft (12m) long tunnel thatched with palm leaves and dotted with observation holes.

Lars Lepperhoff recorded: "When I first saw through the little hole I could not speak because it was such an emotional moment. In front of me, perhaps only 5 metres away, were about 40 Hyacinth Macaws feeding on palm nuts. I could hear them cracking the hard nuts. [Colour page 24.] The sun was shining on the marvellous blue plumage of the playful birds. Some of them took up to three nuts and flew with them to a tree growing nearby. They ate one nut and had another nut in both feet.* The birds always tasted several nuts before they decided to eat one. Most they threw away after they tasted them. In fresh nuts they even found the liquid which was drunk by the birds with enthusiasm" (Lepperhoff, 2002).

Hardened travellers, enduring roads that shook them to a jelly, visited the arid homelands of the Critically Endangered Lear's Macaw (see

Chapter 7). For few parrots is survival more precarious. Brazil did not give up the secret of their location until 1978. A few had found their way to Europe or the USA but their source was unknown to the outside world until the ex-patriate German ornithologist Helmut Sick finally located their roosting site. Riverbeds, dry for decades, dotted the area and the sandy soil was covered with cacti, succulents and thorny trees and bushes. Twenty years after their "discovery" the BioBrasil Foundation was taking tourists to this now-famous location.

The main threat to the Lear's population was poaching. These blue macaws nest in the cliffs. Poachers trapped them by putting a net over the nest entrance. Some former trappers were converted to nest guards. Various organisations, including the World Parrot Trust and BioBrasil, employed them. Some people were sceptical that this approach works. Sam Williams was sure that it does. "Why would they risk their lives climbing cliffs when they can have a steady income – something that is very rare in this impoverished region?" he asks. (The average wage in 2002 was the equivalent of less than £1 per day.) Some of the money to pay the guards came from tourism. From large hides the tourists could watch the macaws feeding in licurí palms. Palm fruits collected for this purpose were placed nearby, along with corn cobs. This also kept the macaws away from farmer's crops.

Bolivia's Red-fronted Macaw

Bolivia was another country where an endangered macaw and farmers shared the same habitat, not always amicably. In the mountains west of Comarapa there were spectacular views over the green, irrigated Misque valley floor far below. Small adobe houses** dotted the fields bordered by trees and giant cacti. Peanut farmers were working in the sun in the habitat of one of Bolivia's two endemic macaws: the Red-fronted. Confined to an area that is a dot on the map of central Bolivia, this endangered species occupied a strange habitat: arid montane scrub

---

* Macaws (captive and wild) can hold several nuts simultaneously to prevent other macaws from taking them. While eating one nut, using one foot and the beak, another nut will be held under the foot used for perching. With smaller nuts, such as pine nuts and even sunflower seeds, nuts can be stored in the lower mandible while another is being cracked. A single macaw does not do this because there is no competition for the food.

** Constructed from sun-died bricks made from mud and straw.

■ *Red-fronted Macaw.*

at 3,600 to 8,200ft (1,100 to 2,500m). Its range was tiny, apparently only approximately 112 miles (180km) from north to south and 93 miles (150km) from east to west.

Its total population was difficult to assess but seemed unlikely to exceed 1,000 birds. Between 1973, when the species was introduced to aviculture, and 1983 when it was placed on Appendix I of CITES, hundreds of these macaws were trapped and exported. It is uncertain what impact this had on its population in view of the fact that it was persecuted as a crop pest by the maize and peanut farmers. Its main problem was that its entire known habitat had been converted for agricultural use.

The people were so poor that the success or failure of their crops was crucial to their survival. Why should they protect the macaws that raid these crops? There is only one reason: eco-tourism potential. I saw what this meant while on a World Parrot Trust members' trip. Our group all gave money to the old, wrinkled peanut farmer over whose land we had been walking. With a hand as hard as cured leather, he pressed these notes to his lips, and then shook us by the hand. We had probably given him more money than he would reap from the potato crop he would plant next week to follow the corn and peanuts. This was the best way to impress on this farming community that Red-fronted Macaws are valuable as an occasional cash bonus, despite any damage they might cause to the crops.

Our group had been fortunate on that chilly August morning. In the field far below we saw

and heard a flock of macaws. More and more were flying in – at least 45! (see colour page 24). Our guide was elated. This was the largest flock he had seen in several years. Far below I could see the macaws playing, feeding, squabbling and walking on the ground or hanging upside down to display their orange wing coverts. Through the scope I tried to count juveniles. In one group of 15 there were three, possibly four.

The bright colours of the macaws were a stark contrast to the reddish-brown, stony soil, the grey trees with light green leaves and the tall cacti, spiny or fluted. We climbed down the slope to the field where the macaws were feeding on remnants of corn from the recent harvest. Jumping across two little streams and climbing a couple of stiles, we crept closer and closer. In so doing we disturbed a family of Blue-fronted Amazons (*Amazona aestiva xanthopteryx*) that had been feeding in the top of a flowering tree. I was sorry that they flew. The Bolivian birds are surely the most beautiful Blue-fronts throughout the whole huge range.

The young macaws, identified by their red-brown foreheads and lack of orange on head and wings, were incautious, the last to move away from the onlookers. A couple just sat in the field, oblivious to danger. The adults were feeding, picking up pieces of corn left from the harvest; they moved further off but stayed for another hour or more. Gradually they drifted away. At 3pm we returned to the Misque valley, hoping for more photo opportunities. The macaws were still there, and we climbed down to watch them again. This time the sun came out, turning them into kaleidoscopes of blue, pale green and orange as they floated down to the field. Shutters clicked as they grew bolder and flew above us, nearly as curious about this strange group of humans who did not work the land as we were mesmerised by their beauty, arguably the most beautiful of all macaws in flight. When a flock landed, it seemed as though the treetop had suddenly burst into orange flower!

Indonesia

On the Indonesian island of Seram the spectacular Moluccan Cockatoo had the same potential to attract eco-tourists but it was almost trapped to extinction (see Chapter 7); accelerating deforestation was another threat to its existence. In 1998 Djuna Ivereigh visited Seram as part of a cave exploring expedition and met several bird trappers. He felt sorry for the birds they trapped but was impressed by their knowledge of the bird life. He immediately saw the potential to train them as eco-tourism guides, thus providing them with long-term careers and encouraging conservation. The villagers of Sawai and Masihulan welcomed this initiative. They built a platform 130ft (40m) up in the canopy on the edge of a valley. From there cockatoos and hornbills could be seen on a daily basis – and tourists were clamouring to use it. Not long after its construction the political problems and violence on Ambon brought tourism to a halt.

In 2003 the airport on Ambon reopened and tourism re-commenced. The first group were Americans with a passionate interest in the Moluccan Cockatoo. The people of Sawai greeted the Americans warmly, even ceremoniously. They had built a new canopy platform at a height of 125ft (38m). It was big enough for bird watchers to spend the night there. Stewart Metz, who slept up in the canopy, described this as "one of the most amazing experiences of my life".

"The land of parrots"

It is ironic that although Australia is often known as "the land of parrots", and many people go there with this in mind, the parrots themselves do not benefit from this popularity. It is too easy to see them, wherever you go! In the eastern part of the country, every park has its complement of Rainbow Lorikeets and Galahs. Many "parrot" tourists do take part in bird tours of the outback, primarily to see such species as Major Mitchell's Cockatoos in the dry interior and Palm Cockatoos and Eclectus Parrots in Cape York. Unfortunately, parrot conservation does not benefit. Private individuals do.

Africa

Eco-tourism started in Africa with safaris, following on from the decades of tourists who shot game rather than watched it. By the last decade of the century numerous tour companies that specialised in bird watching were in existence, and Africa was one of the most popular destinations. However, these tours offered little for the person interested in parrot watching, apart from the probable sighting of a few Senegal Parrots. Africa is the most impoverished continent in terms of numbers of species and lacks any large or spectacular parrots.

At the end of the century, civil wars and unrest in central Africa made it an uncertain destination for travellers. Despite that, gorilla-watching tours were popular. In the same location flocks of Grey Parrots could be seen – and they *are* a spectacular sight. There is potential for Grey Parrot tours to countries such as the Congo, the Central African Republic and Cameroon in a more stable political climate.

The first ever African "psittatour" took place in 2004, to look for *Poicephalus* such as Rüppell's and the Red-bellied, also for three species of lovebirds. Such tours are unlikely to ever attract more than a handful of people and will have little impact on the environment, but they did cater for the growing number of people who wanted to observe parrots in the wild.

Tour companies aiding conservation

By the end of the 20th century it was obvious that there were good profits to be made from bird tours. But were the companies who ran them putting anything back into conservation? Most did not. An exception was the company known as Tropical Birding. In March 2003 it ran a non-profit tour in Ecuador that raised US$17,000 for land purchase in the threatened Chocó forests of Ecuador and Colombia. In 2004, after a thorough search for appropriate property, that money was used to help the Mindo Cloudforest Foundation purchase the land used to establish the Milpe Bird Sanctuary in north-western Ecuador. In the few months that followed, a visitor's centre, a caretaker's house, and superb network of trails were built. This reserve soon proved to be one of the top birding spots in Ecuador. The company organised several tours from which 100% of the profits went to BirdLife International to conserve key threatened areas in the tropics.

Tourism destroys habitat

Tourism was not always good news for parrots, especially on small islands. Situated off the coast of Venezuela is the island of Margarita, one of three islands where the endangered Yellow-shouldered Amazon (*Amazona barbadensis*) occurs. (It is also found in a few locations on the coastal areas of Venezuela.) During the last years of the century there was a huge tourism boom on Margarita. In 1996 the Amazon's numbers there were estimated at about 800 birds, that is, half of the species' entire population. Tourism was responsible for much habitat destruction on an island where little forest remained. It also resulted in sand being taken from creeks and rivers for building. The parrot was already under enormous pressure; up until 1998 more than half the chicks that hatched every year were illegally removed from nests. Had it not been for a forward thinking conservation programme, tourism could have spelt the death-knell for the island's Amazon. By 1996 its numbers had soared to about 1,900, due to the hard work of some very dedicated individuals. There was co-operation from national and local authorities and from the project's community outreach programme (see Chapter 12). Chicks illegally

taken from nests were confiscated. The outcome was better than that for most such chicks: they were successfully re-introduced by fostering them into wild nests.

If this Amazon continues to thrive on Margarita, it will be proof that the sun-seeker kind of tourism and conservation can exist side by side. This is true to a degree on the Caribbean islands of St Vincent and St Lucia. Many visitors pay a few dollars to traverse specially cut forest trails. The income aids forest management and conservation. It also emphasises the intrinsic value of the forests.

However, the question must be asked: as human populations on these islands continue to increase, will man be able to conserve parrot habitat? At this point the answer seems to be a conditional one: yes, if eco-tourists continue to bring in the dollars. But there is another side to this equation. Will increasing numbers of eco-tourists and other holiday-makers who visit the rainforests eventually have such a detrimental impact on the environment that parrot numbers will decline? This seems unlikely if the forests are well managed, as they are on the islands that are most popular with tourists. Nevertheless, there is a lesson to be learned from other fragile eco-systems, such as the Galapagos Islands.

Future parrot tourism sites

A critically endangered cockatoo, the Red-vented (see Chapter 12) might be the next attraction for parrot-tourists. A conservation programme was started on the small Philippine island of Rasa during the last years of the century. It was so successful that in 2003 plans were being made to expand it to the island of Dumaran, with a community-based sustainable tourism programme.

Parrot-tourism could be the catalyst for conservation in many tropical countries. In Central Africa it could protect Grey Parrots, in New Guinea it could save Pesquet's Parrots and in a poverty-stricken area of Bolivia it could save Red-fronted Macaws and bring much-needed income. Furthermore, it could show countless parrot lovers the joy of wild parrots, thus reinforcing the message that no more should ever be taken from the wild.

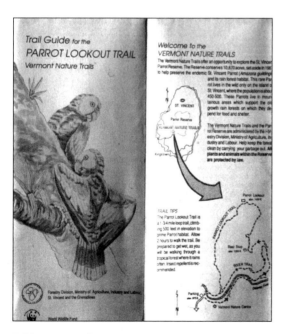

■ *Visitors to St Vincent can pick up a brochure about the Parrot Lookout Trail.*

19. A NEW AGE OF AWARENESS

During the last decade of the 20th century the intelligence of parrots and their capacity to interpret facts and even to understand abstract thought was brought to the attention of many people worldwide who had previously attributed them with a much lower level of intelligence.

Joanna Burger is no ordinary woman. She is a Professor of Biology at Rutgers University, the author of 14 books on bird behaviour. Her style is eminently readable but it is her empathy with her Amazon and her ability to interpret his feelings and behaviour that make her book *The Parrot who owns me* remarkable. As I read it I realised its significance. It had the potential to change the way people perceive their parrots, to provide their owners with a deeper understanding of their bird's needs which can improve their quality of life to an unimaginable degree. In this age of careless acquisition of parrots and often even more careless disposal, this book was timely. It conveyed the message that a parrot is a remarkable being that deserves the utmost respect and understanding.

Tiko was a Salvin's Amazon (*Amazona autumnalis salvini*) whose elderly owner died. The way his story unfolds will provide an insight into what an unwanted parrot suffers and perhaps make parrot owners more responsible for their actions. The touching story of how Joanna Burger won his heart is one of inspiration for anyone who rehomes a parrot or takes on a wild-caught bird. Her remarkable insight and perception of what Tiko needed would give entry to many people into a hitherto unknown world. The door to this world too often remains closed and it prevents them from forming a happy and close relationship with their parrot. One of the keys that unlock this door is the recognition that anthropomorphic values are highly relevant. However, this statement needs clarification. Anthropomorphism is the attribution of human behaviour to non-human creatures. It would be more accurate to talk of the realisation that animals are not the only creatures that have emotions, or can work out problems, etc. These attributes are not unique to the human race but egocentric man was, for centuries, either unaware or unwilling to admit this. By describing certain actions or behaviour as anthropomorphic, however, it allows some people to understand them better as they relate to animals. I found it satisfying to read in Joanna Burger's book:

"Our training drills into us [scientists] an aversion to anthropomorphic judgments. I once considered it the epitome of bad science to attribute human thought, feelings, and language ability to animals. But over the years I have changed my mind. I have come to regard it as at least equally benighted to automatically assume that animals lack these qualities. I find myself amazed, in fact, that anyone could doubt that the animals closest to us – dogs, cats, horses, parrots (especially parrots) – have emotional responses to the things around them, or that anyone could question the proposition that they form ideas about the situations they find themselves in or the people they meet. ...No one who has lived with a parrot will for a second doubt that they have thoughts and feelings similar to ours."

Unfortunately, many people who live with parrots lack the perception to understand this. Many of the situations that the author describes so lucidly will surely make them aware that their parrot deserves much more respect. With her husband, she tried to uncover Tiko's motivations, and to "ease her way into a bird's eye view". After several years, Joanna found that: "The balance of power between us shifted. I stopped treating Tiko like a pet. I began to see him as an autonomous creature whose dependence on me only highlighted the need to really understand, deep down, that his life was as important as mine, his desires and inclinations equally valid."

We can make it easier by truly trying to understand them, as Joanna Burger understands Tiko, who was 46 years old when she wrote about his life and made so many apt observations. She points out that among animals: "Their capacity for intimacy and connection with one another and with us isn't fixed. It grows and develops. It has untapped depths and reserves. It can, perhaps, be taught. It is influenced by experiences and events."

The dislike of anthropomorphism was so strong during most of the 20th century that it did untold harm to the way people viewed parrots and other animals. It often over-rode personal experience that clearly indicated that the emotions and behaviour of parrots parallel those of humans in countless situations. Denying this fact was to reduce the ability of humans to understand the needs (especially emotional needs) of millions of companion parrots that might otherwise have led much happier lives.

World-famous Alex

Alex became known to millions from television, videos and newspaper articles as the Grey Parrot used to probe the limits of parrot mental ability. He was first taught to recognise objects, colours and shapes and, when questioned, to name them in English. He was able to give the correct answers about 80% of the time. A typical exercise involved showing him several objects, such as a yellow key, a green piece of wood, a blue piece of rawhide, an orange piece of paper and a red box. When asked: "What object is green?", he responded "Wood".

In another test he was shown a round piece of wood, a triangular piece of felt, a square piece of rawhide, a five-sided piece of paper and a toy truck. When asked which object was five-cornered, he replied correctly "Paper". Asked forty-eight such questions he was right 76% of the time. The answers to the questions involving shape were always correct. What is interesting

▌*Joanna Burger with Tiko.*

about these tests is not so much that Alex is able to correctly identify objects but that he also understands the abstract concept of category, such as biggest, smallest and "middlest". Apparently this is difficult even for young children.

Some critics find it difficult to believe that Alex understands the questions and thinks about the answers. They urge caution because the experiments are based on long-term relationship between Irene Pepperberg and Alex and because the experiment is not amenable to normal controls and replication. There will always be cynics! As I see it, however, the major benefit of these widely publicised experiments is that many people who believed that parrots and other birds had little intelligence changed their views. They were astounded by Alex's abilities and began to treat birds with more respect.

Many parrot owners claim that parrots merely repeat what they hear and do not understand the meaning of words. This is often the case because owners do not use words in a way in which a parrot can associate them appropriately. If the owner is intelligent enough to repeat the word "apple" when offering apple, and "water" when changing the water, the parrot has the opportunity to learn to name and even to ask for such items. Irene Pepperberg's experiments might encourage other parrot owners to teach parrots in a more imaginative way.

Alex, and the other Grey Parrots taught with him, proved without doubt that parrots cannot only communicate vocally with people (for example, to request items), but that they can categorise colours and shapes, for example. How Alex achieved this is described in detail in Pepperberg's book *The Alex Studies* published in 1999. After 26 months of training Alex had acquired a fairly extensive vocabulary. It usually took him one or two months of work before he learned to manipulate his vocal tract appropriately to produce a new sound. He could name paper, key, wood, cork, corn, nuts and pasta, for example. After two years he could identify, refuse and apparently request a limited set of objects for play or for food. He also demonstrated a limited capacity to compose multiword phrases from separately acquired descriptions. Many owners of Greys and other parrots will recognise this ability in their own birds – often to the disbelief of others.

The results of the research attracted enormous attention worldwide. In the author's words, Alex "was to change our perception of the term bird brain". Alex has often been called an extraordinary bird. I doubt this. I suspect that perhaps 50% of Grey Parrots could achieve what Alex has achieved. But Irene Pepperberg was truly remarkable, to have initiated research that required an incredible amount of patience, and to have sustained it for 25 years.

Described as telepathic

In New York, artist Aimée Morgana was working with her Grey Parrot N'kisi. His vocabulary of 950 words was remarkable enough but more so was his *reputed* ability to use past, present and future tenses. This seemed to me so extraordinary that it threw a seed of doubt in my mind regarding other aspects of this work. Aimée Morgana said that her parrot seemed to surf the edges of her awareness, responding to moments of discovery rather than to any deliberate projection of thought. If she deliberately tried to send him information nothing happened. Aimée believed that her parrot often described what she was thinking about, reading or looking at in situations where there were no clues. She was looking at a photograph of a purple car. N'kisi, who was out of sight, said: "Oh look at the pretty purple." She contacted biologist Dr Rupert Sheldrake and together they designed a series of video-taped experiments to discover whether or not his comments were based on chance.

She prepared photographic images based on 19 key words in N'kisi's vocabulary. These were placed in envelopes and randomly numbered by an independent observer. In an enclosed room approximately 55ft (18m) away on another floor of the house N'kisi was filmed as Aimée opened the envelopes. Three people who did not know which pictures Aimée was looking at, or when she took a picture from an envelope, transcribed the result. Each time she opened an envelope N'kisi was given two minutes to talk. Sometimes he just chattered without using any of the key words; at other times he said the right words. When Aimé took out a photo of a man talking on the phone N'kisi asked "What ya doin on the phone?" When she opened the envelope containing the picture of a car and noticed a man leaning our of the window, N'kisi exclaimed: "Oh, oh, careful. You put your head out" (but how could a parrot know that this could be dangerous?). The latter was not counted as a positive result because the key word of car had not been mentioned, although it was an appropriate response. When Aimée looked at a photo of a woman with her arms around a man, N'kisi asked: "Can I give you a hug?"

During 71 trials N'kisi correctly used the key word on 23 occasions. An independent computer analysis gave odds of more than 2,000 to one against these results being due to chance. Whether or not these experiments had any significance, as Dr Sheldrake said in the *Journal of Scientific Exploration*: "We hope our work will help people to realise the amazing abilities and awareness of intelligent birds, and encourage greater care of these precious beings and the planetary environment we share." He suggested that the activity of the mind might not only be localised in the brain but also beyond it, through fields connecting the observer and the observed, fields intensified by strong emotional bonds.

There is nothing unusual about a strong bond between a parrot and its favourite human but even in such cases many people under-estimate their parrot's emotional responses. These extraordinary birds can have a close relationship with a human, or humans, and many can communicate with people. Unfortunately, relatively few people are sensitive enough or focussed enough on their parrot to be able to understand this. Even if they can, a message might be beyond comprehension.

Donald Risdon founded the Tropical Bird Gardens at Rode in Somerset. The free-flying macaws there were a much-loved attraction. In her book *The Road to Rode* Betty Risdon, his wife, related the story of Edwina, the Scarlet Macaw:

"She would always come over to our bungalow and knock on the French windows if either of us had been away or ill. One day she did her usual knocking and Don and I couldn't understand her message. We had not been away or ill. Edwina died that night. It was her way of saying goodbye."

This is more than a touching story. Perhaps the macaw had demonstrated that she knew she was going to die and that she understood the concept of death. This means that intelligent creatures like macaws are deserving of the same respect and compassion that we would give to a fellow human.

It suggests that she might have been self-aware – something for which we have evidence in only a few of the higher animals, such as apes. (This is probably because evidence is difficult to acquire.) There is one test that might demonstrate if a parrot is self-aware. If you hold it in front of a mirror and it wants to attack the reflection as an intruder, or it displays to it as a potential mate, it has not recognised its own image, thus it is not self-aware. This might be simplifying the state but one has to start somewhere in trying to assess it.

Some dog owners tell true stories that their dog went out of its way to say goodbye to someone just before it died, when there was no sign to a human that its death was near. I believe that dogs must also be self-aware. That this applies to macaws I have no doubt. I have often looked into the eyes of a large macaw and felt troubled and guilty because I could feel that here was a creature as sentient as I am – and what right have we humans to shut them away from their own kind and the tender affection they give to each other, to stop them flying their graceful flight, to deprive them of their birthright: the rich environment of the green forests, the tropical warmth and humidity?

That humans do not hesitate to keep wild parrots shut up in cages is perhaps a sad reflection of how little we understand some of the higher life forms with whom we share this planet. During the last two decades of the century public opinion demanded that intelligent large apes, such as gorillas and orang

utans, should be given enormously improved standards of living. Gone were the cages with bars like prisons. They were replaced with grassy enclosures dotted with trees and glass-fronted indoor accommodation, "environmentally enriched" with ropes, even with televisions. Perhaps one day these standards will even be applied to macaws and cockatoos. In 2004 the World Parrot Trust produced an 80-minute DVD entitled *Pollyvision*. It consisted of footage of wild parrots for pet parrots to watch. (However, the response to television varies considerably in individual parrots.)

Intelligence

In Canada Andrew Iwaniuk was a biological researcher at the University of Alberta. He compared the brain size and structure of 1,400 species of birds. He found that parrots' brains are especially large in the areas used for processing information for vocal learning and communication. He stated that owners should treat parrots as if they were children, giving them care and interaction to foster their social development.

Scientists define rudimentary intelligence as the most basic kind, that is, the ability to react adaptively to the environment. They define medium intelligence as a greater ability, to learn from new stimuli and to adapt to changed circumstances but with little evidence of what are sometimes called higher cognitive functions. Higher intelligence is defined as having a range of cognitive functions beyond those in the medium intelligence category. Recognition of objects is the first factor that qualifies them for this label. Being able to manipulate these objects and to use them as a means to an end is another. While scientists agree that dogs, chimpanzees and many of the larger parrots fall into this category, by their definition it should apply to nearly all parrots. However, the ability to manipulate objects and to use them is not a fair test of intelligence. Ground-feeding parrots are not as dextrous as canopy-feeding species because they do not need to manipulate objects (such as nuts or grubs) with the feet when they are feeding. As in humans, however, intelligence varies considerably among individuals and this is also related to environment and mental stimulation.

We now know that much attention must be given to the psychological welfare of captive birds and animals, especially those, like macaws and cockatoos, for whom a strong emotional bond is just as important as it is for a human. To deny these parrots the physical and emotional contact that they crave is at least as cruel as shutting them up in small cages.

Scientists also state that another highly advanced characteristic is that of understanding the intentions of others, which implies both self-awareness and the realisation that others have motivations of their own. However, I would question that understanding the intentions of others denotes self-awareness. Most parrot owners can relate anecdotes that confirm that their parrots understand their intentions in many different situations; indeed, they would find it odd if they did not. However, I am sure the same applies to animals of lesser intelligence – rabbits, for example. Parrots are very observant and usually know more about our body language (and habits) than we know about theirs.

Even the most subtle change of behaviour in a parrot has a reason; owners should be alert to this and try to work out what it is, although this is often difficult. One of my Rajah Lories (*Chalcopsitta atra insignis*), a gentle, affectionate bird, bit me when I was refilling her nectar pot. I could not understand why she had bitten me. When I went to the aviary about four hours later I saw that she had laid an egg from the perch. I had removed the nest-box on the previous day as she had laid two eggs from the

▌*Rajah Lory.*

perch (the clutch size is normally two) indicating that she had no enthusiasm to incubate a second clutch (the first clutch ended in failure.) The bite was perhaps a protest at the removal of the nest-box when she was about to lay another egg. On the other hand, it could equally be some other cause that I had failed to interpret.

In November every year when the weather becomes cold this pair was removed from their outdoor aviary to a heated birdroom. The female was susceptible to respiratory problems in a cold, damp environment. One November the male became unbearably noisy, making a continuous unpleasant shrieking sound. What was he trying to tell me? I moved them back to their winter quarters and immediately he became quiet. Of course I have no way of proving what he was trying to communicate to me but the intelligence of these lories is so high that I know he had a reason for acting as he did. (Listen to your birds and observe them: they will benefit.)

They understand our feelings

Scientists know little about whether animals understand the *feelings* of others, when these are not directed at the individual animal. Some believe that understanding has not been documented in animals other than humans. How, they ask, would an animal that does not speak, communicate to us that it had this understanding? Disregarding the fact that parrots can mimic speech, there is anecdotal evidence (what other kind could there be?), that parrots understand very well when humans are sad or angry. Dog owners also know this to be true. Parrots and dogs and undoubtedly other animals that have a close association with a human do feel our emotions; indeed, they often feel negative emotions to the degree that they are affected psychologically. A parrot in a home where two individuals are constantly arguing and shouting can become very disturbed; often the result is feather plucking. (This is well known to the more sensitive type of parrot keeper.)

Dogs, parrots and other animals understand more than we realise, being much more sensitive and observant than humans. Research has shown that dogs know when a human they are close to will have an epileptic fit. They do this by detecting physical and behavioural changes that are too small to be noticed by humans. Some dogs try to take protective action; one dog would push a young girl away from the stairs several minutes before the start of convulsions. Parrots are not large enough to act in this way but they are sensitive to elements beyond the human range.

For example, one Grey Parrot owner recorded that her bird, Jing, knew several hours in advance when an earthquake would occur, including the 1994 San Francisco earthquake whose epicentre was 450 miles (720km) distant. Jing would stare at the ground, as if in a trance, or hang upside down from her perch. Her owner, Jane Hallander, a former research biologist, contacted parrot owners in Turkey and Japan. If their parrots were wild-caught they reported similar behaviour. Owners of hand-reared birds did not (Hallander, 2000). It was not long before Jane Hallander could predict the magnitude of the earthquake by the intensity of Jing's behaviour.

Ability to solve problems

Surely one of the most obvious indicators of intelligence is the ability or the attempt to solve problems. Of all the parrots, cockatoos and Keas show exceptional talents in this respect. Unfortunately, few parrot owners record these incidents. Sheralin observed her Grey Parrot trying to open a nut. Normally he could do so unaided but when one walnut defeated him he held the nut in his foot and pounded it hard against the perch. He pounded it about six times, stopped, and then transferred the walnut to his beak. Then he pounded it with his foot against the perch again. Finally, he placed it in his food bowl and started to play with his toys. Half an hour later he took the nut in his foot again and started to pound it. Although he did not solve the problem of opening the nut, he reacted in a highly intelligent way and might eventually have been successful.

Many people can identify with the big apes – but everyone should acknowledge that other animals are intelligent in different ways and deserve equal respect. Towards the end of the century this concept was much more widely accepted than at the beginning when such views would not only have been heard as a tiny minority, but would also have been considered idiosyncratic.

The contents of this chapter might cause many people to question the ethics of keeping such sentient, emotionally responsive and intelligent creatures in cages for their own entertainment.

20. TWENTY-FIRST CENTURY ETHICS

Parrot welfare issues such as over-production, selling parrots from unlicensed sites (shows and auctions), and re-homing of unwanted parrots, received much more attention and publicity in the early years of the 21ˢᵗ century than ever before. It was a step in the right direction, albeit many years overdue.

Over-production of parrots

In 2001 Danish aviculturist Peter Them wrote: "I find it absurd that, while global aviculture has an increasing problem finding purchasers for domestically bred offspring and the prices of most parrot species and other birds have crashed – there is this huge worldwide trade in wild-caught birds" (Them 2001).

He was echoing the thoughts of the more responsible aviculturists. Concerned about the lack of commitment to such long-lived and sensitive birds, some owners no longer permitted their parrots to breed. They were in the minority. They believed that aviculturists should cease to mass-produce birds because demand for all species except Grey Parrots had declined significantly. This led to wide availability of lovebirds, Cockatiels, and most Australian parakeets, and others, at low prices, thereby increasing impulse buying.

Cheap birds were inadequately housed because even a small cage cost more than the bird. A small cage for a Cockatiel cost £50 in the 1990s but a parent-reared bird could be acquired for £10 – or £15 for a lutino. How could it happen that living creatures had such a low market value? It happened because of over-production by breeders and, the importation of large numbers of low-priced captive-bred birds, such as lovebirds from Thailand and because of massive importations of wild-caught parrots that were offered at low prices. This made it difficult for breeders to obtain realistic sums for their young birds. Cheap birds were not valued and were given away or even liberated when they became too much trouble or when the family went on holiday. When breeders could not sell their young they were desperate to get rid of them, showing no concern for a bird's future. It was not only inexpensive birds that were victims. In the UK a Green-winged Macaw was left attached to a fence in a field, with its food placed next to it. Not only dogs and cats, animals with little commercial value, were thrown out, but expensive beings like macaws. It was a sign of the society in which we lived, in which many people had the money to indulge any whim but not the commitment to follow it up.

Others apparently did not have the money but were prepared to take advantage of the "throw-away" society. Someone seeking a Grey Parrot advertised: "Must be very cheap or free." I felt my hackles rising when I read this. What sort of person has the guile to use these words? It might be said that they debase any parrot to almost worthless merchandise. Whatever the circumstances that led to this form of begging, they were unjustified. If a person genuinely could not afford to buy a parrot, how could he or she buy a suitable cage, veterinary care or pet insurance? Taking on a parrot is a serious responsibility and the cost is only one aspect of this. Only an insensitive person would be capable of placing such an advertisement. This is the reverse of an essential characteristic in the owner of a bird as perceptive as a Grey: a caring and thoughtful attitude.

In the USA the Gabriel Foundation is one of the best-known parrot rescue centres. In 2002 Julie Weiss Murad of this foundation wrote:

"... there are far too many birds being produced for whom there are not enough caring educated families. Unfortunately, there are many production-oriented breeding facilities and corporate pet retailers whose only concern is the bottom line. Right now, the companion parrot market is flooded with improperly weaned and poorly socialized parrots, often sold with the incorrect caveat that in order to bond with a parrot, a potential owner must get it as a baby and hand feed it" (Murad, 2002).

This was partly due to the activities of a huge bird food company, well known for its hand-rearing products; it started to breed parrots and to buy them from breeders in order to flood a huge pet store chain with young parrots at the weaning stage. The stores claimed to keep them until they were eating pellets on their own, supplemented by two hand-feedings daily. Reputedly staff were trained to feed the young parrots but socialisation was totally neglected. By this I mean handling to keep them tame and to inure in them the vital sense of trust, security and even curiosity, without which a hand-reared parrot is unlikely to be a successful companion.

One person who worked in such a store recorded the serious problems. The parrots arrived dehydrated. They were not tame and people who tried to handle them were bitten. Often the young parrots were not fed, the excuses ranging from "I didn't know they were there", to "I don't know how to hand-feed them". This was published in *The Pet Bird Report* of September 2000 but the writer withheld his or her name for obvious reasons. According to the editor, Sally Blanchard, that magazine had received "hundreds of e-mails, phone calls and letters" from people who had had negative experiences in purchasing birds from the large pet chains. Their main complaints concerned their health, compromised pet potential from poor socialisation, and the lack of knowledge of employees. One former pet shop employee worked at a store where hand-reared parrots

were received from the big bird food company. They were shipped in totally inappropriate containers. A Blue-fronted Amazon and a Yellow-collared Macaw arrived in shipping cartons similar to those used for shipping Budgerigars in bulk – one bird on each side.

These parrots were being exploited by huge business concerns; many died because they could not feed themselves or due to disease. Other parrots were totally unsuitable for inexperienced people to cope with. One man bought a young Jardine's Parrot from such a store – out of pity. It was in very poor condition from improper diet. Furthermore, there were "bugs" in her food. When he took her home he had her tested by an avian vet. She had PBFD (psittacine beak and feather disease – a viral disease that is often fatal in young parrots).

Many purchasers lost their money and suffered much heartache. But, as always, it was the parrots who suffered most, dying in sad circumstances or, worse, spending a life of misery because they were unsuitable as companions. It was reported that more than half the parrots that arrived from this source had behavioural problems. The big bird food company and the pet store chains made a lot of money. It was perfectly legal but totally immoral.

In *Animal Machines* Ruth Harrison wrote: "The chick comes out of the incubator and never sees a hen; the calf which is to be fattened for veal or beef is taken from the cow at birth, or very soon after; and even the piglet is weaned far earlier now than it used to be. The factors controlling this are mainly economic." This was written in 1964, before parrot production became big business, but two decades later it would have been appropriate to substitute the word parrot for hen...

Money takes precedence

The November 2000 issue of The World Parrot Trust's magazine *PsittaScene* was largely devoted to parrot welfare and rescue. The Director and founder Mike Reynolds had this question to ask of breeders: "Do you care most about the parrots themselves, or more about the money you make from them? This is the crunch question. Do you support the reduction of mass, abusive, sub-standard parrot keeping, or would this objective be unwelcome to you for financial reasons?"

■ *Jardine's Parrot.*

In some countries where aviculture had been held back by political problems, such as Communist rule (the Czech Republic, for example), parrot breeding for aviaries and for the pet market was booming at the start of the 21st century. However, I predict that in a few years' time, prices will crash. In the developed avicultural countries (Western Europe, the USA and South Africa) supply exceeds demand for many parrot species. This is reflected in prices that were lower than a decade previously and in the escalating number of parrot rescue centres. It is not reflected in the thinking of parrot breeders, many of whom do not stop to consider the result of their actions.

Jamie Gilardi, Director of The World Parrot Trust, said: "We now need to think carefully about how we make use of each bird we have, whether we breed them, and how we allocate our energy and resources to best help the recovery of threatened parrots around the globe. Are we kidding ourselves when we say that we're breeding birds 'for conservation'? It is highly unlikely that parrots now in private hands will ever be of direct conservation value to the species in the wild. We should all think long and hard about why we own birds and, if we choose to breed them, why we've made that choice. There are legitimate reasons to breed parrots in captivity: conservation simply is not one of them."

The breeder's responsibility

What can breeders do to reduce the chances of their hand-reared young ones being rehomed? Those who sell directly to the public can be much more selective in their clients. If they breed Grey Parrots they can afford to be choosy because there are always more buyers than birds. They can test the expectations and commitment of the prospective purchaser with a few questions. They can tell them that not all parrots learn to talk; too many purchasers are interested only in this aspect. They should not be afraid to say "No", explaining that these sensitive birds need a special kind of owner. The prospective purchaser might go elsewhere; on the other hand, the refusal to sell might bring the realisation that successful parrot-ownership demands more time and thought than was anticipated.

If a certain species has taken longer to sell during the previous few years, it is time for the breeder to re-assess whether he or she should continue to produce it. Methods to stop birds breeding without causing them stress include letting the female lay, then replacing the eggs with china or plastic ones or infertile eggs saved for the purpose. The worst way is to withhold the nest-box as this could cause problems, including aggressive behaviour from the male.

Some breeders need to be more responsible in the choice of species they hand-rear. Parakeets suitable only as aviary birds, which are difficult to sell due to over-production, were hand-fed to sell as pets. Aggression and fearlessness towards people is a trait of hand-reared Rosellas. A case in point was a Rosella, described as "extremely stressed and unhappy, constantly pulling out her feathers and very aggressive and destructive". She was too badly plucked to place in an outdoor aviary. Close confinement and her frustrated need to fly had resulted in a psychologically disturbed bird that plucked itself and tried to attack people. Rehoming in this case was not an option and the kindest solution was euthanasia.

Breeders should think forward – by years, especially if their own years are mounting up. Is it necessary to replace breeding pairs with younger stock? These pairs have served the breeder well; they deserve a happy retirement. All too often they are sold to unsuspecting breeders knowing that they are past breeding age, so that in their last years they too end up on the rehoming roundabout. The breeder should be committed to them in their twilight years.

Forced weaning

Some breeders increase the likelihood of parrots ending up unwanted by their inadequate weaning procedures. Weaning is the period during which young parrots learn to feed on their own and to become independent of hand-feeder or parent. It should be a gradual process followed by a period where mainly soft foods are offered, not only hard seed or pellets. It is a time of great vulnerability for those fed by inexperienced or impatient hand-feeders, or with those who mass-produce parrots for the pet trade in the UK. In the USA hardly any breeders wean young parrots; they sell them before they can feed themselves, often before they are even feathered. In my view this should be illegal.

Premature weaning or forced weaning is a major reason why many hand-reared parrots make poor pets. They never recover from the experience. To be young and hungry and deprived of sufficient food is a recipe for never trusting a human again. It is the reason why cockatoos, for example, cry for food for months after they should be weaned. It is the reason for anxious, neurotic young parrots that are so demanding the owners cannot cope.

■ *Young Grey Parrots.*

Why are so many parrots force-weaned weeks before the proper time? It is a matter of economics and ignorance and laziness, probably in equal measure. Weaning requires *much* patience, it is very time-consuming – and time is money. Psychological damage due to forced weaning could be eliminated. Breeders who sell young parrots too soon should be honest enough to tell the breeder that the parrot should be hand-fed (perhaps only once daily) until it no longer demands food.

Many breeders work on the premise that, for example, Grey Parrots are weaned at 12 weeks and Umbrella Cockatoos at 15 weeks (they are not!) and invariably sell them at that age. Here ethics go hand in hand with compassion. Caring breeders know that some young parrots take longer to wean than others, even those from the same nest. They refuse to let them out of their care until they are certain that the time is right. They also offer unlimited post-purchase advice because the welfare of the parrot is of the utmost importance.

Even parrots that are feeding themselves well when they are sold, will beg to be fed, due to the fear of finding themselves in a strange place with unfamiliar people. This is called weaning regression. They should never be refused food. Hunger causes depression and eliminates the desire to feed. It results in weight loss and, if hand-feeding does not recommence, in death. Many young parrots die from starvation after three or four days in the new home. The breeder has not acted responsibly towards the bird or to the seller. This is a major problem and one of which the buyer should be aware.

Forced weaning is especially sad for mass-produced parrots. If you reared 40 human babies and children together without real parental care, just adults to look after their physical needs, you would not expect to produce well-adjusted children. It is the same for parrots. The resulting young are mentally scarred for life.

There are certain species that responsible aviculturists feel should not be in the avicultural domain. One of these is the Moluccan Cockatoo. Found only on the island of Seram, it has been trapped almost to extinction for the pet trade. Almost all breeders hand-rear the young; they are sold to unsuspecting people for a very high price. Many purchasers have no understanding of the demands on one's time and attention of such a bird – or of the assault on the ears if they do not receive that attention. South Africa's most successful parrot breeder, William Horsfield, commenced on a commercial basis in the early 1990s. More than a decade later he wrote: "... my focus gradually shifted away from supplying the pet markets. This was largely due to the unrelenting demand for species like most of the cockatoos as 'silly-tame' pets, which in my opinion were being set up for a life of misery in years ahead" (Horsfield, 2006).

In the USA, Rebecca Margison, director of the Avian Protection Society, believed that Moluccan Cockatoos reared for the pet trade would be the first to be euthanised as a way to control their numbers, despite their Vulnerable species status. She said: "Breeding rates will continue, these birds will continue to flood the pet market, unsuspecting buyers will purchase the feathered cuddle bugs, many of the buyers will fail in their attempts to provide adequate amounts of attention and stimulation, and the birds will act out their frustration by screaming, biting, destroying wood and furniture, destroying their feathers and mutilating their bodies. Then the people will either put the bird in a basement or dark room or give the bird up. Considering their long lifespan, it will simply be too difficult to properly care for these birds long-term. So we

will see them being euthanized, probably within five years" (Calvert, 2003).

I, too, believe that no parrot has suffered so much at the hand of man as the Moluccan Cockatoo. On countless occasions these poor birds have wrenched at my heart-strings due to the inhumane treatment they were suffering. Those big, brown watchful eyes seem to show wisdom and intelligence that is so great that caging them except under exceptional conditions is an act of cruelty. This view will seem extraordinarily sentimental to those who have not been closely involved with this cockatoo. Many of those who have will have experienced (along with the shrieks and the histrionics) tenderness perhaps unmatched by any creature on earth, an intense need for a soul-mate and the capability to express and understand emotions, all to a degree that many would not believe possible in a non-human creature.

One Moluccan I will never forget. He was the male of a pair in the breeding centre at Palmitos Park, Gran Canaria. He had come to the park as a confiscated bird, whose owner did not have the necessary documentation for a CITES I species. I was very happy when he paired up with one of our females: they were so compatible. Several years later it seemed the owner had won a court case to take the bird back. The owner had a restaurant in a popular resort – so the Moluccan went back to where he had come from: a cage in a busy pedestrian area. He shared the cage with doves and chickens. It broke my heart to see him there. The owner's lack of understanding of the psychological and practical needs of one of these remarkable birds was nothing out of the ordinary. This unfortunate cockatoo mirrored the fate of thousands of others of his

■ *Moluccan Cockatoos weaned (by the author) at their own pace – at about five and a half months.*

species who have never been treated with an ounce of compassion.

In the USA one cockatoo breeder was asked, in a short space of time, to take back two of her hand-reared birds from different homes. "Quinn", a four-year old Moluccan and "Woody", an Umbrella, were the victims of a divorce and a jealous husband. The breeder asked herself:

"What am I doing producing more domestic hand-raised parrots, when even perfect parrots, like Quinn and Woody, lose their families and their security, all they ever knew, because two people I thought were ultimately committed to them (not to mention each other) could not get along?"

"My first parrots, were all wild-caught. I would never think of 'getting rid' of them. I am committed to giving them the best lives I can give them. I am responsible for them... Then I ask myself about why I breed birds, given that so many are abandoned. I know that I would have given anything, when I got my first Cockatoo to have gotten a healthy, happy chick like Woody or Quinn. Instead I got an angel from the wild, who had passed through several hands (at a profit, of course) and died in my home of beak and feather disease several years after I got her" (Clyne, undated).

Millions in captivity

In the year 2000 the World Parrot Trust estimated that there might be between 50 million and 60 million captive parrots worldwide and that the estimate for the United States was over five million parrots. Mike Reynolds, Director and founder of the Trust, wrote:

"Even with the restricted inflow [in the USA] of parrots from wild sources brought about by the Wild Bird Conservation Act, the ease with which parrots are now aviary bred means constant pressure of an excessive supply of young birds at ever lower prices. The result is a vast population, perhaps in the millions, of parrots in transit from one home to another, or to a shop, or to some kind of 'sanctuary'. It is a testament to the genuine commitment of some many hundreds, perhaps thousands, of concerned parrot people, that all over the developed world parrot sanctuaries are being opened."

Rescue centres

In 2000 The World Parrot Trust proposed the following guidelines for anyone considering starting a parrot rescue centre.

1. Sufficient funding, wide experience or working with parrots, suitable accommodation, expert veterinary support and sound methods of assessing foster homes.
2. The motivation must be rescue, rehabilitation and the long-term welfare of the birds. Profit has no place in parrot rescue.
3. Stability: total commitment on the part of those involved, plus a reasonable financial status. A business plan is recommended.
4. Some expertise in public relations. This is needed to maximise publicity, to promote the service available and to acquire funds and other forms of support. It will also assist in working with local parrot people, clubs and authorities.
5. The quality and range of facilities must be adequate. Separate quarantine, hospital, rehabilitation and pre-release sections are essential.
6. Re-homing skills. This requires inspection of potential foster homes, the education of those taking on the responsibility for a parrot, the preparation of a document recording the commitment and following up the adopter and bird to ensure that all is well.
7. In the UK the knowledge required to deal with Defra concerning species on Appendix I of CITES, and in other countries equivalent knowledge.

Welfare and cage sizes

Animal welfare was almost totally neglected by the British parliament during the 20th century, at the end of which the 1911 animal welfare laws and the Pet Animals Act 1951 were unchanged, outdated and inadequate. It was not until 2004 that a new animal welfare bill was proposed.

Major welfare issues result from buying cages that are too small for the species. Many parrots, especially wild-caught ones, show behavioural problems and aggression due to fear, when they are too closely confined. The purchase of a cage that is too small is, in part, due to the low prices of wild-caught parrots such as Greys, Senegals and Orange-winged Amazons. Most people who buy a cheap parrot will not buy a large expensive cage. In the UK there are no regulations regarding cage sizes. The only requirement is that a bird should be able to stretch both wings simultaneously. Some countries had, by the end of the 20th century, brought in legislation that stipulated minimum cage sizes for certain parrots.

In Germany, for example, a pair of *wild-caught* macaws of a large species must be kept in a cage or aviary measuring at least 20ft (6m) square. For captive-bred macaws the stipulation is an aviary 13ft (4m) square.

In Sweden a law was passed in 2001 relating to minimum cage sizes for birds in pet shops and breeders' cages. For a parrot whose length was between 26cm and 35cm (approximately 10in to 14in), such as a Grey, the minimum cage size would be 84cm (2ft 9in) square. For those measuring more than 75cm (30in) in length, such as a Blue and Yellow Macaw, the required size was a minimum of 6.5m (21ft) square. This means that, for example, only a few of the larger pet stores would stock macaws. I believe that this would reduce impulse buying. In Switzerland, legislation regarding minimum cage sizes came into force in 2002. It was drawn up with the assistance of officials of EXOTIS, the society for keepers of exotic birds.

It would seem that worldwide legislation is needed to prevent parrots (especially breeding pairs) being kept in cramped conditions. Unfortunately, in this respect standards deteriorated drastically as the century progressed. In the 1920s Lord Tavistock wrote that his Galahs bred readily in an aviary measuring 24ft (7.2m) x 8ft (2.4m). Today the same space would be more likely to house six pairs, each in an aviary 8ft x 4ft. This battery-farming approach is totally unacceptable in an age when animal welfare issues are increasingly under the spotlight.

Never again from the wild

The early part of the 21st century was and is perhaps the most important period in the history of parrot aviculture. Aviculturists have in their care many wild-caught birds of species that will probably never again be imported from the wild. These include all Australian parrots and cockatoos (except in the case of egg-smuggling), the rarer Indonesian parrots (fig parrots and some lories) and cockatoos that are prevented from entering Europe under an EC directive, and all the large macaws except the Blue and Yellow and the Green-winged. Theoretically certain Amazon parrots should never again come from the wild but smuggling might maintain the supply of wild-caught Amazons. Import and export bans, plus the threatened or endangered status of many species, had ended trade in some of them, or trade to Europe and/or the USA. Availability of other wild-caught parrots will be reduced as their numbers decline.

It seems that the future for most wild parrots can only deteriorate. Brazil is just one example. Its promises to slow down the rate of deforestation were nothing more than wishful thinking. In 2003, 9,170 sq miles (23,750 sq km – an area the size of Wales), was deforested partly to grow non-genetically-modified soya, for which there was a huge demand in Europe. Trees were cut down to graze cattle; the number of cows there doubled in a decade. Brazilian beef was in demand for its disease-free status and Brazil had become the world's leading exporter of beef.

With the loss of more and more of the Amazon rainforest came global warming. This was a high price to pay for food that could be produced elsewhere. When the trees fall Brazil's extraordinary rich bird life grows ever poorer; wonderful bird species are brought to the edge of extinction. They have nowhere to go – but the fauna are not the only creatures to suffer. All human beings and all wildlife will ultimately be affected by global warming and climate change, as a result of man's folly in destroying the world's most precious natural resources.

▌ *Green-winged Macaw.*

Private initiatives

Government support for conservation was usually sadly lacking in the neotropics yet many wonderful individuals, either as a private initiative or part of non-governmental organisations, were becoming a force to be reckoned with by the early years of the 21st century. In Ecuador, for example, a reserve of 17,000 acres of cloud forest and pre-montane wet tropical forest was established by land-owner José DeCoux in conjunction with the Centro Investigacion de Bosques Tropicales. Los Cedros Reserve lies at the southern end of the Cordillera de La Plata, north-west of Quito. It is important as a southern buffer zone for the 450,000 acres Cotocachi-Cayapas Ecological Reserve. Los Cedros is home to a number of interesting parrot species, including the rare and beautiful Rose-faced Parrot (*Pionopsitta pulchra*) and the Bronze-winged Pionus.

Forest protection in this Chocó region is vital. Since 1960 more than 40% of the forest has been cleared or heavily degraded and deforestation is accelerating (Smith, 2004). Without private reserves there would be little hope for the survival of many parrot species. Nevertheless, the reserve is under constant threat from illegal loggers and illegal sale of the land.

More responsibility by aviculturists

The Rose-faced Parrot is unknown to parrot keepers. However, equally threatened parrots in aviculture could die out without more careful planning and a greater sense of responsibility on the part of those who hold them. Some might say that if aviculturists act irresponsibly regarding the avicultural future of the rarer species, and towards individual parrots, it might be better if these parrots are lost in captivity.

All such birds are potential founders of the stock with which future generations must work. If they have not already reared young, they, and they alone, can pass on genes not already present in captive stocks. To ensure that their breeding will be successful for an unlimited number of generations, the gene pool must be as wide as possible. Most aviculturists know about the effects of in-breeding, that is, pairing together closely related birds (genetically very similar). After two or three generations this results in

small and often degenerate specimens, and in decreasing fertility.

A serious threat to parrots in aviculture results from breeders who do not manage them in a responsible way. They give little or no consideration to the future of the species because they are motivated by financial gain. The wild status of many parrots is not well known, but one out of three parrot species is known to be endangered. It is often stated that parrots in aviculture should be preserved for future generations but the hard truth is that this will happen only if a species is commercially viable.

There are several ways in which breeders endanger the captive survival of the rarer parrots.

1. *Failure to co-operate with other breeders or studbook co-ordinators*

Rare species are obtained by breeders who have only one pair of the species – and usually a collection consisting of many different species. If they breed, the young are usually sold as soon as possible. Ideally, the buyer should already keep the species and can provide unrelated partners. Or, he or she will obtain at least one other pair from another source. There are two reasons for this: one is to prevent in-breeding and the other is that selling young which are destined to be the only pair of their species in a collection is the quickest way to ensure its extinction in captivity. When one bird of a rare species dies, the owner either cannot find another to replace it, or cannot afford to do so. Yet he or she might not make the effort to enquire who might need the survivor.

Studbooks are important in assisting the survival of a rare species in aviculture in a certain country or continent. The studbook keeper can locate surplus males or females, if they exist, and place young birds where they will be used to their best advantage. Some studbooks operate in Europe. Just knowing the location of rare species might be important at some stage. However, the stipulations of some studbooks have made it difficult for private breeders to co-operate or unfair demands have been made on them. As an example, one successful breeder of the Philippine Cockatoo in which there is a serious lack of captive females, was expected to pass all his young females to a zoo. Studbook keepers must be realistic!

2. *Producing rare species which are unsuitable for breeding*

Another threat to parrots is producing young of rare species that are unsuitable for breeding. Young of Moluccan Cockatoos, Palm Cockatoos, Hyacinthine Macaws and Golden (Queen of Bavaria's) Conures are hand-reared from the egg to increase production, because their value is high and/or they are perceived as desirable pets. Although a few of these birds might find their way back into breeding situations, many of them will not breed. If they have been without contact with their own species from independence until one or two or more years of age, they have not had the opportunity to learn appropriate behaviour. Some present greater problems in this respect than others. Male cockatoos and Eclectus kept in this way are more likely to be useless for breeding than Amazons, for example. It is not possible to predict if hand-reared birds can breed successfully as much depends on the circumstances of the individual parrot.

When I hand-reared Moluccan Cockatoos to produce birds for display at Palmitos Park, I isolated them from the age of five or six weeks. Their only companion was an adult male Moluccan. Because of the extraordinary affectionate and gentle nature of this species, I found it was perfectly safe to place an adult male with the chicks that were feathering up. As soon as the young ones could fly, they were released from their cage to fly with the adult. Moluccan Cockatoos *not* hand-reared in this manner cry continually and make food soliciting calls for many months whenever they see a person. Those reared in an adult's company show normal behaviour and vocalisations.

Aviculturists should ensure that a percentage of the young reared are suitable for breeding and are placed in a breeding situation. Failing this, when the wild-caught breeding pairs die, there will be no suitable birds to replace them.

3. *Failure to comply with legislation*

Over 120 countries were members of CITES at the start of the 21st century. Some of those responsible for implementing this treaty lost sight of its purpose, which was to prevent species becoming threatened by excessive trade in wild-caught birds. Not only had CITES failed to do that in many instances, but in some cases it obstructed the work of genuine breeders. Much of the wording of the treaty was vague and was interpreted differently in various countries.

▮ *Male Eclectus Parrots being hand-reared. If, after weaning, they are kept without contact with their own species, they might be unsuitable for breeding.*

Some breeders ceased to keep Appendix 1 species to avoid the paperwork involved in registering adults and selling young. In the UK breeders of Appendix 1 species were required to micro-chip the parents and to give proof of their origin. If no proof existed the case would be discussed with the relevant official at Defra. When the parents were registered and the young are ringed or micro-chipped, an application to sell them could be made to Defra. Identification of individual birds was essential to prevent the system being abused.

4. *Lack of exchange of information*
Many breeders accumulated information that would be of great value to others rearing the same species. Unfortunately, much of this information is never accessible. If aviculture is to realise its full potential, it is vital that breeders share such knowledge, preferably in the form of the printed word. Avicultural literature is full of successes with rare species but detailed accounts of experiences with common species are much rarer. Everyone should carefully record and publish, in words and pictures, accounts of the species with which they have most experience. It might be considered as a duty, in return for the privilege of keeping these wonderful birds.

Irresponsible and inhumane acts

Every occupation or interest in which items of high value are involved attracts an undesirable element. When it is live animals that are involved the suffering can be incalculable.

A Green-winged Macaw was taken to a parrot rescue centre in the UK. It was found flying free and advertising failed to locate its owner. The bird shook with fear for months after being caught. It was found to be suffering from cloacal papillomas and was operated on for their removal. Birds in this condition would not be welcomed by breeders because the disease can be contagious. Veterinary treatment would be expensive and the papillomas might recur. This macaw might have been liberated when found to have the disease – or it could have been stolen. Viral-induced cloacal papillomas (small growths) are very common in wild-caught birds imported from Guyana, such as Green-winged Macaws. This was not an isolated incident of

inhumane disposal. In the Leeds area someone noticed a brown paper bag at the roadside. On stopping his car to investigate he found a Grey Parrot inside. It was known to have been there for some hours. The Grey was tame but very badly plucked. In the hands of a caring rescuer it feathered up in nine months and was then rehomed for breeding. Although there are rescue centres and help lines that obviated the need for such callous action, some people cannot be bothered to seek them out.

Legislation

It is not only the ethics of individuals that will influence parrot welfare and survival. Governments and their policy-makers are even more influential. In 2002 the Indonesian government reduced the export quotas of wild-caught birds to zero – seemingly a giant step forward. However, in view of the huge scale of the illegal trade, in a country where corruption is the norm, this action might not have much impact.

The other factor that gives cause for pessimism is the number of Indonesia's wild-caught parrots that are exported as captive-bred. For example, during the years 1997–2001 the total number of wild-caught Pesquet's Parrots exported legally was given as nil but the number of captive-bred birds was listed as 47 – possibly more than the total ever bred in captivity worldwide. This is patently ridiculous! Likewise for Salvadori's Fig Parrot (*Psittaculirostris salvadorii*), 144 wild-caught birds were reported exported and 189 captive-bred birds. This species, threatened by habitat loss, is very difficult to breed in captivity, even in the most sophisticated breeding stations. The figures for the closely related Desmarest's Fig Parrot (*P. desmarestii*), equally difficult to breed, were even more ludicrous: 656 wild-caught and 1,363 captive-bred exported.

Moral standards

Moral standards and principles relating to parrots progressed very slowly indeed during the first part of the 20th century. Towards the century's close there was more understanding of the physical needs of parrots and a growing band – but still very small – who insisted that parrots should be kept in large aviaries where the emphasis was on environmental enrichment. As related in Chapter 19, the intelligence of parrots was increasingly being recognised. The importance of training them to perform basic requests, often avoiding or eliminating behavioural problems in the process, was gaining greater credence among companion parrot owners. Indeed, progress in this respect was marked during the 1990s along with a much greater understanding of the psychological processes of parrots. This gave great hope for a future in which all aspects of parrot welfare would be improved. Many more people than ever before were questioning the trade in wild-caught parrots and some were actively opposing it.

Moral responsibility is important in another area – that of aviculturists and collectors who must say no to the acquisition of illegally imported birds. The survival of one endangered species, Lear's Macaw, will depend on this. If collectors continue to create the demand, there is no doubt that Lear's will face the same situation as Spix's Macaw – and become extinct in the wild.

Bigger penalties for smuggling

Enlightened governments were taking smuggling more seriously. In Australia, Customs officers severely disrupted an international smuggling racket in 2004. Customs Investigations carried out the biggest ever operation to identify and prosecute smugglers, raiding premises in Queensland, New South Wales, Victoria and Western Australia. Large numbers of eggs and birds were seized. The penalties for trafficking in wildlife under Australia's federal laws included maximum fines of $110,000 and/or ten years in jail.

The future

Only by raising the profile of parrots will their status as highly intelligent creatures that must be protected from commercial trade (like gorillas, for example) and from abuse, and from over-breeding (like dogs in puppy farms) be recognised. More active measures will be necessary. World Parrot Day, organised by the World Parrot Trust on May 31 2004, set the tone.

■ *World Parrot Day 2004. The scene in London's Trafalgar Square.*

The press reported that: "A flock of protesting parrots converged on Downing Street yesterday to demand that the prime minister does more than merely repeat empty electoral promises. Tony Blair was probably out enjoying the bank holiday weather as illustrator Quentin Blake – with a large blue and yellow macaw perched on his shoulder – arrived to deliver a petition calling for an end to the importation of wild birds. On what was World Parrot Day, wildlife campaigners urged the government to ban a trade which, they claim, is threatening the survival of numerous species. The director of the Cornwall-based World Parrot Trust, Jamie Gilardi, said: 'Parrots are among the most intelligent species of bird and we are campaigning for the end of importation of wild birds into the EU.'

"The Labour party, he said, had made a statement in 1997 in support of such a ban and he wanted Mr Blair to follow up on that. 'We want this [trade] stopped.'"

A Green-winged Macaw carried to Trafalgar Square for the protest, posed with a notice declaring "Born to be wild" clasped in its beak. Could this be the start of an era in which parrots are treated with the respect they deserve?

21. THEY MAKE YOU LAUGH AND THEY MAKE YOU CRY!

On of the most notorious parrots of the 20th century was a Hyacinthine Macaw named Blue Boy. He was an extraordinary bird with an extraordinary owner. Evan, Lord Tredegar, had apparently purchased the macaw in the late 1920s – and the two were rarely apart. In South Wales, the Morgan family's dynasty started in the 13th century and continued until the 20th. Their seat was Tredegar House in Gwent.

On one occasion, Evan (a Roman Catholic convert and Chamberlain to the Pope) was entertaining the Archbishop of Cardiff who, seeing the remarkable bird, approached Blue Boy and asked him how he was. Blue Boy replied with a pithy phrase of no more than two words, telling the Archbishop exactly where to go. Evan apologised profusely, but the Archbishop replied: "Don't worry. I get the feeling a lot of people would like to say just that to me. It is rather refreshing to hear it said straight out for a change!"

The photograph of Blue Boy perched on Evan, Lord Tredegar's shoulder at a garden party is without doubt the most famous image of that irrepressible bird. The other characters in this evocative 1930s photograph (the Alderman of Newport, his wife, and housekeeper) look rather shocked. One lady has her hand to her mouth as if to stifle surprise. Many have joked that Blue Boy must have said something outrageous (Busby, pers. comm. 2006).

Blue Boy's language was remembered by the footmen at Tredegar House. He would sometimes perch himself on a windowsill in the Butler's Pantry and swear ferociously as the footmen attempted to clean the silver. Blue Boy was also capable of polite remarks. He would often sleep in the Servant's Hall. If anybody poked their head around the door at night and said "Goodnight, Blue Boy!", he would reply: "Goodnight." One footman, testing the macaw, entered the Servant's Hall in the morning and said: "Goodnight, Blue Boy." The macaw ignored him, and, apparently, gave him a look of great disdain.

Blue Boy was treated with apprehension by guests. He would often lull them into a false sense of security by snuggling up to them, and then he would bite the buttons off their shirt or jacket and break them in two. He also had a penchant for attacking the pearls on ladies' necklaces, and nipping the heads of bald men. Evan entertained widely and was a most entertaining, if sometimes alarming, host. He greatly disliked bores. It is said that if a guest displeased him he would whisper to Blue Boy who would drop down onto the floor, go underneath the table, and nip the ankles of the offending guest. H. G. Wells was once pecked by Blue Boy, and claimed that he could never "gratify that damn bird".

Blue Boy's end was sad and swift during World War II. According to Evan: "He crawled up a broomstick and as he reached the top it started to topple over. He took a terrible blow on his head. Haemorrhaging set in, and the poor boy went under very quickly." The loss of Blue Boy, his partner in crime, upset Evan greatly. He never bought a replacement. That was unusual for he had owned many birds over the years.

A story is recounted which illustrates his affinity with birds and his ability to shock. Evan was wandering around Thame Market with a friend in the 1920s. They came across a stall selling birds, including an Australian Parakeet described as "witless and uncontrollable". Evan, perhaps sensing a challenge, bought it. Within a month he walked into the packed Café Royal in London to show off his new party piece. Remarkably, he had trained the parakeet to crawl up the inside of his trouser leg and poke its head out of his fly!

Parrots have occupied a special place in the human heart for many centuries. Even native people, who were more inclined to eat them than cherish them, kept some as companions. In the year 1900 Walter Goodfellow recorded how, when he was travelling in Ecuador for two years, he would often come across Archidona Indian women with Orange-chinned Parakeets (*Brotogeris jugularis*) on their shoulders. They would carry them in that position while doing household tasks, also on long journeys through the forests (Goodfellow, 1900).

From the first decade of the century to the last, Greys and Amazons were riding high in the popularity stakes. In or about the year 1900 a Double Yellow-headed Amazon called Polly was purchased by a family for their spoiled only child, Edward. He would ride around Merced, California, in his cart with his two favourite companions, his dog and his Amazon. Polly was not a young bird and she could sing an old Civil War song as well as a risqué sea-faring ditty.

During that decade travelling shows visited small towns. An actress called Little Eva was the star of one such show in Merced. After the performance Edward's family hosted a party for the theatrical troupe. The beautiful Eva arrived glamorously attired and wearing a stunningly expensive hat – probably from Paris. Eva put down her hat and Polly found it. During this important social occasion Polly worked hard on the hat, shredding every piece of straw and picking off every flower. She destroyed it. Little Eva was not amused – and the family had to hide their mirth.

■ *Lord Tredegar and Blue Boy. Did the macaw's language shock garden party guests?*
Photograph: Tredegar House, Newport, South Wales

Polly ate the middle of a fried egg, toast and jam for breakfast and enjoyed coffee in a doll's cup every morning of her life. During the summers she would patrol a long, low fence, walking up and down and calling children, dogs, chickens and cats. They all obeyed her! That was an age of innocence – when you could give a parrot freedom and safely leave it outside knowing that it would not be stolen. What a good life Polly must have had! After almost 50 years with her family, she died peacefully one morning (Perrin, 1999). Lucky indeed is the parrot that spends most of her life with one loving family. Lucky indeed is the parrot that is treated as a family member, not as a "pet" for entertainment.

An unusual mimic

It was usual for Australian parakeets to be kept in aviaries but in 1903 Dr George Creswell was short of aviary space. He put his aviary-bred Redrump Parakeet in a cage where he became an amazing mimic. He could whistle almost the entire repertoire of the Song Thrush. Then he copied a Siskin x Canary hybrid in the house – an especially accomplished and energetic songster. This performance was made even more interesting by the interjection of phrases spoken by Dr Creswell's Blue-fronted Amazon, Polly. Billy gave them various inflections, just as the parrot did, according to the voice of the teacher! Now and then a couple of bars of "Pop goes the weasel!" were introduced, without any break in the song (*Bird Notes*, July 1903).

Every day Billy would perch in a corner of his cage on one of the lowest perches, with his feathers ruffled and his head tucked in his back until he looked like a green ball. Almost in a whisper, he repeated the phrase he was learning. Eventually a female was acquired for Billy and he took up residence in an outdoor aviary. Sometimes, when the female was in the nest he could be heard singing the old songs in a low tone.

In Australia it was the white cockatoos who were most likely to become unforgettable companions. Archie, a Western Slender-billed Cockatoo, lived with the local barber in a farming town north of Perth in the 1930s. Arnold was a champion golfer and would often practise his swing. Archie would stand with his legs apart and swing his head from side to side,

at the same time making a whooshing sound. He roamed the town at will and could often be seen in a storm-water pipe that ran under the main road. When anyone walked past he would pop his head out, repeat some really bad language, then disappear from sight. Strangers blamed any unfortunate man who happened to be close! Archie enjoyed going down to the station and jumping in the van of the goods train standing there. When the train reached the next siding, seven miles south, the guard would put him in the van of another train going north! He was so well known he always arrived home safely.

A blue treasure

Of the 350 species of parrots in existence only about one seventh are regularly kept as companions. Sometimes unusual species are found, unidentified. Surely the strangest story ever concerned a parrot in Denver, Colorado, that had been kept with a Double Yellow-headed Amazon for 25 years. When the Amazon died in 2002 the woman phoned an avian vet's office for advice on the surviving bird, reputedly a Spix's Macaw. This macaw was then extinct in the wild and the captive population consisted of only 60 individuals. The call was answered by Michelle Muck, a parrot enthusiast and a member of The World Parrot Trust. She was a little sceptical but eventually the owner invited her to see the bird. Her heart skipped a beat. In a small cage, in poor plumage, with a deformed and overgrown beak and little strength in its feet, was a listless blue macaw. Because it was a wild-caught bird and did not enter the USA legally, the World Parrot Trust and American and Brazilian officials worked together with the owner to return it to Brazil. Over the next weeks its diet was changed (it had been fed only pellets), and its feet were exercised. Some weeks later, "Presley" as he was called, weighed nearly 400g (from an underweight 300g) and was deemed fit to make the journey to Brazil, to go into quarantine at Sao Paulo Zoo.

There was highly optimistic speculation that this thirty-plus macaw could breed, that he might even be the saviour of his race, as he was perhaps unrelated to all others. Although the larger *Ara* macaws can reproduce at this age, Spix's Macaw is very different in so many ways that the same reproductive potential might not

54 Paradise Parakeet (*Psephotus pulcherrimus*) as illustrated in Greene's *Parrots in Captivity* (CHAPTER 17). **55** Queen of Bavaria's (Golden) Conure (*Guaruba guarouba*), the subject of a bizarre escape story (CHAPTER 21). How many more new species will be described? **56** The Pintoi Conure (*Aratinga pintoi*) was already in captivity but had not been distinguished from the Sun Conure (CHAPTER 16).

Photo: Roland Seitre

56

Elizabeth Butterworth

57 No one knows when the Glaucous Macaw (*Anodorhynchus glaucus*) became extinct
(CHAPTER 17).

Photo: Sam Williams

58

58 Lear's Macaw (*Anodorhynchus leari*) is critically endangered, due to the activities of illegal trappers (CHAPTER 6).

Photo: Parrots International

59

59 Red-fronted Macaws in their Bolivian habitat. **60** Hyacinthine Macaws (*Anodorhynchus hyacinthinus*), Piaui, Brazil – a major destination for parrot eco-tourists (CHAPTER 18).

Photo: Lars Lepperhoff

60

apply. Nevertheless, his discovery could still benefit his species. When feathers and a blood sample were sent to San Diego Zoo for DNA testing to determine his sex, cells were isolated and preserved in the zoo's frozen bank. This was the only known frozen sample of the species' cells.

A moving story

A very moving story concerned a much-loved Moustache Parakeet. Lloyd Barker, a 24-year-old American soldier, whose hobby was falconry, was posted to Vietnam. One day he visited the village of An Khe and saw a young boy hitting a small creature with sticks. Concerned, he investigated to find it was a parrot. Its tail feathers had been pulled out and one of its toes was broken. Lloyd gave the boy the equivalent of 80c and took the bird away. "Bird" soon became tame and went everywhere with Lloyd who was

■ *Moustache Parakeet.*

assigned to fly as the door gunner in a helicopter. On these assignments Bird would hang on the webbing on Lloyd's back and look over his shoulder. When shrapnel clipped the top of his head, the army vet treated him.

Then Lloyd was assigned to office work and Bird would ride on the typewriter carriage. When the bell rang at the end of the line, he would hang on tight when the carriage returned. At night he would climb up a chord to the liner of the tent, enter a hole and roost there. In the morning he would climb along the chord to the back of the tent, where the major had his office, and climb down to the light bulb to wish the major "Good morning". Then he would return to Lloyd and jump on to his typewriter. Bird was wounded again during a mortar attack, when a piece of shrapnel hit him in the breast, exposing his muscles. The vet sewed him up and saved his life again.

When the time came for Lloyd to return to the USA there was much concern because Bird would eat only if Lloyd fed him. Lloyd knew that Bird would die unless he took him home with him. The only way was to travel to Saigon and obtain an export certificate from a vet; the certificate had to be signed within 72 hours of departure. Saigon was a restricted area with no passes allowed. The major told Lloyd: "Bird has brought too much joy to too many soldiers to have him starve here in Vietnam. I will give you a seven-day pass to go to Saigon."

Bird and Lloyd set off by helicopter and plane. The health certificate and the export certificate were obtained and Lloyd went to an air base and put Bird on a commercial flight to Idaho. He said: "I cried all the way back to the hotel." His tears were justified. He was delayed for four days in Asia so it took him eight days to get home. Bird had died the day before. Lloyd wrote: "My heart broke. He had given so much and entertained so many, and, most of all, he had helped me survive the horror of a year in combat" (Barker, 1997).

The ending was so sad and perhaps need not have been so. Bird would probably have survived if he had been crop-fed via a tube. Most vets (and many aviculturists) could do this.

Mutual adoration

So often tender and affectionate, it is not surprising that cockatoos tug at the heartstrings, such as the Umbrella owned by a 13-year-old American girl. The cockatoo had a prolapse (part of his intestines would appear when he defecated) and had been operated on several times without success. He needed a loving owner. Jacque took him on. They adored each other. The girl would have a half-hour cuddling session in bed with the cockatoo every morning. He would sit with her while she did her homework every evening, then they played together like two children. Jacque gave him medication and a healthy diet. She took the responsibility very seriously.

Despite the loving care the cockatoo's problems returned and once more surgery was necessary. After the operation he could eat only certain foods. Jacque would feed him, one seed or one piece of vegetable at a time. When he returned to the vet to be given fluids intravenously, tests showed his liver function was impaired. He returned home, to be watched over 24 hours a day by one or other member of the family. A few days later he became very weak; he lay in Jacque's arms, not even opening his eyes. Her tears were wetting his feathers.

"Suddenly," recalled Jacque's mother, Cynthia Drury, "an amazing thing happened. He opened his eyes, stood up and rested his head on Jacque's shoulder. The love and comfort Jacque was giving him seemed to give him strength, he rallied and began to say Jacque's name." He was rushed to the vet's surgery where he was again given fluids. But he died in her arms – of kidney failure. She held him for half an hour. Her grief was inconsolable (Drury, 2001).

▌ *Umbrella Cockatoo.*

An unwanted Goffin's

A poignant story with a happy ending concerned a Goffin's Cockatoo discovered in a bar in Benson, Arizona. It had deformed legs and no one wanted it. One man took it home and unwisely put it in an aviary but he could not tolerate the sight of it dragging itself along the ground with its beak. He gave it to a woman known as the "Bird Lady" who, equally insensitively, placed it in a small cage with sanded paper on the floor and left it outdoors.

He took it back and gave it to a friend. Barbara did not want any more parrots but when she saw the sick, dirty and frightened little cockatoo she knew that she had to help it. She was told it was a young captive-bred male that had been hatched deformed. It was an adult female wearing an open quarantine band. The unnatural position of the most badly affected leg, that pointed upwards, suggested a bad break. The right leg was pointing backwards. Nails were missing and both feet appeared to be useless. The little cockatoo appeared to be in pain, and pulled herself along with her beak and her right wing, the end of which was missing, making flight impossible. What courage this cockatoo had! Obviously she had not been imported in this condition. One dares not ponder on how she received these terrible injuries...

The next day Barbara took the cockatoo, now named "Jordy", to an avian vet. Various tests were carried out and the cockatoo was found to be positive for chlamydia (psittacosis). Thus started six weeks of daily handling to give medication. The treatment was successful. Because of her lack of mobility the Goffin's became covered in her own faeces and her underside was naked and raw. Pressure sores developed and testing revealed an *E. coli* infection. As soon as the medication ceased the infection returned. The vet thought that surgery would do more harm than good. Barbara became very discouraged. The cockatoo seemed to be in constant pain so a different vet was consulted. After taking x-rays he pronounced: "A piece of cake! I can operate this afternoon."

He shortened the badly broken leg, straightened it and pinned it. The leg healed well and Jordy became more active and affectionate. She was able to walk on her hocks, with her head up, and then she could run and even hop a little.

▌*Female Goffin's Cockatoo.*

Most of her activities took place on furniture, in her padded cage or on the floor. Just eight months after Barbara took her on, the little cockatoo would run to her, her eyes bright and expectant. She did everything with enthusiasm and loved to play and bathe. She was learning to scratch her head with her foot. She spent her evenings being cuddled by family members. Barbara called Jordy her "little darling" and marvelled over her "special spirit and willingness to trust, even when she had been so mistreated by humans" (Bailey, 2000).

Some parrots are as cherished as children. A marital breakdown can result in neither partner wanting to relinquish their treasured pet. In a twist to a typical 20th century custody case, in 1987 a court in Covington, Kentucky, awarded custody of the parrot to the male partner. His wife was awarded visitation rights at weekends. However, there was a stipulation: the husband would not be permitted to take the parrot to bars when he went out drinking!

Amazing Amazons

Amazon parrots are loved for their joyous personalities and their sense of mischief as Sarah Huber's story about her Amazon Rocky illustrates. She thought she had a problem with the volume control on her tape recorder. When the sound fluctuated she peered into the room expecting to find that the Amazon was to blame but he was sitting quietly eating a Granola bar.

She went back into the next room and the volume changed again. When she returned to the room the Amazon looked up innocently, said "Oh, hello" and went on munching. Sarah went back to her room when suddenly the music stopped. She returned to Rocky's room and turned on the tape recorder. This time she stood by the door and opened it a little way. She saw Rocky run over to the tape recorder with the Granola bar in his beak and press the buttons until it shut off. As he saw Sarah open the door he whipped his head round and pretended to munch on his Granola. She turned on the tape recorder yet again, went out and peaked through the door. As he reached for the tape recorder she opened the door; he was so quick that his beak touched the Granola bar before the door was open (Huber, 1997).

For an Amazon to play the innocent it must have a sense of self-awareness. This can be said only of remarkably intelligent animals such as the great apes. Furthermore, the Amazon had worked out how to bring Sarah back into the room. It is the clever and often unexpected actions of parrots that set them apart from other pets. There is no doubt in my mind that Amazons, and a few other parrots, have a sense of humour or at least a sense of mischief.

Almost everyone who has a close relationship with a parrot has a story to tell about its accomplishments. Living with a parrot can be an incredibly rewarding experience if you have the time, patience and sympathy to empathise with it and to treat it like a treasured member of the family. Err on the side of over-estimating its intelligence and you will be on the right track. Make a real effort to understand it – and I do not mean its mimicry. Individuals of many species of parrots, small and large, can make the most wonderful companions – *in the hands of the right person.*

We never own them

When referring to many parrots that have a close relationship with their owner, I hesitate to use the word "pet". It somehow demeans the independent spirit that is, for example, a macaw or an Amazon. We might be privileged to share our lives with these birds but we never own them. We co-habit. The relationship is quite different to that with a dog or a cat.

This is somehow especially true of the large macaws. They are extraordinary creatures with whom one can interact almost as one would a human. They understand much more than most people realise. The most popular companion macaw is the Blue and Yellow (Blue and Gold). Too few people can offer these highly intelligent birds sufficient time and commitment. The cognitive abilities of ALL parrots are under-rated, perhaps none more so than this macaw. I am saddened by the thought of the many large macaws that spend years of torment with unsympathetic owners.

The affection that they can show is exceptional. G. A. Perrot described his Blue and Yellow Macaw as being "capable of most tender, almost sensuous, affection frequently demonstrated". (Sensuous might seem a strange word to use about a parrot but I believe it to be true of certain macaws and cockatoos.) He commented: "They alternate rapidly between mischief and contrition. A loud 'No' plus an angry gesture and Mac immediately looks all apologetic and very gently holds one's finger and licks it with his tongue or else rubs his head along one's arm or against one's head in a gesture of affection" (Perrot, 1978).

In the USA a wild-caught Blue and Yellow Macaw called Charlie was bought from a bird farm in 1978. To start with Charlie was taken out of his cage every day. He went on holiday in the family's motor home and was left unattended on his stand while they went out for the day. Asking for trouble? Of course. Charlie gnawed the Formica counter tops and was thenceforth relegated to a life inside his cage in the bathroom of the family's home. Unfortunately, there is nothing unusual about his story so far.

Nineteen years later he was still in the bathroom but he was in poor condition, plucking his feathers and had lost all interest in preening. He was suffering from depression. Leslie Beatty came into his life and saw immediately that his owners were afraid of him. Charlie was a mass of pin feathers and his tail feathers were still in sheaths – a sign of a poor diet or lack of moisture on his plumage, or both. Leslie went over to Charlie and scratched his head. He did not object. He let Leslie preen him all over, much to the amazement of his soon-to-be former owners.

Charlie settled in with Leslie. Next morning he removed him from the cage with a stick, and Charlie stepped onto his arm. Soon he was begging to be preened. "He let me cuddle and hold him. I'd never felt anything quite like it. It was as though I could feel his every thought; all the loneliness he'd experienced and the absolute relief and gratitude for his new home."

Leslie's four year old Blue and Yellow and three year old Green-winged Macaws became Charlie's teachers. He copied all they did, from shaking off excess water after a bath to eating with the family. When he first saw them his eyes changed from a "listless stare to a look of pure delight".

He could not be petted enough after all the years without any physical contact. He wanted to be held, touched and preened continually. It is my belief that it is just as cruel to deprive macaws and cockatoos of physical contact (avian or human), as it would be to deprive a child. Leslie Beatty wrote: "Charlie is now a very happy macaw and is adapting to his new flock. He is a wonderful addition to our family. I'm so glad to have him as part of our lives. He is truly a cherished parrot treasure" (Beatty, undated, published in 1996).

Macaws seem to have such a deep need for affection that they can put past cruelty or neglect behind them when they find someone to whom they can relate. Sometimes macaw and human have a relationship that is mutually beneficial or therapeutic. Carol Gomez had a passion for flying microlights. After six months of training, in 1996, she took her first solo flight with near fatal consequences. The microlight she was flying crashed 160ft (48m) to the ground at almost 100mph (160kmph). Her limbs were smashed and her abdominal artery was ruptured. She nearly bled to death. The consultant who treated her found it hard to believe that anyone could survive such an accident. She was rushed to the operating theatre where she underwent surgery for 14 hours; her chances of survival were only 20%.

She did survive, after three months in intensive care, but she was told that she would never walk again. For more than a year she was wheelchair-bound. Then she started to walk with the aid of crutches. One day she went to a garden centre. She had never kept a parrot and had no intention of buying one – until she saw a Blue and Yellow Macaw. Carol said: "We just looked at each other" – she could not explain further. It seems to me that there is a higher level of communication between a large macaw (and between macaws) and a human than exists with other parrots. Here were two beings who desperately needed emotional commitment from another and, in that instant, they found it. The macaw let her rub its head. It was a screamer and not tame, but was less than two years old, Carol was told. She bought it.

▮ *Carol and Maxine.*

Carol called her Maxine. When she got her home she opened the cage. Maxine ran up her arm, pecked her face (not hard) and laughed. Carol thought she had made a big mistake. She was still on crutches and wondered how on earth she was going to deal with this big macaw. Right from the start she treated her like an intelligent being, talking to her all the time and telling her what she was doing. A new neighbour could hear Carol communicating with what she thought must be a child with special needs, and she sometimes heard the "child" reply.

The macaw went everywhere with Carol who was still walking with crutches; it was not long before Maxine had gnawed through one set! Within six months Maxine was very tame

and closely bonded with this remarkable and courageous woman. Carol was determined that she would walk again unaided. Sometimes it was hard to get out of bed – but she got up for her macaw. "Looking after Maxine stopped me from sinking into depression," said Carol. "She's like a piece of magic. Who is to say that we are cleverer than they are? They can communicate in our language. We can't speak theirs. Sometimes I will say to her: 'Do you want a sandwich?' Maxine will reply: 'Can I have a look?' and she might say: 'What's that?'" The macaw does not like loud noises. When the mower is in use she shouts: "Shut it off! Off!" Maxine does not like the cat and it is frightened of her. Sometimes she will steal its food and say "Oh, that's nice!"

Carol's strength and courage through years of pain and sadness should be an inspiration to everyone who complains at the slightest hardship. She can explain it: "Maxine was my saviour." She helped her recovery and, a few years later, Carol was able to continue her favourite pastime – flying microlights! "When you are up there you feel as though you are flying, as though you stay in the air by just flapping your wings." Carol loves the sensation of flight. Alas, many companion parrots are permanently deprived of it.

Parrots in the news

Described as the most famous parrot in the world at the time of her death, "Polly" lived in an almost equally famous pub in Fleet Street, the heart of London's newspaper world. She was a Grey Parrot who resided at Ye Old Cheshire Cheese for 40 years. When she died in 1926 news of her death was broadcast by the BBC. The sad event was reported in more than 200 newspapers throughout the world.

When I visited Ye Old Cheshire Cheese in 1972, I saw "Polly" behind glass, the work of a skilful taxidermist. I examined some of the framed newspaper cuttings in which her death was announced. According to the *North China Star* she was "probably the best known parrot in the world". The *Penang Gazette* believed her to be "the biggest personality in Fleet Street". The *Manchester Guardian* told an amusing story of how, on Armistice night, when the Street went mad, Polly pulled 400 corks without stopping. During her reign at the city pub she had been introduced to many of the most notable people of four decades. She had "kissed" Princess Mary, and ordered "Scotch" for Prime Minister Baldwin. Not surprisingly, she could imitate the popping of a cork and the gurgle of wine being poured.

Polly had been delivered in a cigar box as a gift from a Liverpool shipper. She became a fluent talker and a New York newspaper described her as "an expert in profanity". She would whisper strong words in the ears of men patrons but with ladies her language was impeccable. Always a great attraction with American tourists, one such visitor offered £300 for her. But Polly was one item that money could not buy.

Some parrots make news because they have a famous owner. Whether Sir Winston Churchill's macaw was an avian celebrity during the great man's lifetime is unknown. According to *The Guardian* newspaper Churchill acquired him in 1937 and he was his companion until Churchill died in 1965. In January 2004 almost every UK newspaper carried the story of Charlie the Blue and Yellow Macaw. Allegedly she had belonged to Churchill and had now reached the extraordinary age of 104 years! In these stories the emphasis was not on her age but on the rude comments she made on Hitler and others. According to the *Daily Mirror*, which carried a full-page photo of feather- plucked Charlie, "she can still be coaxed into repeating them with that unmistakeable Churchillian inflection".

There is well documented evidence that if macaws reach their fifties they are crippled with arthritis or nearly blind due to cataracts. According to a study made in the USA by well-known avian veterinarian Susan Clubb, degenerative changes occur in macaws over 40 years old. Most macaws of known age die in their late forties to mid-fifties. In old birds the facial skin alters, with cysts, wrinkling, spots of pigment and wart-like blemishes. Thinning of the skin is evident on the face and on the feet. In the photographs Charlie showed no such signs of age. Many parrot owners would have great difficulty in believing this nice little story. When the *Mirror* wrote about Charlie, it obligingly published a photograph of Churchill with his macaw on his shoulder. The macaw was a Scarlet! Even in black and white the differences (light upper mandible, lack of feathered lines on the face and dark breast colour) are glaringly obvious. Charlie was an imposter!

World leaders and parrots are not an unusual combination. Apparently the most famous parrot in America at the turn of the century was Eli, a Hyacinthine Macaw that lived in the White House during Theodore Roosevelt's administration. Roosevelt wrote to a friend describing Eli as "the most gorgeous macaw, with a bill that I think could bite through boiler plate, who crawls all over Ted and whom I view with dark suspicion".

Ted was Roosevelt's son and obviously had no qualms about playing with his big-beaked companion. For the last word from a president's parrot we must go back to the 19th century. At the funeral of US President Jackson in 1854, Pol, his pet Yellow-naped Amazon, yelled obscenities – and was ejected.

In 1958 a Budgerigar called Sparkie Williams shot to fame in the UK. The BBC organised a competition to find the best talking bird and Sparkie beat 2,768 other entrants. Touring the country, he could repeat 583 words, including eight nursery rhymes, and made a record that sold 20,000 copies. Sparkie can be seen today in the Hancock Museum at Newcastle-upon-Tyne. No other member of the parrot family in the UK has ever equalled his fame.

Newspaper editors love quirky stories about parrots. We have all read them! Often they relate to the parrot's ability to mimic, which has led to some bizarre situations. There was Percy the Yellow-fronted Amazon, for example. Percy was rehearsing for the role of Long John Silver's parrot in a children's pantomime to be performed

■ *Scarlet Macaw.*

▌*Red-lored Amazon.*

in Dorset in 1999. He learned his classic line "Pieces of eight" as any good parrot would, for his acting début, after his owner answered an advert for a talented parrot. He looked just the part. However at the final rehearsal, when his big moment came, all did not go smoothly. He blurted out an extremely rude phrase. The actors around him collapsed into hysterics. Nothing stimulates a Yellow-front more than laughter, so Percy then decided to run through his repertoire, and demonstrated it with a stream of even ruder words. He was sacked on the spot!

In Manchester a Ducorp's Cockatoo called the police when the house-sitter accidentally locked herself out. While waiting for a neighbour with a spare set of keys, she was surprised and embarrassed when a police car arrived. The officer informed her that a 999 call had been received from that address. Assuming that it was a mistake, she went to the back of the house where the cockatoo was seen standing on the telephone, with the receiver off, pecking at the numbers! (*Daily Mail*, May 17 2001).

Recognition of his owner resulted in Barney, the Red-lored Amazon, being returned to Georgina Morgens from whom he was allegedly stolen. In court in Surbiton, Surrey, the defendant claimed that he had bought Barney at an auction. When the parrot saw Miss Morgens in the witness box he let out a wolf-whistle and climbed along his cage to be near her. He let her scratch his throat and whistled in tune with her. The judge was astonished that the lawyer had not noticed an important point. The only name the Amazon had spoken while at the police station was "Barney"! The defendant was found guilty of handling stolen goods.

A happy ending

Escaped parrots are more likely to bring tears than laughter – but there are some happy endings. During the 1980s, when I lived in London, I received an unusual telephone call one New Year's day. A lady told me hesitantly: "There is a *yellow* parrot in a tree across the road..." This was before the days when yellow mutations of Ringnecks, Kakarikis, *Neophemas* and Quaker Parakeets would have sprung to mind. She had anxiously telephoned the police to be met with the understandable response, in the season of good cheer, "Madam, I believe you have celebrated too well!" In desperation she telephoned the local fire station. Perhaps a long ladder could be used to catch the bird? "A *yellow* parrot?" She received a similar reaction to that of the constable. Finally convincing him that it was no joke, the fire officer gave her my telephone number. (I don't recall how he knew it.)

She related the story to me and was extremely relieved that I did not question whether she was sober. That she had been able to contact me was extremely lucky. I knew the only man in London who kept and bred Golden or Queen of Bavaria's Conures (*Guaruba guarouba*) (see colour page 21). He lived three miles away, in the opposite direction to the wandering bird's temporary domicile. When I telephoned him he admitted that one of his birds had escaped. We both jumped into our cars and met at the spot described by the lady. She was definitely not inebriated! Sure enough, feasting in a tree of berries was the truant Golden Conure. It finished its meal and, after some minutes, made its way down the tree to its owner. Capture was easy. It had had enough of adventure and wanted to go home!

REFERENCES CITED

Anon, 1999, Yellow-eared Parrot: New hope for its survival, *Cyanopsitta*, 53–54: 30–34.

Bailey, B., 2000, Jordy – The bird I didn't want, *Pet Bird Report*, 9 (4): 58–59.

Barker, L., 1997, The Bird, *Bird Talk*, January: 56–58, 60–62.

Beatty, L. L., undated (1996), *Pet Bird Report*, Charlie Reborn, 6 (5): 50–51.

Beissinger, S. R., and N. F. R. Snyder, eds, 1992, *New World Parrots in Crisis*, Smithsonian Institution Press, Washington and London.

Bignell, A., undated, *Lady Baillie at Leeds Castle*, Leeds Castle Enterprises Ltd.

Bucher, E. H., 1992, Neotropical Parrots as Agricultural Pests, *in* Beissinger and Snyder: 201–219.

Butler, P., 2000, *Promoting Protection through Pride*: a manual to facilitate successful conservation-education programmes developed at RARE Center for Tropical Conservation, *International Zoo Yearbook*, 37: 273–283.

Cahyadin, Y. M, P. Jepson and B. I. Manoppo, 1994, *The Status of* Cacatua goffini *and* Eos reticulata *on the Tanimbar Islands*, PHPA/BirdLife International.

Calvert, K., 2003, Moluccan Cockatoos, *PsittaScene*, 15 (1): 8–9,12.

Chalmers Mitchell, P., 1931, *Guide to the Gardens and Aquarium, Regent's Park*, Zoological Society of London.

Chassot, O. and G. M. Arias, 2002, Great Green Macaw: flagship species of Costa Rica, *PsittaScene* 14 (4) (No 53): 6–7.

Clubb, S., 1992, The Role of Private Aviculture in the Conservation of Neotropical Psittacines, *in* Beissinger and Snyder: 117–131.

Clyne, T., undated (1996), Was 'A Matter you Cockatoo? *Pet Bird Report*, 6 (5): 16–17.

Cokinos, C., 2000, *Hope is the thing with Feathers*, Jeremy P. Tarcher/Putnam, New York.

Collar, N., and T. Juniper, 1992, Dimensions and Causes of the Parrot Conservation Crisis *in* Beissinger and Snyder: 1–4.

Conway, W., 2000, The changing role of zoos in the 21st century, *EAZA News*, 298–13.

Cotton, D. E., 1940, A wonderful Tovi Parrakeet, *Avicultural Magazine*, Fifth Series, vol V (3): 81–82.

De Grahl, 1987, *The Grey Parrot*, TFH Publications, New Jersey.

Delacour, J., 1966, *The Living Air*, Country Life, London.

Derrickson, S. R. and N. F. R. Snyder, 1992, Potentials and Limits of Captive Breeding in Parrot Conservation, *in* Beissinger and Snyder: 133–163.

Desenne, P. and S. D. Strahl, 1991, Trade and the conservation status of the family Psittacidae in Venezuela, *Bird Conservation International*, 1 (2): 153–169.

Dingle, S., 2003, My introduction to aviculture, *Bulletin Avicultural Society of America*, 72 (2): 5–10.

Drury, C., 2001, Dundee, the gift of love, *Companion Parrot Quarterly*, 54: 83–85.

Farrar, C. D., undated (1920s?), *Through a Bird-Room Window*, F. V. White, London.

Forshaw, J. M., 1989, *Parrots of the World*, Third (revised) ed., Blandford Press, London.

      2002, *Australian Parrots*, Third (revised) ed, Alexander Editions. Queensland.

Fuller, E., 2001, revised ed., *Extinct Birds*, Comstock Publishing Associates, New York.

Garnett, S., 1999, Cockatoos and Peanuts at Lakeland, *PsittaScene*, 11 (3): 14–15.

Garrett, K. L. and K. T. Mabb, 2004, Naturalized Parrots in California, *ASA Bulletin*,73 (2): 13–16.

Gedney, C. W., 1879, *Foreign Cage Birds*, Vol I, The Bazaar, London.

Goederen, G. de, 1951, A visit to the Zoological Gardens of Wassenaar, *Avicultural Magazine*, 57 (4): 139–142.

Goodfellow, W., 1900, A Naturalist's Notes in Ecuador, *Avicultural Magazine*, VI: 65–72.

　　　　　　　1906, Notes on Mrs Johnstone's Lorikeet, *Avicultural Magazine* new series, IV (3): 82–88.

Guild, E., 1938, Tahitian aviculture: acclimatization of foreign birds, *Avicultural Magazine*, Fifth Series, vol III (1): 8–11.

Hallander, J., 2000, In my experience – Earthquakes, *Parrots*, 33: 42–43.

Hartley, R., 2001, The people who live with Lear's Macaw, *PsittaScene*, 13 (1): 10–11.

del Hoyo, J., A. Elliott & J. Sargatal, eds, 1997, *Handbook of Birds of the World*, vol 4, Lynx Edicions, Barcelona.

Helwig, V., 1989, *Remembering the Tody*, Castenchel Editions Inc., Quebec.

Horsfield, W., 2006, Profile – William Horsfield, *Avizandum*, 18 (1): 16,18–19, 33.

Huber, S., 1997, Amazons are never innocent, *Amazona Quarterly*, 13 (1): 21–22.

Jupp, T., 2000, The status of cockatoos in south-west Western Australia and conservation efforts by Perth Zoo, *International Zoo Yearbook* 37: 80–86.

Knobel, E. M., 1948, Amazon Parrots, *Avicultural Magazine*, 54 (4): 138–150.

Lepperhoff, L., 2002, A Journey through Brazil, *PsittaScene*, 14 (2) (no 51): 10–13.

Low, R., 2000, *Why does my Parrot...?*, Souvenir Press, London.

Low, R., 2001, Reintroduction and conservation education in Trinidad, *PsittaScene*, 13 (3): 12–13.

　　　　　　　2002, Travelling Home, *Parrots*, No 50: 26–29.

Lucker, H., 2000, The European Endangered Species Programme (EEP) for red-tailed amazon, *International Zoo Yearbook* 37: 202–205.

Lydekker, R, ed., 1895, *The Royal Natural History*. Vol IV, Frederick Warne & Co., London.

Macias-Caballero, C., E. C. Enkerlin-Hoeflich and M. A. Cruz, 2003, Thick-billed Parrots in Mexico, *PsittaScene*, 15 (4): 2–4.

Metz, S., 2001, Why we must help conserve parrots in the wild, *Pet Bird Report*, 10 (1): 26–29.

Munn, C. A., 1992, Macaw Biology and Ecotourism, or "When a Bird in the Bush is Worth two in the Hand", *in* Beissinger and Snyder.

Murad, J. W., 2002, How YOU can make a difference, *Companion Parrot Quarterly*, 57: 36–42.

Nichol, J., 1987, *The Animal Smugglers*, Christopher Helm, London.

Nilsson, 1981, The bird business, a study of the commercial cage bird trade. Washington, District of Columbia, Animal Welfare Institute.

　　　　　　　1989, Importation of Birds into the United States in 1985, Washington, District of Columbia, Animal Welfare Institute.

Norley, L., undated, Rupert: In my own words, *Pet Bird Report*, 7 (6): 24–25.

Pavlis, R. R., undated, Comments on organic article, *Pet Bird Report* 7 (2): 81.

Perez, M. R., M. Failla, V. Seijas, P. Quillfeldt and J. F. Masello, 2005, Burrowing Parrots – an agricultural pest? *PsittaScene* 17 (4): 10–11.

Perrin, C., 1999, Polly, *Amazona Quarterly*, 15 (2): 21–22.

Perrot, G. A., 1978, We bought a Macaw, *Magazine of the Parrot Society*, XII (2): 29–35.

Pittman, T., 1997/1998, The Glaucous Macaw: Dead or alive? *Just Parrots*, Dec 1997/Jan 1998: 46–48.

Plath, K., 1951, Breeding of the Goldie's Lorikeet, *Avicultural Magazine*, 57 (4): 133–135.

Porter, S., 1938, Notes from South America, *Avicultural Magazine*, fifth series, vol III, no.8: 289–298.

Ryan, T., 1980, Quarantine Centre Mortality, *Magazine of the Parrot Society*, XIV, (5): 113–114.

Salaman, P., 2001, New Tradition for the Catholic Church saves Palms and Parrots, *PsittaScene* No 51: 4.

Saunders, D. A., 1979, The availability of tree hollows for use as nest sites by White-tailed Black Cockatoos, *Australian Wildlife Res.*, 7:257–269.

Schooley, M., undated, Fauna Smuggling, *Australian Birdkeeper*, 3 (3): 135–136.

Sick, H., 1993, *Birds in Brazil*, Princeton University Press, New Jersey.

Smales, I., P. Brown, P. Menkhorst, M. Holdsworth and P. Holz, 2000, Contribution of captive management of Orange-bellied parrots to the recovery programme for the species in Australia, *International Zoo Yearbook* vol 47:171–178.

Snyder, N., P. McGowan, J. Gilardi and A. Grajal (eds), 2000, Parrots: *Status Survey and Conservation Action Plan 2000–2004*, IUCN, Gland, Switzerland and Cambridge, UK.

Stap, D., 1990, *A Parrot without a Name*, Alfred A. Knopf, New York.

Stern, J. and M., 1990, Parrots, *The New Yorker*, July 30: 55–73.

Stringer, R., 2004, Lest we forget D-Day, *Cage & Aviary Birds*, Sept 16: 11.

Taylor, J., 1991, Report from Indonesia, *PsittaScene*, 3 (1): 6–8.

Them, P. H., 2001, We can breed birds, so why still import them? *Cage & Aviary Birds*, May 12: 9.

Vane, E. N. T., 1947, Parrakeets – then and now, *Avicultural Magazine*, 53 (2): 60–67.

Vaughan, C., and J. Liske, 1991, Ecotourism and the Scarlet Macaw (*Ara macao*) Population: a case for commensalisms? *Proceedings of the First Mesoamerican Workshop on the Conservation and Management of Macaws:* 35–19.

Waugh, D., 2004, Conservation of the endangered El Oro Parakeet, *Parrots*, January: 24–27.

2005, Tourism and conservation *ex situ*, in *Dialogue on Tourism, Cultural Diversity and Sustainable Development*, Responsible Tourism Institute.

Wiley, J. W., 1981, The Puerto Rican Parrot (*Amazona vittata*): its decline and the program for its conservation, *in Conservation of New World Parrots*, ed R. Pasquier, ICBP Tech. Pub. No 1.

Williams, H. P., 1951, Longevity in Parrots, *Avicultural Magazine*, 57 (4) 152.

Williams, M., 1906, Toys for Parrots, *Avicultural Magazine*, New series, vol IV, no 8: 289.

Wright, T., and C. Toft, 2001, Nest Poaching for Trade, *PsittaScene*, 13 (3): 6.

Yealland, 1940, Some Parrot-like birds at Sterrebeek, *Avicultural Magazine*, Fifth series, vol V (12): 288–293.

INDEX OF SPECIES

(Note that parrots are listed under the initial letter, eg, Eclectus is under E, while families of parrots, eg, conures and lories, are listed under the family.)

Bold type indicates a photograph of the species.

Colour illustrations are numbered and preceded by C.

INDEX OF PEOPLE (selected) mentioned in the text

About the Author

Rosemary Low has been passionately involved with birds since she was five years old. It was a pet duck that she pushed around in a doll's pram! As a teenager she kept and bred Budgerigars. When she was 16, her first parrot arrived (a Grey). Between the ages of 20 and 30, she started to keep the species she has since never been without in her own aviaries: neotropical parrots and lories and lorikeets.

In the Canary Islands she was curator of two of the world's largest parrot collections, **Loro Parque** in Tenerife and **Palmitos Park** in Gran Canaria.

Rosemary Low has had more than 20 books on parrots published, including *Endangered Parrots*, *Encyclopedia of the Lories*, *Amazon Parrots: Aviculture, trade and conservation* and, on parrot behaviour, *Why does my Parrot …?*

Her books have been translated into German, Spanish, Portuguese, Italian, Dutch and the Czech language. Her interests in conservation and the impact that trade in wild-caught parrots has had on parrot populations worldwide are reflected in this book.

She has travelled widely, speaking at international bird conventions and observing over 100 species of parrots in the wild in more than 30 countries. Watching parrots in their natural habitat, from the critically endangered Kakapo in New Zealand to tiny Pygmy Parrots in New Guinea, and the world's largest parrot colony in Argentina, gives her more enjoyment than anything else.